GRETA'S PASSAGE

 IBEX MEDIA

ANDREW WARREN

GRETA'S PASSAGE

Shelter Island
Aug 16, 2015

To Cornelia and Kasi
wonderful friends &
the best hosts ever.

Andrew Wossley

IBEX MEDIA

Cover design & Interior by Deborra J. Dodson

1. Fiction / Historical

2. Fiction / Political

ISBN: 9-780991-4944-08

Published by Ibex Media, New York, New York, U.S.A.

DEDICATION

To my mother, whose unflinching constancy of courage, perseverance, and love has provided me with an inspiring, as well as illusive model.

ACKNOWLEDGMENTS

I would like to thank the world around me for helping me get to this point in my life when everything seems easy, or at least easier. Much of the credit goes to my wife Robyn, whose love has lightened my heavy heart. I'm also indebted to my two awesome children, Judy and Alex, who, though having a complex life of their own, have remained close-by, both emotionally and physically.

I thank my mother, Sylvia, who has been the constant, dependable presence of all my years, and who, at 90 is still the dominant force of my family. This book is dedicated to her.

I would be remiss at this point if I didn't mention Deborra Dodson who has helped me tremendously putting this book in the form you see here.

Andrew Warren

CHAPTER 1
Ghimeş
1924-1939

At first there is nothing but a monotone hissing sound. Then a voice pierces the silence. It is raspy and suffused with odd inflections, betraying its Eastern European origins. It is a woman's voice, an old woman's voice. She sounds awkward, anxious. She's evidently not comfortable talking into a recorder.

"Hm...Ehm...Hellooo?...I don't think it's on...Hellooo?!...Okay?"

The sound suddenly cuts off.
"Hello? Okay. This is Greta Sobel...No...Forget that."

There are groans of frustration and then the sound cuts off again.
"Hm...Can you hear this?...Oh yes, I see; it's turning...Okay. I will talk about my life in Europe, before I came to America. That was the best part of my life. I was young then, young and craving for life, so when my time came, I grabbed it and sucked on it like a child does a piece of candy, until all its sweet tantalizing liquor filled my being, leaving me aching for more. Now I am old and gray and have the time to reminisce but, alas, there is no one left to listen. Most of the people who knew me as I was are gone. I was afraid you were gone too, my darling."

There is a long silence intermittently interrupted by distressing coughing sounds.

"My body is failing, but my memory is still good. I wish it were the other way around. Life is designed to disappoint, so I learned the only way to avoid heartache is to only desire those things you already have.

"You asked me to tell you everything...from the beginning. I was never bashful or prudish, so I'm not going to start now. Years ago, I was concerned about what people thought of me; I wanted them to think that I was a good woman. But now I know that a good woman is just someone everyone can push around. I'd rather be remembered as a tough woman who gave as good as she took. There were those who would have put a knife in my back had I looked away for a second. I guess they thought I had it coming: my crime was that I did what they only allowed themselves to fantasize about.

"When I was very young, I wanted someone to take care of me, but it didn't turn out that way, so I had to learn to make it on my own. I had it tough at first, especially since I didn't have an education or skills. But I had one great asset: me. I was beautiful and I was smart, not book smart, street-smart and resourceful. I don't know where I got it from, but I always had boundless confidence in myself. No matter what, I knew I'd always land on my feet. And throughout much of my life – there were the occasional moments of misery – I stayed optimistic and cheerful. Looking back, I don't think I would have done anything differently. Oh, maybe one or two things. I wasted too many good years on one sad man whom I didn't love. But I got even. Once I freed myself, I made up for lost time without guilt or regrets. Then God punished me by giving me a cold, cruel son. I tried to soften his heart, not for me, but for all the other people I knew he'd end up hurting. I failed...maybe because God knew I had wanted a girl. I even had a name picked out – Ingrid after Ingrid Bergman. She was my favorite actress. No one showed emotions, passions the way she did."

The muffled sounds of a throaty laugh come through the recorder's reluctant speakers.

"I'm a bit nervous...I'm afraid you've already made up your mind. But hear me out before you render your judgment. You're asking me to talk about things that happened so long ago that now don't even feel like they were ever part of my life..."

There is silence, except for the whirring sound of the recorder.

The old woman's voice returns, but now it sounds shrill and petulant.

"Why now? Why have you waited so long? That was so cruel of you."

There is another silence.

"What I did was because I had to survive and had to keep my son alive too. He would never understand that. But will you forgive me… if I tell you everything? And then you'll see that if I did anything to hurt you, it was not intentional. I don't care now anyway. It is just too late. I'll probably be dead before you listen to these recordings."

The voice bursts into guttural laughter.

"I have these jars inside my head where instead of fresh preserves I put up discarded memories that were never intended to be opened. I'm afraid that if I decide to unseal them now, these wayward memories will burst out and ravage whatever shred of reason I may have left. So if I do, it better be perceived as an act of final atonement, of full payment of all outstanding debts, real or only charged with. They'll call it "The reckless life of a romantic woman."

Loud throat-clearing sounds reach out of the recorder followed by a long silence.

I

I was born in a small village in Transylvania called Ghimeş. It doesn't exist anymore. In addition to Jews, there were Gentiles – Hungarians and Romanians – living in Ghimeş. They lived on one side of the river; the Jews on the other – that was our *shtetl*, which was like no other kind of place. When I lived there, I thought that the whole world was Jewish. All the store signs were written with Hebrew letters and everyone spoke Yiddish. And as I walked down the street, strangers would smile and wish me a nice day. Everyone was so friendly.

Most of the time, the Jews got along with the Gentiles better than they got along with each other; the Hungarians were Catholic, while the Romanians were of the Eastern Orthodox faith. There were two hills on their side of the river and the Catholic Church was built on one and the Orthodox Church was built on the other. On Sundays, they would close the bridge leading to the *shtetl* while everyone was in church. They were worried that the Jews would come and steal their chickens. When I was just about four years old, a Hungarian peasant claimed that some of his chickens disappeared while he was in church, and, of course, the suspicion fell on the Jews. This Hungarian peasant called on his friends and they all rode across the bridge on their horses and, when they got to the middle of the *shtetl*, they drew their swords and began slashing away. Three people were killed that day, including my cousin, my mother's sister's eight-year old daughter.

The bridge gate was installed after that. The Jews paid for it. It was a tall metal fence that could only be locked from the Gentile side, and the Jews paid the sexton from the Romanian Church to lock it before church every Sunday. That's not to say there were no more thefts on the Gentile side; there were plenty, but at least they didn't blame them on the Jews.

In the *shtetl*, the Jews spoke only Yiddish, and since most of us had little contact with the Gentiles, we didn't need another language. Some did though, like my father, if they did business with the Gentiles. Naturally, none of the Gentiles spoke Yiddish. But despite the language barrier and the differences in religion and customs, as I remember, everyone got along pretty well. If I said there were no more problems with Gentiles after the bridge gate was installed, I meant until about a year before we finally left Ghimeş.

Over the years, I've avoided telling my age, and when I did, I usually skimmed off a few years. But this time I'll tell the truth: I was born in 1924. That makes me 88 years old. Yes, I am an old woman now. But although this might make you think that my spirit is worn out, I feel no different than when I was a young girl. Ironically, my body seems to follow a different agenda. But don't worry; it's strong enough to be around to finish this.

II

I was born in an old, weathered clapboard house, which my father had to winterize every fall with dead leaves mixed in dry mud. I was delivered by a midwife who was also the butcher's wife. My mother had a very hard time during delivery. Everyone assumed she wouldn't make it, but she did, although the trauma changed her into a bitter, morose woman. She had once been, I was told, good-natured and gay and a terrific dancer.

Our house was on a side street – a narrow dirt path, to be exact – and smaller than most of the other houses in Ghimeş. I remember it as if I was still living there, even though it's been almost 75 years since we left for the last time on a rainy day with just our tattered clothes on our backs. Our front door, a squeaky mishmash of twigs and straw held together with nails and twine that had to be replaced at least every other year, opened into our living room, which I remember to be pretty spacious, but of course it was more than just a living room; it was our dining room, our kitchen, and, in the winter, our communal bedroom. It was the only room of the house, with its great big fireplace, that was heated. Around the first of December of every year, my father would announce that it was time to drag our straw mattresses into the living room. I was always cold, so I put my mattress as close to the fireplace as I could. My brother Sammy, macho boy that he was, would always drop his mattress on the opposite side of the room. My mother picked a spot right outside her bedroom, while my father always chose to be by the front door. He was a heavy cigarette smoker, and since my mother didn't allow him to smoke in the house, he had to skip out several times in the middle of the night for a quick smoke.

To the right of the front door, there was a long wooden all-purpose table – nothing more than a heavy oak board with four pieces of round lumber nailed at the corners – which we ate on. But my father also used it for business and that's where my brother did his homework. Above the table there was a small window that looked out onto the chicken house that my father built. At dinnertime, which was the only meal we had together, I sat at the far end of the table, while Sammy sat at the end near the front door. My parents sat next to each other or rather there was a chair next to my father's that was meant for my mother, but she was always running back and forth to the kitchen.

When I got to be about eleven or twelve, I started helping my mother, or so I thought, though she never stopped complaining about my uselessness, and to prove it, she would rip out of my hands whatever I was about to carry to the dinner table. She didn't really want me to help her; it would have undermined her martyr status.

The kitchen area was on the other side of the living room. It consisted of another long narrow table, with two or three levels of shelves beneath the tabletop. It was made of the same rough wood board as the eating table, but it had been painted white. The shelves were filled with pots and pans of every size and shape, except for the side closest to the fireplace where my mother kept two stacks of white china dishes in various stages of infirmity: dinner plates and soup plates. Since my father was a tinker, we had the best pots and pans in Ghimeş. The dishes had been part of my mother's dowry, something I didn't know at the time, though

I should have guessed since she constantly reminded us of their lofty pedigree: "They are *Rosenthals*." I didn't understand why she was so proud of an ugly heap of chipped and cracked dishes with a sissy, floral design, which I always thought she had gotten second hand from our neighbors from across the street who were even worse off than us, the Rosenthals.

My mother did all her cooking on the fireplace, which Reb Berger, the blacksmith, outfitted with metal rods across the top so my mother could hang her cooking vessels. She even did her baking in that fireplace, and she never burned anything. To the left of the fireplace, there was a load of chopped wood that my mother kept replenishing from the big pile that stood outside on the side of the house and which my father kept restacking with dried logs that he brought home in his tinker cart.

Everyday when I got home from school, the house smelled differently, depending on what my mother was preparing for dinner. I was a very finicky eater, and, had my mother not been such a phenomenal cook, I would have starved to death, or so she told me. As soon as I walked through the door, tantalizing aromas would drive me, trance-like, towards whatever pot was hanging in the fireplace.

One day there would be the scent of beet borscht with boiled potatoes and sour cream; the next day I would be overpowered by the smell of chicken soup with matzo balls; the next day there would be cabbage borscht, which my mother made with beef and a big bone that she would have bought that morning from the kosher butcher; the day after that the house would smell from stuffed cabbage and mamaliga or potato pierogis, which my mother garnished with fried onions. My father loved gribenes on a fat slice of black bread, which my mother would bake fresh. Nothing ever beat the rude smell of hot chicken fat for getting one's saliva flowing. I'm forgetting the kosher salami that my mother always kept on hand exclusively for my father who would eat it with a big gob of mustard on a slice of black bread as soon as he woke up in the morning – Sammy and I were not allowed to have any, though I often saw my mother slicing Sammy a piece when she thought I wasn't watching.

There was never any liquor in the house, but whenever my father came home from the pub reeking from beer, my mother would have him eat a piece of kosher salami – it seemed that the combination of meat and garlic and spices did a great job masking the odor and sobering him right up.

The living room floorboards were covered with a wild assortment of cheap rugs that I later found out were also part of my mother's dowry. Many years later I visited a mosque, and it reminded me of how the rugs were laid out in our house in Ghimeş, but of course I knew those rugs were not cheap.

The far wall of the living room opened into a narrow hallway. My parents' bedroom was on the left side of the hallway, while Sammy's and mine were on the right. Sammy got the back bedroom not just because it was bigger but it was also a corner room with windows on two sides. At the end of the hallway there was a small door that led to the backyard. The door was used mostly at night for quick access to our latrine. The house had no plumbing. Going by the big round hole on the side of the latrine, it must have functioned as a guardhouse at one time, but, in its new capacity, it came with a piece of heavy burlap nailed on the inside, which nonetheless gave my mother yet another reason to kvetch, because she felt exposed.

I remember my cell-like bedroom, particularly as a place to escape the tumult of the house, and by tumult I mean the arguments between my parents. In addition to my bed, there was an armoire where I stored everything I owned: clothes, my school stuff, and a few damaged dolls that were handed down to me by neighbors whose girls had gotten married. On the ledge of my small window, I had a potted poppy plant that bore the most beautiful red flowers in the summer. In front of the window, my father put a small desk and a chair where I could do my homework. However, all I ever did sitting at that desk was watch my poppy plant and daydream.

I slept on a lumpy straw mattress, like everyone else in the house, which my father had made by filling an empty potato sack with hay that he literally took from our horse's mouth. My pillow was made the same way only smaller.

We had no electricity; the only source of light at night was a small kerosene lamp that was hung above the living room table. When my brother got older, my father bought a second kerosene lamp so that my brother could read in bed; he was a great reader.

In the winter, when we all slept in the living room, my father was responsible for keeping the fire going overnight. I once offered to take his place for only one night, but he refused. He said that a young girl had to get a good night's sleep so she would look beautiful the next day and make all the boys in town run after her. My father was the best man I ever knew: kind, tolerant, and always in good spirits. There were many times when everyone around him, especially my mother, was in the grip of panic and despair, yet he remained infectiously cheerful. My mother never really appreciated what a terrific man she had.

As soon as I got home from school, my mother met me holding up an empty milk can, which she would shove in my hand as she spun me around towards the door. Milking the goat was the low point of my day. Our goat was extremely temperamental and always managed to kick me while I was milking her. I knew she liked me, but she was probably angry at me because she felt that I wasn't enjoying her company.

I preferred playing with mice. There were many field mice around the house, and I had a knack for catching them with my bare hands. One year I brought them into my room where I put them inside a large baking pan my mother used to bake *challah* on Rosh Hashanah and watch them run around in circles. I was planning to return the pan before the holidays, but I forgot and my mother discovered my crime and reacted with uncharacteristic nastiness even for her.

The fact that she immediately discarded the baking pan seemed reasonable; the fact that she slapped me hard across the face seemed reasonable as well. But not letting me wash my hands for a month afterwards was, I thought, excessive. We all washed our hands in a common washbasin that my mother filled with fresh water every morning from the deep well we had in our front yard. She decided that it would take a month for the mouse *choleryah*, as she called it, to wear off my hands, and even after that, she always made sure I was the last one to wash my hands before dinner.

My parents didn't talk much to each other except to fight, and they were always fighting about the same topics: my father's smoking and my insolence. As the years passed and my father's coughing got worse, my mother became more and more caught up in her messianic fervor to prevent my father from smoking. She would scream at him that he was killing himself and that he would leave her a penniless widow with two young children. Then she would raise her hands and beg God to spare my father. Thinking back, I can't decide whether this was my mother's lame effort at showing affection for my father or just her selfish fear of losing the lifestyle that she otherwise grumbled about all the time.

III

At dinner, my father would hold court with fantastic stories that he either heard about at the pub or that he claimed he actually witnessed. The near certainty that my father had made up these stories had absolutely no impact on my unreserved delight at hearing them. I still remember one story my father told us one night. I was eight or nine at the time.

"You all know Ahuva Gotnick," my father started. Of course we did. She was the Rabbi's wife. We also heard the rumor that a long time ago, something only the oldest residents of Ghimeş would remember, when Moishe Gotnick returned from rabbinic school in Chernowitz, he brought back a wife, who, unfortunately, soon got sick and died. Later, after waiting the proper amount of time according to tradition, Rabbi Gotnick remarried; Ahuva was his second wife.

My father continued.

"A long time ago, when Rabbi Gotnick was still married to his first wife, he went to pay a shiva call to a young widow who had just lost her husband in a logging accident. When he got there, the young widow, howling with despair, grabbed the Rabbi's sleeve with both hands and demanded that he find her a new husband. The Rabbi told her that he didn't know any eligible young men appropriate for her, but that she shouldn't worry because she was young and attractive and won't have any trouble finding a new husband. The young widow was not placated and kept on howling and screaming that it was a *shandah* for a healthy woman like herself who hadn't experienced the blessing of motherhood to die alone. And to convince the Rabbi of her worthiness, she grabbed his hand and ran it across her hard breasts and thighs.

"The Rabbi, about to pass out, sat down and asked the young widow for a glass of water. By the time she returned, he had regained enough of his composure to offer, what he was convinced would be a most reassuring pronouncement, that if he weren't already married, *Baruch Hashem*, he would marry her himself. Still inconsolable but evidently a step back from the brink, the young widow inquired if the Rabbi wanted to further confirm her worthiness, to which the Rabbi sprung to his feet and made a dash for the door, though still possessing enough judgment to wave his arms in the air and assure the young widow not to worry that much, happiness was still ahead of her.

"Once on the street," my father continued, "Rabbi Gotnick thought about the foolish oath he had made to the young widow and shuddered, but quickly calmed himself by remembering that his wife had never been sick a day in her entire life. A week later, the Rabbi's wife, this paragon of health, lay dead from some terrible fever. After the funeral, while the Rabbi was still sitting *shiva*, in came the young widow demanding that the Rabbi make good on his promise. You guessed it – her name was Ahuva. A few months later they were married – they would have been married sooner but for all the gossip – and, as everyone knows, Ahuva gave the Rabbi six fine children, three sons and three daughters. But what people don't know is that the week before the death of the Rabbi's first wife, Ahuva spent all her time locked inside her house *davening* furiously and calling out *Shabbatai, Shabbatai.* She was summoning Sabbatai Zevi, the 17th century mystic who claimed to be the Jewish Messiah and who later died under very mysterious circumstances, but only after vowing with a vengeance that he would return.

"A few days later, a man appeared in Ghimeş who people thought very much resembled the excommunicated Shabbatai Zevi, wearing a turban and an embroidered silk kaftan. The man walked straight into the young widow's house, as if he had been there before, spent some time inside, and then headed for the Rabbi's house, where he stood outside reciting the forbidden Tetragrammaton over and over again – that's the unutterable name for God – while shaking his finger at heaven. Afterwards, everyone knew what Shabbatai had done: he placed a *kishev*, a curse, on the Rabbi's wife. The next day, the poor unsuspecting woman got sick and never recovered. And then Ahuva became the Rabbi's second wife, and what a good wife she's been."

I love that story and my father told it so well. I remember me and Sammy at the edge of our chairs, our chins resting on our elbows, listening breathlessly. My mother sat for a minute, but got up and kept herself in the kitchen.

IV

Despite the almost constant state of hostility between my parents, an unexpected, short-lived cease-fire settled on our little home every Friday night. My mother would spend the whole day cooking. When I got home, she ordered me to watch over whatever kettles she had going in the kitchen, while she would go into her bedroom to change. When she came out, a half hour later, she was thoroughly *oysgeputst* – white silk blouse, a fashionable long skirt, and dark leather pumps – and her hair would be in a crocheted hair net. A short string of pearls, which must have been fake, hung around her neck. The rest of us also wore our best clothes. This was the only time I remember my father wearing a suit, except at my wedding many years later. My mother would light the Shabbat candles and my father, holding an old, leather-bound Siddur, would recite the *bruchas*. Then the three of us, as if in a race, lunged at our Shabbat meal, slurping and belching and grinning with delight. Even though she never allowed herself to share in our happiness, I know this was the best my mother could ever feel.

V

We didn't have a real synagogue in Ghimeş. During the High Holy Days, Ahuva and Rabbi Gotnick, opened their house. They emptied their living room except for a small table that they placed at one end of the room to act as the *bimah*. Ahuva, who was good with a hammer and nails, was in charge of hanging a string from one end of the living room to the other, on which she draped a bunch of long bed sheets. Everyone was supposed to bring his own chair: women to the right of the *machitza*, the men to the left. We didn't have a Torah in Ghimeş, so every year the synagogue in Tirgu Ocna lent us one of theirs.

Yom Kippur is the one holiday I remember most fondly. All the adults had to sit through endless services in Rabbi Gotnick's makeshift synagogue while the kids ran wild, freed of paternal supervision. Once we reached the age of thirteen, we were also supposed to fast, but I don't think many of us did. In fact, while our parents were sitting in prayer in Rabbi Gotnick's living room, we had our choice of kitchens to raid. My mother, being onto us, always hid all the food she prepared for the *break fast*, but other mothers were not quite so vigilant, so I think back with mixed emotions at our Yom Kippur attacks and all the poor families whose *break fast* we ruined.

My mother always fainted during the Yom Kippur fast. It was a sight to see. By three-thirty or four in the afternoon, she would slide off her chair and land on the floor with a heavy thud. Everyone knew it was going to happen, so by three o'clock we all had our eyes peeled to one of Rabbi Gotnick's living room windows, staring at my by then famous mother, and she never disappointed.

She knew she was going to faint, but even though everyone, including the Rabbi, pleaded with her that given her condition she didn't have to fast, she kept doing it. To prepare for her inevitable fainting spell, the day before Yom Kippur, she picked a big red apple and stabbed it with small pieces of cinnamon. On Yom Kippur day, before she went to services, she gave the cinnamon-encrusted apple to me, with the admonition to be outside Rabbi Gotnick's house by 3 o'clock or else. As soon as she fainted, I was supposed to run in with the apple and hand it to my father who would then place it under my mother's nose. Miraculously, within seconds my mother would come around. Apparently the combined smell of cinnamon and apple was strong enough to revive her. My mother would then get up off the floor, apologize and wave to the Rabbi to continue the service.

One year I didn't think it would be fair to cut the performance short; after all there were kids who had been waiting for months to see it, and decided not to hand over the apple. When old Tzeitel Tishman rushed out and demanded that I produce the apple, I told her that I had been robbed. She didn't believe me, so when they finally managed to revive my mother, Tzeitel the Shrew, as she was better known, told my mother of my delinquency. My mother told my father to fetch me, assuring him that all she wanted to do was talk to me. Of course, by then all the services came to a halt. When I walked in, she grabbed my hair and began yelling at me and pounding my head. I begged her to stop, arguing that she was making God angry for beating me in God's house on the Day of Atonement, the one day in which even God forgives his children. She was wobbling perilously and there wasn't much sting in her punches, so I kept waiting for her pass out again, but she didn't. After my father intervened, I broke loose and services were allowed to resume.

Back on the street, I was hailed as a hero. The following year and all the years after that, I never missed handing over the cinnamon apple. The only other memorable moments happened after services ended and people went home to discover that their holiday meal was gone, and the air filled with the groans and cries of the *balebustes* of Ghimeş who had nothing to feed their husbands.

Another incident I remember in connection with Jewish holidays happened before a Passover. There was no specialty bakery in Ghimeş, so the Rabbi would send someone to Tîrgu Ocna to bring back a cartful of matzo. On the day before Passover, starting around six o'clock in the morning, the women would line up outside the Rabbi's house for their share. The line stretched past the kosher butcher's shop, which was three long blocks away. The Rabbi began distributing the matzo around eight o'clock in the morning, and it took until about ten to take care of everybody. Each family was supposed to get three boards of matzo; if they wanted more, they would have to travel to Tîrgu Ocna on their own.

When I turned eleven, my mother decided that it was my job to wait on the matzo line and, despite my objection that only married women stood on line, the edict prevailed. On the day the Rabbi was due to distribute the matzo, my mother woke me up at five-thirty in the morning, and even though I explained to her that it made no sense to get there that early, my mother insisted that I had to be on line by six. Needless to say, I was the first and waited another half hour before the next woman showed up. The following years, my mother took care that I would always be first, rejecting my arguments by asking me, while staring me down with her merciless eyes, what I thought our Passover would be like if they ran out of matzo.

The best part of waiting on line was hearing the wild arguments that broke out. Some women were screaming that they needed extra boards of matzo because they had relatives coming from out of town; others argued that they had a bigger family than the average and therefore deserved more matzo; and still others pounced on newly married women or widows as they didn't qualify for a full ration. In the end, the Rabbi somehow managed to appease them all. I loved the spectacle, which was why I stayed around to the end. My mother never knew why it took me so long to get home even though I was the first one on line, and sloughed it off as another sign of my colossal uselessness.

VI

There was only one public school in town and it was run by Romanians, and when I turned six my father sent me there, despite my mother's grumbling that all those *goyem* were going to contaminate me. It was not uncommon for a girl to be kept home. After all, the only education a girl needed was to cook, keep house, and raise children, and my mother was going to teach me that.

The school building had a room for each grade, and each room had three rows of benches, enough for about fifteen children. In the early grades, they taught us Romanian and arithmetic. In the higher grades, they added geography and history, mostly Romanian history. None of this mattered to me; I never learned anything. All I did in school was stare out the window: in the summer there were millions of colorful flowers covering the ground and graceful birds dancing in the air, and in the winter there were huge banks of white snow and howling winds that picked up the snow and swirled it up to the sky. At first, Mrs. Constantinescu, my teacher, would say, "Greta, stop daydreaming!" Then she realized that it didn't make any difference, so she left me alone.

When I graduated at the end of the seventh grade, we had a big celebration with folk dancing and singing. My father and Sammy came to see me. I danced the *hora* with the other girls, dressed in a typical Romanian peasant costume that the school had lent me for the occasion and which my mother filled with safety pins to make it fit me. The next year, that same outfit was probably worn by a much heftier Romanian peasant girl.

I was a terrible student. I wasn't stupid, but I couldn't remember anything. I couldn't remember the multiplication table no matter how many times Sammy practiced it with me. If there ever was any doubt about how bad my memory was, this next story takes care of it.

We were assigned to memorize a poem written by Romania's greatest poet, Mihai Eminescu. It was called "La Steaua," (To The Star); it had four short stanzas. I knew it would take me a while to memorize it, so I locked myself in my room and started the process as soon as I got done with my chores. I read each stanza over a hundred times, and then I tried memorizing one line at a time. After hours of effort, I fell asleep on my bed with the book in my hands. I woke up the next morning and fretfully started the whole process again. I left for school and, on the way, I kept reciting the poem as I walked. When I got to the dirt path that led up to the school – the school was on top of a steep hill – I ran into one of my friends who was in an earlier grade. I cried to her how I couldn't remember the damn poem and showed it to her. She read it twice or three times, closed the book, and recited the poem flawlessly. During class, the teacher called on me. I managed the first stanza, but then I got stuck. After that, there was no doubt that I just couldn't remember anything, yet here I am reminiscing about things that happened over seventy-five years ago. I don't understand it.

VII

One year, a photographer came through Ghimeş and my father had all four of us pose for a picture. I still have that photograph. Almost forty years ago, when I traveled back to Romania to bury my father, I found it in his wallet tucked between lottery tickets. It's probably the only thing I took back with me. It shows me and my brother standing in front of our dining room table, while my parents are sitting on either side of us. The photograph's once-elegant scalloped edges almost disappeared and there is a blotch on the side of my mother's face, most likely the result of somebody's sweaty thumb that makes her left cheek look like an erupting volcano. I am dressed in a drab country dress and tall lace-up boots, and look radiant sitting between the two men in my life. They're guarding me and I feel safe. I have long blond hair braided in two pigtails that hang down the flowery bib of my dress and deep blue eyes that stare directly into the camera. It's a black-and-white photograph, but I remember.

I was naïve and silly, but so pretty. My father understood it wasn't enough and that the world was changing, and even girls needed to know how to manage on their own should fate, God forbid, leave them without a man. My father's decision proved, many years later, to be one of the keys of my survival. It turned out, despite my lousy memory, I was terrific at languages. In school, I quickly learned Romanian. I also learned Hungarian, because a lot of the children were Hungarian, and I wanted to talk to them too. So by the time I was eight or nine, I was fluent in both Romanian and Hungarian. At home I only spoke Yiddish.

VIII

Ghimeş had its own little weekly Yiddish newspaper. I couldn't read it – it used Hebrew letters – but my father read it to us during dinner. It was the only contact we had with the outside world, and the news was always terrifying – it seemed that the world had had enough of us Jews and needed us to disappear. But I was sure that didn't mean me because everyone loved me and would always want me around.

Ghimeş even had a small hospital, but all it did was take care of broken bones or deliver babies; it didn't have a real doctor. If you needed a doctor, you had to go to Chernowitz, a three-day horse ride, where they had a real hospital. There were closer hospitals, but they didn't allow Jews.

We didn't have a movie theater in Ghimeş, but, in the summer, a few of the locals staged live plays. These plays were held in the kosher butcher's barn. The butcher had built a platform to be used as the stage at one end, leaving the rest of the barn open for spectators.   Most people would watch standing, but those who wanted to sit had to bring their own chairs.   The actors were neighbors of ours: the butcher and his wife – they usually grabbed the lead roles – the blacksmith and his sister, and a young widow who lost her husband when he got hit in the head by a rolling tree log. Ghimeş was a big logging town; lumbermen would chop down trees and then push them down the side of the mountain towards the river, from there they would float down to the lumber plant.

I used to go to the theater with my brother. He liked it more than I did, but I went with him because he always bought me a hot, cinnamon-scented apple-filled pastry that only the butcher's wife knew how to bake.

The only play I remember was written by the butcher himself. It was called *Othniel the Butcher and Hid Beautiful Wife Delilah*. In the play, Othniel was a wealthy butcher married to Delilah, the Rabbi's daughter, but, despite his money, he always felt that he wasn't good enough for Delilah. Idan worked for Othniel in the butcher shop, but before he worked for Othniel, he had had his own butcher shop, which he lost to gambling. Throughout the play, Idan incites Othniel by telling him that while he's in the shop, working himself into an early grave, Delilah is fooling around with Chaim, a Talmudic student who's lodging in their basement. At the end, Othniel, ravaged by jealousy, kills Delilah with a kosher meat cleaver, a big *shandah*. Years later I realized that the butcher stole the idea from Shakespeare's *Othello*, but I still think the Yiddish version was better than the original, more realistic.

IX

There was even a library in Ghimeş filled with Yiddish books. Long ago, the building had once been the mayor's office for Jewish issues, but once the town's elders, who all lived on the gentile side of the river, decided that all Jewish issues had been resolved, the place was abandoned. It was a sturdy building, made of brick and stone, and with a solid tile roof. At first no one wanted to set foot inside an unkosher place, but Ahuva Gotnick, the Rabbi's wife, made a special *brucha* and hung a big mezuzah by the front door. From then on, the place became a big social center, especially after a large number of very comfortable armchairs were discovered in its basement.

Since the armchairs were considered unclaimed property, within a day of their discovery, a big meeting was held in the library to decide what to do with them. Everyone agreed that now the chairs belonged to the Jews, but not how they were to be distributed. An enormous shouting contest ensued, some people claiming that the allocation should be based on size of family, others arguing it should be done by secret raffle, and still others, who had counted on not leaving empty-handed and had brought along their entire family, that everyone should leave from the meeting with the chair he was already sitting on.

Just as the meeting was about to collapse into chaos – people were menacingly facing each other, waving chairs above their heads – Ahuva climbed onto her chair, lifted her arms skyward, and, in a voice that made her seem possessed by a dybbuk, began invoking Yahweh, the early wrathful vision of God who destroyed Sodom and Gomorrah and later drowned all His people in the Great Flood. Soon everyone was sitting and breathlessly gaping at her. Ahuva commanded that the chairs be left where they were as the library was meant to become a place where people could meet and quietly schmooze and even read if they wanted to. Before long, there were thousands of books that had either been left by the front door or that Ahuva bought with money people had donated, and the library became the virtual social center of Ghimeş.

Sammy came home one day all excited having found stacks of books in French, English, and Romanian in the back of the library's basement. He was there every chance he got, taking out new books and returning the ones he read. He kept on reading for the rest of his life; that's how he knew so much. Of course, he knew Romanian and French, but I was the only one who learned

Hungarian. He thought Hungarian was a useless language; I thought it was the language of love.

There was also a lot of fun stuff going on in Ghimeş. Once a year, a traveling circus stopped in town for about a week. No one ever knew exactly when they were due, other than in the summer. Then one morning I looked out my window and there it was, a huge tent dwarfing our little homes. Tickets were sold by fire-eaters carrying body-size placards over their colorful costumes. Every time someone bought a ticket, a giant flame would gust out of their mouths, scaring everyone half to death.

I loved the circus, but not as much as my father who, during the entire time the circus was in town, canceled all his appointments and attended every performance. It wasn't the acrobats or the wild animal acts that appealed to him though; he only wanted to see the clowns. They made him laugh. He laughed so hard that tears would stream down his face, and, because he was a heavy smoker, every once in a while he'd smother in his own laughter, and then cough his lungs out for the next hour. Even though he was coughing so hard that, at times, I thought he would choke to death, he never stopped going and he never stopped laughing.

X

My father was a tinker. He had learned the trade from his father. He was the only Jewish tinker throughout the whole area, which took in about ten or twelve villages, *shtetls* just like ours. In order to make sure that he didn't miss anybody, he had made a map of his territory and each day he would go to a different village. When he completed a full round, he'd start all over again. This way people didn't have to wait more than about three weeks to have their pots and pans fixed.

He was a big man; he was over six feet tall, but to a child of nine or ten – that's how old I was in that old photograph – he looked like a god, except I didn't think gods had wispy, dapper moustaches and sly smiles to cheer up their faces. He had huge hands; when I was little whenever I asked him for an airplane ride, he would splay his hand on the table for me to sit on, and then I would feel his fingers gripping my sides like steel claws, as he lifted me up above his head.

When my father traveled to a nearby village, he would come home at night. But if he went to one of the more remote villages, he would be away sometimes for two or three nights. When he returned, he always brought my brother and me a present. Once he brought back a gramophone and one record. The record played the voice of Joseph Schmidt, a big opera star, but very few of us had ever heard him sing. He was born in a *shtetl* not far from Ghimeş. No one before had made it big right out of a *shtetl*. He became a big singing sensation with performances all over the world, in spite of great personal handicaps: limited musical education, tiny stature, but mostly his Jewishness. I still listen to his songs; my favorite is "Ein Lied geht um die Welt." Ultimately, it didn't matter how famous he was; he was killed in a concentration camp along with many nameless Jews. A Jew will always be nothing but a Jew.

At first, my father carried all his tools and materials in a small cart that he tied to an old mule that followed behind him on his long business trips. When the mule died, he offered to fix an old widow's pots and pans in exchange for a disheveled, old horse. This was Alborak, but that's not exactly how my father wanted the story remembered. He came home one night telling us that some poor old widow who couldn't pay him for fixing all her pots and pans had offered her horse instead. My father thought the widow had some chutzpah trying to get him to take a decrepit old nag as payment for his great craftsmanship. When I heard that, I jumped for joy and begged my father to get Alborak. I had seen him in town pulling the old woman's cart, and had stopped to pet him; one day he ate a big ear of corn right out of my hand, and he took it gently with his lips brushing the palm of my hand and then bowed his head as if to say thank you.

My father argued that we could get a much better horse for

all that work, besides we didn't need a horse, we needed a mule –
much cheaper to feed and a harder worker. But I jumped in my
father's lap and hugged and kissed him until he finally gave in.
But not before he said that I would never make anybody a good
wife because I was impractical and impulsive. He was right about
that. But I got my Alborak.

I'll always remember Alborak as having given me some of
the best times of my childhood. Sammy named him. He had
read somewhere that was the name of Mohammed's winged
horse, and he thought the name might inspire it to great deeds.
Sammy never told anyone other than me what the name meant,
so no one appreciated the irony: Alborak's idea of a gallop was an
exasperatingly slow shuffle.

At home, my father kept the cart in front of the house covered
with a piece of burlap. On snowy days, me and Sammy would
steal the burlap cover off Alborak's back and use it to slide down
the hill behind our house. My father would rather have seen us
use the sled that he had built, but Alborak never complained.
Winters were cold, but not as windy and raw as here in New York.
I remember Sammy playing in the snow in short pants; he didn't
even own a pair of long pants until after he was *bar mitzvahed*.

My father was the jolliest, most lovable man in the world,
but a rake – everyone adored him, except my mother. She had
her reasons, though. Many of my father's out-of-town trips were
in truth nights when he went to the pub, got himself drunk, and
then engaged one of the town's many prostitutes, or *curvah*, as
they were called, and spent the night with her. Sometimes he
wouldn't come home for a couple of days. My father didn't make
too much of a secret of his escapades, since he obviously didn't
care, so the neighbors knew about them, and naturally my mother
found out. I only learned about them years later overhearing my
mother's anguished account. Interestingly, no one ever seemed
to be annoyed with my father: it was, first of all, difficult to ever
hold anything against him, and besides everyone figured it must
be hell living with my mother. In the end, both men and women,

seemed to not only sympathize with him, but blamed my mother for it. Ironically, after my mother finished her tearful confession, the acquaintance excitedly remarked, "Oy, what a man."

XI

When we were small, Sammy took me with him wherever he went. He was three years older and, as I look at the photograph, a good head-and-a-half taller. He was blond and sweet and everyone loved him. In the photograph, he's wearing a pair of embroidered *spiel-hosen* and he has his arm lying across my shoulders, and his proud expression is saying: "I'm her brother." I, on the other hand, look like I'm too busy trying to come across cute to be aware of what's going on around me.

Even though Sammy and I were very close, we fought all the time over the stupidest things. One day, my father returned from one of his overnight trips carrying two tiny kittens. He gave one to each of us. I must have been seven and Sammy ten. Within days we began arguing whose kitten was the prettiest. My kitten was mostly white with two black and gold blotches over her eyes. Sammy's was black and white with gold stripes across her back. Our differences of opinion, which initially started as juvenile teasing, quickly deteriorated into ferocious screaming and name-calling. We were in the back yard by the chicken house, as my mother did not allow us to bring the kittens into the house. I told Sammy that our father gave me the prettier kitten, because I was prettier than him, to which Sammy called me stupid. Before I knew what I was doing, I was on top of him pummeling his head. He tried to stop me by grabbing my hands, but he didn't hit me back. We had many fights when we were children that ended up in brawls, but he never hit me, which was my license to hit him at will. After that incident, the kittens disappeared. One morning we woke up and went looking for them in the chicken house, but they were gone. My heartless mother must've drowned them in the latrine.

My father didn't say anything when I went to him the next day while he was busy cleaning up the backyard and blamed my mother for killing my kitten, but a few days later he brought home a puppy, a pure mutt, and said that it belonged to both Sammy and me and we had to share him and love him and conduct ourselves like responsible parents. We immediately fell in love with Bercu – that's what my father named him – and forgot the kittens and the hurt of losing them.

I can't say that Sammy didn't love Bercu, but, between school and Torah studies, he was just too busy. I was okay with that. Bercu was my dog. He was mostly sheep dog with large paws, so I knew he was going to grow big.

Bercu went to school with me; of course, he had to wait outside, but he didn't seem to mind. After my parents turned in for the night, I would sneak him in through the back door and have him sleep in my bed. Of course, it didn't take my mother long to sniff out my deception. One morning, as I opened my eyes, there was my mother leaning over me, spraying spit, hollering and cursing. She grabbed Bercu by a paw and threw him out the window. I almost fainted. She then ripped the sheet off my bed and threw it out – it had been contaminated. Then she turned to me and started hitting me with both hands until I sank to the floor, crying hysterically. I was never able to forgive her that display of cruelty, and neither did my father or Sammy, but I don't think she cared; she had already distanced herself from all of us. I was grateful to see that Bercu was okay, but I never dared to bring him in the house again. My father never reproached my mother, but he did build Bercu a beautiful doghouse. The only way he could respond to her acts of meanness was to confront her with his kindness.

XII

We used to play *ţurca* on the street with neighborhood boys. It was a Romanian game similar to baseball. I was the only girl, but I was one of the best players. I was a terrific batter. The bat was just a short stick, and instead of a ball, we used a chunk of wood that looked like a large *dreidel*. I used to hit that *dreidel* farther than most boys, and then I would run as fast as I could and slid, feet first, into a bundle of boys' shirts – that's how we marked the bases. We played right on the street, and since the streets were not paved, you can imagine what I looked like when we got home. Sammy didn't look much better, but I was the only one who got smacked. I once dared to ask my mother, why she was only beating me, and never Sammy, and she answered that Sammy didn't have to grow up to be a lady. When I told her that I didn't want to grow up to be a lady, she just hit me harder. She used to either slap me with her bare hands or hit me with her wood-soled slippers. Whenever she had been cooking and her hands were covered with flour or chopped meat, she would take off one of her slippers and smack me with it. I preferred the slippers. Her hands stung like rug beaters; the wooden slippers felt much better. Luckily by the time I was a teenager, her strength started waning, and she began using the slippers more and more, as they didn't take as much out of her.

XIII

My mother was an honest, hardworking woman, but without a sense of humor, and the fact that she was very sickly didn't help her mood. As I look at the old photograph, I try to remember what she looked like in life. She's been dead for well over a half a century, yet I feel closer to her now than I ever felt before. In the photograph, my father, Sammy and I are grinning as if we're all doing a toothpaste commercial; in an unsettling contrast, my mother, with lips pursed and a grim face, glares out menacingly.

She looks barrel-chested, but I suspect that was only because she swathed her enormous breasts in some tight-fitting undergarment that resembled a war shield, which was exactly what she needed to protect her from what she perceived to be the alien environment of her existence. Yet I often think about her now, and I feel something for her – love or maybe just pity. Either way, I know she suffered a lot.

Her ill health probably started from the time of my birth. I was told I should have had a twin sister, but she died before birth. So the midwife delivered only me. We didn't know there was a dead baby inside my mother until years later when her stomach started swelling up and she began complaining of a lot of pain. Since she had always been a big complainer, my father kept ignoring or placating her, but after a while he realized that this was different, so he finally took her to the hospital in Chernowitz. I was there in the room with my mother when the doctor took out of her stomach this fully formed fetus of a girl. It was covered with hair and it was green, but otherwise it looked perfectly normal. I'll never forget. That was my sister. I still think about her. After the operation, my mother ended up with a big scar across her stomach and no bellybutton.

XIV

Country life was hard. When I came home from school, which was around two o'clock, my mother would put me to work. I fed the chickens; we had about twenty. I also picked up whatever new eggs they had laid. I milked the goat. We didn't have a cow; that would have been too expensive. The goat's name was Bette; she was named after Bette Davis, the Hollywood actress. My father had seen one of her movies on one of his out-of-town trips and liked the picture so much that he decided to name the goat after her. When I finished my chores and I had some time for myself, I rode Alborak. Sammy didn't get home until after five. He finished school at three-thirty, and then he went to shul

35

for two hours of Torah study. Actually we didn't have a *shul*; the Rabbi held Torah lessons every day in his living room, the same room that was used for the High Holy days. The Rabbi was a kind, modest man, the head of a big family with big expenses, and, though he didn't get a salary, he never complained. It was Ahuva who finally spoke out and made everyone feel guilty about how they were taking advantage of the Rabbi. From then on, everyone started contributing to the Rabbi fund, and things go a lot easier for him and he became a lot cheerier and Ahuva had two more children.

My mother always complained that I wasn't much help to her. I was always daydreaming, mostly about how one day some handsome boy would reach down from his horse and whisk me into his arms and take me to his castle where I would be allowed to play with many cute little mice. According to my mother, I frightened the chickens while I was feeding them (I sang to them) so they didn't lay as many eggs or I played with the goat's teats while I was milking her (I tied little color ribbons around them) so she didn't give us as much milk.

My mother was not one to tolerate what she considered my uselessness. And since she hardly ever acted with her heart, her decisions were firm and unarguable. When I was about eleven, my parents sent me to spend a couple of weeks with a distant aunt on my mother's side who lived in Tîrgu Ocna, a big town about a day's ride from Ghimeş. The woman, who happened to be well off, had taken a liking to me during one of her infrequent visits to Ghimeş and told my parents how much she would like to have me come and spend time with her. So my mother gladly sent me away.

While there, this woman, whose name I vaguely remember to be Fruma Meshkin, kept telling me how much she had wanted to have a child just like me, but God had denied her. She seemed like a good person, although easily overcome with emotions. She cried at the slightest irritation, even though her husband, who played a minor supporting role in that household, always did all he could to cheer her up. The woman blamed herself for everything: the *flanken* being overcooked, the wilting of the flowers outside the windowsill of the room I was sleeping in, but most distressingly, the fact that she was barren. It was difficult to like this woman; she was always in such a state of emotional upheaval. Though I felt sorry for her, I was happy when the two weeks were up and I went home. As I was about to leave the woman's house for the last time, she rushed over to me, wrapped her arms around me, and started bawling. I stood there, gasping for breath, as she squeezed my head into her chest. I was convinced the woman was out of her mind.

When I got home, I was not asked one question about my time with Fruma Meshkin, but I noticed that after dinner my parents suddenly developed the habit of walking outside in the back yard, away from the house, for what looked like secret discussions. These discussions often led to fierce arguments that ended with my mother calling my father a blind fool.

One night, when the recurring argument ended earlier than usual, my parents walked back into the house, and my mother told me to sit; she had something to tell me. My father looked ashen. She started by asking me in an uncharacteristically sweet voice if I remembered Fruma Meshkin who had been so kind and loving to me when I visited her in Tîrgu Ocna a few months back. I froze, which for once didn't seem to aggravate her. She switched to a firmer tone, telling me that we were very poor, and I would probably never get married because we didn't have enough money for a dowry. Then she stopped and looked into my eyes for my reaction. I didn't show any. She placed her hand on my head and told me that if I went to live with Aunt Fruma, I would have the best clothes and, when the time came, a big dowry so I could marry a rich, educated man.

I immediately started crying hysterically saying that I didn't want to leave, that I wanted to be with my brother, and my horse, and that I loved my family. My mother, never one to be impressed by emotional displays, said that she and my father had already decided what would be best for me, and that I better start packing because I was going to leave in the morning. I began screaming that I wasn't going to live with that crazy woman, and tried to explain how weird she had been, how she was always hiding behind closed doors and crying sometimes whole days at the time.

My mother dismissed my arguments as lame excuses meant to embarrass her, as she had already written to Aunt Fruma, letting her know that I was coming. Besides, Aunt Fruma had already sent them a lot of money, which they were going to spend on Sammy's education. I had to go, my mother concluded, or else Sammy wouldn't get an education and I would never get married.

I ran out of the house shrieking and hid under the burlap cover of my father's cart. I just lay there, under the damp cover, with my knees against my chin crying as quietly as I could, wishing I were dead. After about an hour, my father pulled the cover off, and picked me up in his thick arms. It looked like he had been crying too. He told me that I didn't have to go, that he had convinced my mother that I could remain in Ghimeş, and, with a glimmer in his eye, pointed out that a beautiful girl like me didn't need a dowry to marry a handsome boy. After that day, my mother said very little, not just to me, but to everyone else in the house. She simply put herself beyond our reach and turned herself into something mechanical, devoid of human emotions. I was delighted that my mother stopped picking on me, and as far as my father and Sammy were concerned, they too seemed satisfied with my mother's new attitude. From that point on until just before she died, she was solely the housekeeper.

With my mother's toxic behavior in check, I began enjoying myself again. As I mentioned earlier, we had a horse, an old broken-down nag that I loved. My father had him pull his tinker's cart whenever he went out-of-town, but whenever he was home, Alborak was mine, all mine. I loved riding him, but my butt was always sore for days after that. Then I had a brilliant idea. I tied one of my mother's old aprons around his belly, after stuffing rags into the front pocket. When I climbed on his back, I made sure the rags were between my butt and his back. Afterwards, I never had a sore butt again.

As soon as Alborak knew I was on-board, he started moving, but at a pace that even chickens beat us. I would kick his ribs and yell "Giddy up" again and again, but to no avail. Undaunted, I would close my eyes and imagine that I was flying. I had the best of times on Alborak's back exploring the woods around Ghimeş or looking down into people's homes. And then he died. I cried for two days until my mother came up to me and slapped me and told me to shut up. That was one of the best lessons she ever taught me.

XV

We left Ghimeş in August of 1939, about two months after Alborak died, so God was kind to Alborak. We probably would have had to sell him to the Gentile butcher on the other side of town before we left if he had still been alive. Fate wasn't quite so kind to Bercu. Despite all my "whys," we left him behind and I sensed that even my father concurred with the decision. I don't know why, but I'm crying now thinking how I used to run to school with Bercu between my legs, climbing up that muddy hill and kissing him 'good bye' and instructing him to wait for me like a good boy while I was inside learning how to be a princess.

The reason we left Ghimeş was not because we were running away from the Germans; the Germans didn't start rounding up Jews until much later. It was the Hungarians. They were just as bad as the Germans. Suddenly they started showing up in bands of eight or ten on horseback. They carried leather whips and guns. They beat people up just for being on the street while they were riding through. If someone tried to run away while being whipped, they shot him in the head.

The Hungarians didn't make killing Jews the science project the Germans did with their ovens and gas chambers, but they killed them just as heartlessly. The Hungarians didn't have the German temperament; when they found a Jew, they just shot him right then and there, no big production.

The thing I've always found baffling about the Germans was not their hatred of Jews, but their ability to control their feelings while they were perfecting their so called 'final solution'. It took years of scientific research to develop new improved methods for killing people. First they had to discover a new lethal gas and then invent an oven the size of a barn. Think of all that engineering: drafting blue prints, letting out government contracts, and finally building those vast steel and concrete structures that would befit the glory of German ingenuity. The Hungarians had a soul, granted a dark, miserable soul, but a soul nonetheless. The Germans were just machines.

The Jews didn't count. When the war broke out, the Hungarians began their murderous raids on Jewish villages. My father wasn't going to wait until it happened to us, besides the Gentile who had been selling my father tinkering supplies for twenty years suddenly decided that he wasn't going to do business with my father because he was Jewish. My father thought it was very ironic because this man had been to our house, always bringing little gifts for me and my brother, had dinner with us, and even played with me on his lap.

My father, who was very smart, knew that the world had turned upside down and told us one morning that we should pack whatever we could carry with us and that we were leaving. By the next day, or maybe it was the day after, we left Ghimeş. I heard my father tell my mother that we were going to Galaţi. I had no idea where that was.

We said good bye to the people we knew, the men cried, the women wondered who was going to fix their pots and pans, and then we left on foot with just the things on our backs. We walked out of our house, leaving behind everything as it was, furniture, china, and most of our clothes. My mother kept cursing my father under her breath; the furniture had been her dowry. But it was cheap, old furniture, and even she realized that was not enough to risk our lives. The fact that the Hungarians raped a young woman who lived next door the night before finally swayed her.

XVI

We walked from Ghimeş to Galaţi, a big port city on the Danube River; my father knew that trains were patrolled by the security forces of Antonescu's Fascist regime. My father walked ahead strapped to his cart like a beast of burden, never complaining, never asking Sammy to relieve him; Sammy was seventeen at the time, tall and brawny, yet he never offered. Whenever we saw a town coming up the road, we avoided it, not knowing what kind of reception we might receive. The rules of hospitality did not apply to Jews.

We had been on the road for about a week; nights were cool and pleasant and my brother and I slept under a rough, itchy burlap cover my mother brought along. It looked like the same one that my father used to cover his tinker's cart. I remember staring at the sky and asking Sammy if God was looking down at us making sure that we were safe. He would turn away from me and mutter that I was a bigger fool than he ever thought, and that, after two thousand years of unrelenting suffering, punctuated every couple of decades with massacres justified simply by our mere existence, any Jew who still believed in God was either an idiot or a useless daydreamer. Sammy said that he didn't want to be either. I silently begged God not to take him seriously, and that he was only a boy who could get moody at times.

On occasion, we passed other travelers, but no one gave us any trouble. We exchanged brief greetings, sometimes just a few nods of the head, and then my father politely asked if we were on the right road to Galaţi.

The only thing out of the ordinary that happened during our journey was passing a gypsy caravan. There was a single line of maybe ten horse-drawn carts packed with people and furniture. The women, dressed in colorful skirts and blouses, were either driving the carts or sitting on a bench at the back of each cart talking gratingly in their own language, though I got a pretty good idea what they were saying watching their hand movements.

My mother grabbed me and turned me around, while spitting "Feh! Feh!"

The men looked like they were resting on beds inside the carts. The children, and there were many, were playing around the carts, screaming and yelling, and jumping in front of the horses and the screeching cartwheels. I was trying to turn my head to watch the spectacle without my mother noticing when a little gypsy girl came up to me and offered to sell me a small bouquet of roadside flowers. I told her I didn't have any money and then my mother told her to shoo. The girl gave me a smile that showed her missing front teeth, pushed the bouquet into my hand and ran away. As we were walking away, I turned back and saw the little girl perching her head from behind one of the carts. She was laughing with her whole face and blowing me kiss.

CHAPTER 2
Galati
1939-1942

*G*reta *had one of her better days. When she woke earlier, she didn't feel any pain, and her energy, something that she had felt waning alarmingly over the last ten or so years, seemed to have at least temporarily returned. She had just come back from spending an afternoon in the Oak Room at the Plaza with Kitty. She doesn't remember having laughed so much in years. They each had a large cappuccino and a plate of chocolate cookies. It was delightful to spend time with an old friend. She hadn't seen Kitty in ages, but this burdensome assignment of recording her life story has suddenly filled her with the urge to be with someone who knew her in the old days. Kitty is the last of her once many friends still living in the City. The few others still alive are either down in Florida or across the Atlantic.*

She's back in her apartment comfortably attired to continue her project and she turns on the recorder.

I

When we arrived in Galați, we went to the house of a man my father knew. The man was from Ghimeș, but left before my father got married. They had been best friends from the time they were little children. When my father walked up to the man who was sitting on his porch, he didn't recognize my father at first, but after they spent a minute staring at one another, the man threw his arms around my father and hugged him and blessed him. Then he showed us into his house, which was a lot bigger than our old shack, and he lived there alone with just his wife.

Their last name was Balter; I don't remember their first names. They had no children. Sammy and I got our own room and my parents ended up with a huge room with its own private bathroom.

We never saw such a big house before. They had electricity, and a huge kitchen with running water, and the street outside the house was paved. The house was made of brick and mortar, not like our house back in Ghimeş, which consisted of strips of clapboard nailed together that my father had stuffed with clumps of hay and dried mud to keep out the wind and the rain. It was heaven, at least at first. There was a great library in one of the rooms that my brother just couldn't get enough of. During the time we lived there, he must have read every book. I didn't read anything; all I wanted to do was to get boys to run after me, and they did.

We lived in Galati for three years – a long time – though I don't remember much happening during this period other than two activities that seemed to have occupied most of the time the six of us spent together: celebrating Shabbat, which took up Friday evenings and Saturdays all day, and listening to the radio, which was observed just as faithfully on Sundays.

II

My father went into business with Mr. Balter. It was some kind of shipping business. Mr. Balter owned a silo, where farmers would come and sell their grain, mostly wheat and corn, and then Mr. Balter would arrange to have all this grain loaded onto ships that traveled up the Danube. The ships went to Hungary and Austria, but most of the grain ended up feeding German soldiers, and this bothered Sammy.

I remember Sammy, his face red with rage, shouting at my father and Mr. Balter that, since one of the objectives of the Germans was to cleanse the world of Jews, my father and Mr. Balter were accomplices in the annihilation of their own people, and because of that they deserved to be sent to a concentration camp. News of the death camps was rumored everywhere. This was early 1941.

III

The Balters and my father wanted to send me to school. They had a big public school just down the street, but my mother said I knew enough, besides I was needed around the house. She was losing her strength, which made her angrier and even more intolerant of everyone. In Ghimeş she had been as strong as an ox, but it always seemed to me that all her strength came from pent-up fury and displeasure with everything and everyone around her.

In Galaţi, I was perfectly happy not to have to go to school any more. I had already been through seven years of school, but never very good at it; besides, I could sit on the front porch and watch the schoolboys walk by in the afternoons as they passed on their way home. My mother kept wondering why I had to be outside the house everyday around the time the school let out. I told her that I was waiting for Sammy with a glass of fresh lemonade.

Everyday around three o'clock, Sammy, a senior in high school, would emerge from behind the red brick house at the corner, in the company of several other sober-looking schoolboys. Every one of them looked grown-up and smart, but Sammy was the most handsome. He was easily a head taller and, with his neatly cropped blond hair, he looked like a studious version of Clark Gable – just add a pair of horn-rimmed glasses and erase the pencil moustache. As soon as I saw him, I would run up to him, flashing a great smile, and hand him the glass of lemonade. Then I would run back in the house before the other boys, who at that moment seemed to have been zapped into state of deep freeze, had a chance to decide whether I was real or just a mirage.

IV

One day, Sammy brought home one of the boys he met at school. His name was Otto. He had a dark complexion and his brow was furrowed, making him look like he was in a constant state of irritation, though I think he was just squinting. Sammy

45

had him over to play ping-pong. The Balters had a ping-pong table in their basement – actually a rough piece of plywood on top of two saw horses. I was there watching them play. During one game, Otto bent down to pick up the ball and his glasses fell out of his shirt pocket. One of the lenses popped out and I picked it up. It was thicker than the proverbial Coke bottle. I handed it back to him, and he smiled and thanked me. He wasn't bad looking. He was slim and quite tall and his black hair was brushed straight back, very grown-up. But what I think attracted me most was the shape of his mouth, which arched downward giving him a perpetual look of sadness. I also liked the fact that he wanted me to like him: why else would he not wear his glasses.

Otto started coming over almost everyday after school. And I could tell that he had just removed his glasses; the deep red notch across the bridge of his nose gave him away. Sammy liked playing ping-pong with him. He had told us that Otto was the best ping-pong player in school. Yet, Sammy could easily beat him at home. I was the only one who knew the reason. Otto cared more that I liked him than winning at ping-pong. He also got so red when he saw me.

My mother knew I was turning into a woman and that I would soon need a husband. Her only prerequisite was that he was rich. She didn't want me to have her life – just poverty and suffering. All I wanted was to meet a handsome prince who would take me to his castle and make passionate love to me. By then I had outgrown my earlier fantasy of having a prince take me to his castle so I can play with mice all day without being yelled at.

One day, after Mr. Balter had added another light bulb in the basement, Otto, still without his glasses, finally won a game. I was impressed and I let him know by giving him a smile. The next game, he won again. I again gave him a smile and congratulated him. In the third game, I could see that Sammy was getting frustrated and playing recklessly. Sammy, who up until then had always kept the score, began cheating. A few times, he called Otto's ball out, when in fact it had tipped the table. Otto never

Andrew Warren

challenged him; he just raised his game another notch.

Then, when the score was tied 19-19, Sammy smashed the ball, but it went long. Otto called it out. Sammy lost his cool and started screaming that the ball tipped the edge. Otto apologized but stood firm. Suddenly, out of nowhere, Sammy lunged at him and started swinging his fists, but none of them landed, which got him even more frustrated. Otto had no intention of hitting Sammy back, but grabbed his wrists and forced him down to the floor. I then jumped on Otto's back and started punching his head to which Otto responded by standing up and waiting for me to stop. That's when my mother showed up and lifted me off Otto's back. Otto turned to my mother, bid her goodbye, and quickly walked out. That was the last time I saw Otto.

My brother never invited anyone else to the house after the Otto incident. Yet my mother kept asking him to bring boys over, especially if he knew they came from "a good family." My brother angrily refused, saying that he didn't want to be involved in slave trading his sister. I knew my brother was trying to protect me out of love, but I wouldn't have minded if a rich boy came and paid my parents a lot of money, which would have made their lives easier, and then taken me to his great mansion where I would sit around eating bonbons, when he didn't want to make love to me. Years later, a rich man came, but no bonbons.

V

The Balters were much more religious than my parents and Shabbat was a big deal in their house. Every Friday, Mr. Balter came home smelling from *brilliantine* as he would have stopped by the barbershop on the way home. Even though he shaved that morning, he would always get the barber to give him a few smoothing touchups. In the meantime, Mrs. Balter would always take a bath, which included scraping the soles of her feet with a large pumice stone, but not before she cleaned the house from top to bottom and placed fresh cut daisies in every room.

While Mrs. Balter was fixing the house, my mother would reign in the kitchen. For Shabbat she always baked two challahs; when we lived in Ghimeş, she only baked one, but Mr. Balter had explained that two loaves were necessary to remind us of the double portion of manna that fell on the Jewish people during their 40 years of wandering in the Desert.

During the first two years we stayed in Galaţi, the kosher butcher carried a large assortment of meats and my mother would always surprise us with a great Shabbat meal: one week we had beef, the next week we had chicken, but only once in a while she made fish, though she only made it because Mr. Balter loved fish. By 1941, with the war raging at our door, the kosher butcher stopped carrying meat, and my mother needed to expand her repertoire of fish dishes, which she did, though not without her usual complaints. In the last couple of months we stayed at the Balters, we ate carp almost every Shabbat, a fish that local fishermen had caught that morning in the Danube.

Everything had to be finished right before sunset, and just when I was sure that something was going to go wrong – Mr. Balter wouldn't be home on time or my mother wouldn't be finished with her cooking or Sammy wouldn't yet be home from school – a miracle always happened and everyone was ready.

Mr. Balter would start every Shabbat by telling us why we celebrated this greatest of Jewish holy days, and even though he had said it the week before and the week before that, he would still take the time, and sometimes it was more time than my stomach was willing to tolerate, to give us the reasons: "We celebrate Shabbat to honor God's creation of the Universe in seven days; we also celebrate Shabbat to commemorate our redemption from slavery in Egypt. *Umein!*"

Then Mr. Balter would lead us in the blessings over the wine and challah. My father was in charge of pouring the wine, which Mr. Balter had brought up that morning from his cellar. Right about the time of our arrival, Mr. Balter had bought a large stock of kosher wines from the local wine merchant; he wasn't much worried about what the Germans were going to do to him, but he wasn't going to take any risks with his kosher wine supply.

At the proper time, my mother would enter the dining room with her two beautiful challahs concealed under an exquisite blue and gold embroidered challah cover that had been part of Mrs. Balter's dowry, and everyone, in unison, would go "aaah," and my mother, who rarely showed emotions, would purse her lips as if trying to cover up a modesty-laced smile.

After dinner, Mr. and Mrs. Balter and my parents would go to the neighborhood *shul* and not return sometimes until after nine o'clock. Sammy and I stayed home and played cards, usually gin, as that was the only card game in which I would occasionally manage to beat Sammy.

The next morning, Saturday, Mr. Balter and my father went back to *shul*, while Mrs. Balter and my mother spent the time gossiping. Mrs. Balter seemed to have become my mother's confidant, and my mother relished telling and retelling stories that she had heard back in Ghimeş, which, as I remember, kept constantly changing, evolving into bawdier tales. Mrs. Balter had lived a very sheltered life that greatly limited the number of stories she could offer my mother in return, which was why about a year into our stay in Galaţi, the gossip sessions between Mrs. Balter and my mother were reduced to occasional reminders of next day's menus.

Sammy would often spend the day with his school friends while I simply did nothing, but somehow I never felt bored. In the afternoon, after Mr. Balter and my father came back from *shul*, we engaged in the most controversial activity of all our time in Galaţi: we played Rummykub. I remember once Sammy called Mr. Balter a hypocrite, but Mr. Balter, choking with emotions, defended himself by saying that Rummykub is allowed to be played on Shabbat because it is not one of the 39 categories of *melakhah* specifically mentioned in the *Mishna*, the book of Jewish laws. For months afterwards, Mr. Balter revisited his defense at the beginning of every Rummykub game, each time adding a new point to support his argument.

"They didn't play Rummykub during the building of the Tabernacle, did they?" I remember Mr. Balter once saying with great aplomb. My mother and I didn't play; we just kibitzed. But the men and Mrs. Balter were involved in what seemed like crucial tactical battles, which, though they separated the winners from the losers by only pennies, they otherwise precipitated the most animated debates over proper playing strategies. It was not uncommon to have Mr. Balter reduce Mrs. Balter to tears over an innocuous comment, like "I was a bit confused, *schatzi*, when you tossed that red 10."

VI

Sundays were devoted to listening to the radio. The Balters had a huge Telefunken radio in their bedroom, and although on week days we were not allowed in, on Sundays, the radio would have been moved to a corner table, and six chairs were placed in a semicircle around it, two in front and the other four right behind them. During the hour and a half devoted to listening to the radio, Mrs. Balter made sure that no one went hungry, as there was always an ample supply of small sandwiches of liver pâté embedded with sliced gherkins.

I would have preferred to go for a walk or just sit around and daydream, but it seemed that failure to attend the Sunday radio sessions was perceived by my mother not just as an act of disrespect towards our hosts, the Balters, but also as confirmation of my otherwise undeniable crass stupidity. I frankly didn't care, but she seemed determined to get me to fall in line. I was too old to get slapped and withholding food was never a big deterrent for me, so, as a sign of her dissatisfaction with what she called my nasty disposition during the previous radio session, she resorted to small cruelties, like throwing out the flowers in my room or spilling out the lemonade I had made for Sammy just before I had a chance to bring it out to him when he came home from school.

On Sundays around 10 o'clock, we would all converge on the Balters bedroom, where Mr. Balter would already be sitting on one of the front chairs slowly turning the dial while keeping his ear right up against the radio's giant speaker, looking like an expert safecracker. Our presence did not seem to distract him, as he continued to move the dial ever so slowly searching for news of the world around us. My father would take the chair next to Mr. Balter, while the rest of us would sit behind.

Mr. Balter's search would invariably lead to one of the Romanian-language stations which broadcast comedy programs, like Radio-Papagal with Tudor Arghezi or Stroe și Vasilache in *Alo, alo, aici e Radio*. I thought they were hilarious and I would always beg Mr. Balter to stop and let us listen in for a while. Mr. Balter would respond by looking at my father for help, but before my father had a chance to intervene, my mother would decree that the programs were stupid and I was stupid. When I tried to get Sammy's support, he gave me a look I might have expected if I had been a foul piece of carp on his Shabbat plate.

Years later I met Nicu Stroe at one of Lena's parties and I told him that I had wanted to listen to his radio program when I was a young girl, but my parents wouldn't let me, so he said he would make it up to me and that night he put on a live program just for me. He actually made up a song on the spot with 'Greta' in it. It was great fun.

I know I promised not to digress, but here I must. Earlier, I checked, as I've often done since I've been recording my life story, the Romanian-language Wikipedia – yes, this 88-year old woman has a computer and knows how to surf the Internet – and read under the entry for "Stroe și Vasilache" that the program was started in 1932 by the Jewish Nicolae Stroe and the Romanian Vasile Vasilache. I am sure the writer did not mean to be unkind, but the article was perfect evidence that, no matter for how many generations a Jewish family had been on Romanian soil, it would never qualify as Romanian.

Mr. Balter's interest in the radio was the news, news of the world, news of the war, news of what might happen to us, Jews of Galati, as we seemed to be right in the middle of the German Army's path on its way to Russia. The news never came from Romanian stations as they, like me, seemed to take little interest in the war. Most of the programs Mr. Balter found of interest were either in German or English, a language that he alone understood.

Mr. Balter's anxiety came mostly from what he heard during the English broadcasts, which he would later translate. I had rarely seen Mr. Balter show emotions; usually, he was of a calm, cheerful disposition, mostly interested in making sure everyone around him was comfortable. But on two occasions while listening to the radio, I saw his face suddenly contort with worry, as he screamed from the top of his lungs, "Oh my God! Oh my God! Oh my God!" – once when he heard that Germany occupied Poland, as Mr. Balter's brother lived in Cracow, and another, about a year later, when we all heard during German-language broadcast that all Jews had to wear Yellow Stars.

Although I should not have been surprised, it was still interesting to hear how differently the German-language broadcasts presented the news compared to Mr. Balter's gloomy translations. I remember hearing a German female announcer joyously announce that the glorious German Army entered Paris and the Parisians welcomed them with flowers. By contrast, the English-language broadcast, announced the fall of Paris to the Germans as one of the bleakest days in history.

The last broadcasts I listened to before we left Galați covered the German Army's advances in Russia, and for once the English announcers, though they may not have shared the happy mood of the German broadcasts, seemed to agree that the Germans were rapidly advancing and the fall of the Soviet Union was imminent. I remember Mr. Balter, in a rare exhibition of emotions, grabbing my father's arm and violently shaking it while yelling at him that if Russia fell, it would be only a matter of time before Germany won the war, and that would be the end of us Jews. Mr. Balter had lost his mind I thought: how could that be, there were just too many of us Jews in the world. I also remember Sammy running out on the street and shouting obscenities.

VII

One night I was in bed just about to fall asleep when I saw Sammy climbing out the window. At first, I didn't realize it was Sammy; I thought it was a burglar, so I started screaming. Sammy jumped at me, wrapped his hand around my mouth and told me to shut up or else he'd beat the crap out of me. He told me he had an important meeting. I told him that a date with a girl did not qualify as an important meeting. He told me that he was going to a real meeting with men, real men – resistance fighters. This was the beginning of his connection with the Communist Party. It was madness because if he had gotten caught, he would have been shot on the spot. But he didn't care. It was a miracle he survived. During the war the Communists made him go on the most dangerous missions, like blowing up bridges and sinking ships docked in the port – some of them probably carrying grain from Mr. Balter's silo – and then puffed him up by calling him one of the bravest fighters of the Romanian Communist Resistance. But after the war, they never rewarded him or even officially thanked him, as they did for his comrades, which made him very bitter.

By 1942, things got very dangerous for the Jews in Galați. The Germans had taken over the city, and Jewish families were being methodically rounded up and deported. By then the rumors of concentration camps were confirmed as eye witnesses found their way back and talked about them, yet we still were afraid to even mention the words "extermination camps" to ourselves. That's when my father decided that we must once again get on the road, and we did.

This time it was Sammy who was against leaving, but no one could argue with my father. When he said go, we went. Maybe that's what saved Sammy's life. Had he stayed and kept doing his nighttime activities, he would have ended up dead. But he didn't see it that way. He saw it as desertion. I never saw him so angry – he spat at my father. My father wiped the spit off his face and grabbed Sammy by the scruff of his neck and shouted at him that as long as he was still the head of the family he expected his family to obey him, besides he was not going to stand by and allow his son to be killed fighting for people who cared for us Jews as little as the Germans. Obviously, my father knew all along about my brother's nightly "dates." Sammy made some lame attempts at arguing with my father, but I suspect that he was himself beginning to realize that these resistance fighters were no friends of the Jews; they just allowed guys like Sammy to join them as long as they could use them for their riskiest missions. The future proved my father right. The next day we left the Balters. My father tried to convince them to join us, but Mr. Balter reasoned that the Germans would never touch him because he ran a successful shipping business that helped the German war effort. We found out years later that two weeks after we left, he and his wife were deported to a concentration camp. No one ever heard from them again.

VIII

Two days later, we were in Bucharest. We snuck onto a freight train and by morning we found ourselves on the outskirts of the great city. To stay on the train any longer would have been risky, as the rail yards were patrolled by armed guards with dogs, so we jumped off. Well, Sammy and I and my father jumped off; we somehow had to pull my mother off the train. She was paralyzed with fear even though, miraculously, the train had stopped. She kept screaming that the train could start moving again at any moment, and, with her luck, she would end up with one leg on and one leg off and she'd be ripped in half.

My mother never loved me, nor do I think she ever loved anyone else, with the possible exception of Sammy. As I said earlier, my father dealt with it by occasionally getting drunk and by indulging in meaningless dalliances. Sammy dealt with it by immersing himself in fanatical causes, where the only prerequisites were an abundance of passion. Her early death, of which I will talk about later, allowed the three of us to begin building the myth of the suffering woman, dedicated to her family, despite great physical afflictions.

IX

I'm about to digress again. It's the lingering image of my screaming mother half on and half off the train that reminds me of something I've been wanting to say for years, but always felt that I had to behave like a lady and keep my mouth shut. I want to get it off my chest now. Whenever I mention Transylvania I get the same reaction: raised eyebrows, a stupid smile, and, once in a while, the question: "Isn't that where Dracula's from?"

Dracula is a novel about a blood-sucking fiend who lived in Transylvania. Apparently, the writer was inspired by a story he heard of the medieval Romanian king Vlad the Impaler, who killed his enemies by shishkebbabing them on ten-foot spears and then leaving them in plain site as a warning against those who sought to defeat him.

The real Vlad, Vlad III, who happened to be been born in a region of Romania called Transylvania, is a national Romanian hero for having kept the far greater Turkish armies from overrunning Romania, and for that matter much of Christian Europe. Since his tiny band of men would have been trounced had he been foolish enough to directly engage the Turkish hordes, he resorted to cunning and intimidation. One night, he and his men, disguised as Turkish soldiers crept into the enemy camp while everyone was asleep. Thousands of Turkish soldiers were hacked to death that night and the few who survived fled across the Danube. Vlad knew the Turks would be back with a vengeance, so he had the road leading from the Danube crossing to Bucharest lined with giant spears on which he impaled the bodies of the dead soldiers. That's how the name Vlad the Impaler came about. So you see, Vlad was simply defending his land in medieval fashion, no crueler than any of his Western contemporaries, so there is no logical connection between him, a man of great courage and cunning, and a vampire.

The image of my terrified mother, with one leg on the train and the other dangling precariously above the ground, worried that she'd be torn in half, reminded me of Vlad the Impaler. Ultimately, the Turks captured Vlad and extracted their revenge by having his body yanked apart by four camels strapped to his limbs.

CHAPTER 3
Wartime Bucharest
1942-1945

Long moments of silence pass. The recorder is still running, yet only soft humming can be heard. Suddenly there is a loud coughing sound, Greta's, followed by the gurgling sound of liquid slowly draining down a throat, no doubt Greta's, no doubt not water.

I

We finally arrived in Bucharest. This time we were without friends or connections, and my father without any marketable skills; a tinker in Bucharest was as much in demand as a tent maker. What kept us hopeful were Mr. Balter's parting words to my father that Bucharest had a big Jewish community and we should have no trouble finding someone to help us. He also told my father to watch out for German soldiers, as Bucharest was inside German-occupied territory. Surprisingly though, I did not see many German soldiers, and the Jews of Bucharest, as I remember, didn't seem much worried about either the war raging just beyond the city gates or, worse, about being deported to a concentration camp.

The only reminder of the German presence in Bucharest was the enormous red flag with a black swastika at its center that flew over a building on Boulevard King Carol that had once been one of King Michael's palaces. I remember walking underneath it and not experiencing the kind of dread and anxiety one expects under the circumstances. I even remember passing a German soldier who acknowledged me with a tip of his head and a smile and a "Gutten tag." I smiled back and wished him "Viel Glück." Imagine! Years later, when the Soviet Army occupied Bucharest, things were a lot worse, but more about that later.

After we left the rail yard, we started walking aimlessly through the city, each of us carrying a big rucksack on our backs and one large fishnet bag in each hand. Several times we thought of stopping someone to ask for directions, but we realized there was no point since we didn't know where we were going, and it was probably of little use to ask a stranger where good fortune was likely to be found. Around midday, we stopped on a city bench and ate a stale sandwich of chicken liver on thick black bread that Mrs. Balter had prepared for us before we left Galaţi. There were street vendors selling carbonated drinks of different colors, which I would have loved to try as they looked awfully good, but my mother gave me a dirty look, so I settled for water from a spigot that came out of a building.

It was getting dark and my mother told us that if we didn't find something soon she would lie down in the middle of the sidewalk. My father assured her that we would soon find a place to stay the night, but I was looking in his eyes and I knew he didn't believe it.

Suddenly, we found ourselves walking inside a big, deserted park – I later found out it was called Chishmigiu. We were trudging through the park when my mother suddenly slumped on a park bench and yelled out "Ich ken shoyn nicht." My father looked around, and then started laughing hysterically. Sammy and I thought he had gone mad. My mother cursed him, but that didn't quench his enthusiasm. He finally calmed down enough to share with us his realization.

"Your mother has found us the perfect place to camp," he shouted. "Look what we have here: two long benches back to back, one for your mother, the other for me and a nice soft grassy place under that huge oak tree, where you two will be sleeping. We have a water fountain on one side of the benches and a large garbage can on the other. What more do we want? It's a perfect spot for squatters like us."

It was a warm, clear night, so we didn't mind, except for my mother, who by then was complaining about everything. One of the rucksacks, the one Sammy was carrying, was filled with food that Mrs. Balter had packed for us; in addition to the stale chicken liver sandwiches, we had hard salami, feta cheese, a few tomatoes, an onion, two loaves of black bread, a jar of *gribenes*, and some wild cherry preserves. There was even a carton of cigarettes for my father, which my mother threw in the garbage can before my father retrieved it.

We all went to sleep right away; we were exhausted. We didn't even take our shoes off. In the middle of the night I opened my eyes and caught sight of my father putting blankets on all of us. When he saw that I had my eyes opened, he smiled and gently tapped my head. I went right back to sleep.

When we woke up that first morning, we saw a few people, and they saw us, but when they didn't seem to get perturbed about our presence, we relaxed. I imagined something good would happen.

My mother had been up for a while and had prepared breakfast; she had had a good night's sleep and was in the best spirits I had seen her in a long time. She had cut up thin slivers of bread on which she placed combinations of salami and feta or gribenes and a slice of onion or tomato and feta. It was delicious, although I would have enjoyed a glass of hot tea on the side. She had never mixed foods before, so I took this as a good omen.

After breakfast, my father took off. He told us he'd be back later. Nothing else. Sammy and I walked over to a pond within sight of our camp, and watched the swans swimming in circles. We found some week-old breadcrumbs in our pockets, and we scattered them on the grass in front of us. Suddenly dozens of swans stormed out of the water and surrounded us. They were making terrible noises, but I loved it. Later we walked around the park. That took us along beautiful, winding gravel paths that swerved gently around big old trees and small ponds covered with pink and blue lilies. There were birds in the trees and flying above our heads that chirped frantically as if they were auditioning for the loudest peep. And the sun was streaming down on us. We had no idea where we were heading, and hardly saw anybody along the way, but an hour or so later, we found ourselves back at our camp and the noisy swan pond. It felt like I was in paradise.

As we were standing on the side of the pond searching our pockets for more crumbs, my mother found the strength to come over and bawl us out for wasting food on those stupid, evil birds. For a while she entertained the idea of catching a swan and roasting it right there in the park. Not surprisingly, when my mother showed up, all the birds fled back into the water. We returned to our camp.

It must have been one or two o'clock when I saw in the distance my father's figure sauntering towards us. He quickly informed us that he had found an apartment just outside the park at a very reasonable rent and we could move in that afternoon. The landlady was a Jewish widow who was looking for a good family to move in.

Sammy looked at my father, "I thought we didn't have any money. How are we going to pay any rent, even a very reasonable one?"

My father smiled and reached inside the lining of his coat. In his hand he had a small roll of frayed bills. It amounted to 250 lei that he had saved during the time he worked with Mr. Balter. The rent would be forty lei per month and we should be able to feed ourselves for about sixty lei, which meant we had nothing to worry about for at least two months.

We loaded our stuff back into the rucksacks and followed my father towards our new residence. As we were passing the gates of the park, I looked back and promised myself that if I ever lost my way, I would return to the spot we spent our first night in Bucharest, and I would be all right. It wasn't a long walk. We crossed the wide boulevard outside the park and entered Saint Constantine Street. Our apartment was at No. 12 on the second floor. My father already had the key, so we climbed the two flights of stairs and walked right in.

The apartment came furnished with some old furniture, which after the widow died two or three years later became my parents' since no one ever came to claim it. It was a big apartment, but very dark. Past the front door, there was a long hallway lit by a feeble electric bulb that hung precariously from the ceiling. To the left of the hallway, there was a small bathroom with an old cast iron bathtub that sat on three lion's paws and two bricks stacked on top of each other. Next to the bathroom was the kitchen that came with a wooden table and four invalid chairs that over the years my father kept trying to fix until he finally gave up and chose the two best ones and threw the others out. By then Sammy and I had long gone out on our own.

There was also an ancient wood stove that more than once threatened to burn down the apartment. Beyond the kitchen there was a dining room commanded by an imposing oval table that, given the serious gashes in its top, seemed to have been involved in some grim conflict. The dining room chairs, in solidarity with the kitchen chairs, bobbled just as perilously. In fact, during a dinner my parents gave a few months after we moved in, one of the guests, a woman, whose only attribute I remember was her ample size, crushed one of the chairs as she crashed to the ground. The dining room's only attractive feature was its relative brightness as it had windows on two sides.

On the other side of the gloomy hallway, there were two rooms separated by an open pantry that, given the large oil stain on the floor, seemed to have been used by the previous tenant as storage of automotive parts. The room before the pantry became Sammy's bedroom, which he shared with ceiling-height piles of bric-a-brac left to us by the widow with her full blessings. When, however, my mother suggested to her that we didn't really need all that junk, the widow got very offended and accused us of being a bunch of ungrateful peasants. The room on the other side of the pantry became my parents' bedroom. It had an old-fashioned armoire that also seemed to have been subjected to a series of vicious clashes and a large bed in slightly better condition, though a big squeaker whenever my father got into one of his late-night coughing bouts. I left the pantry for last because that was where I ended up.

That first day we moved into the apartment, my father and Sammy, on the widow's counsel, brought up from the basement a metal cot, which they placed in the pantry against the wall to my parents' bedroom. Since it had no mattress, I had the choice of one of the several dusty, threadbare rugs rolled up in Sammy's room. I picked the two thickest ones and took them down in the courtyard where I wacked them with the rug beater for a good hour until they finally stopped spewing dust. I often remember that small, uncomfortable bed and the sappy dreams I had lying on it. When I left that apartment to get married a few months later, the only thing I remember asking about my future life was whether I was going to end up sleeping on a soft bed in a sunny room. The rest I didn't care about.

My parents lived out their lives in that apartment. After my mother passed away fifteen years later, my father continued to live in that apartment for another twenty years with his second wife.

II

Within two weeks of our arrival in Bucharest, we received a note carried by a livery boy dressed in a snazzy uniform. To this day I have no idea how anyone found out we existed, but there it was: a note from a distant relative of my mother's, a second cousin or aunt or maybe even more distant than that, inviting us to tea at 4 o'clock on a weekday afternoon. The note was signed 'Mrs. Regina Schoenfeld'. The three of us looked at my mother, as she was desperately searching the deepest recesses of her brain for a connection, but none surfaced. My mother came from simple, peasant stock from northern Transylvania, around Satu Mare, and she could not imagine one of those people becoming a Bucharest socialite.

My father went out every morning knocking on doors, looking for work. He didn't find any, but in the two weeks preceding the arrival of the note, he got to know the city, and concluded that this Mrs. Schoenfeld lived in a very fancy part of Bucharest. He had walked through that neighborhood because he had heard that all the buildings in the area kept a handyman on staff in case something went wrong with the building, like a super does today. Sammy and I shook our heads when we heard what kind of jobs my father was looking for. After all, this was a man who spent his whole life fixing pots and pans and drinking beer in a town without electricity or plumbing. What did he know about elevators, gas ovens, or coal-fired boilers? But we agreed that if there was ever one man who could succeed at doing something he had no idea about, it was our father.

The invitation to Mrs. Schoenfeld's was for two weeks later, which gave us a lot of time to worry, but not enough time to do anything about it. We had no fancy clothes or decent shoes. The only one who we thought had something appropriate to wear was my father. It was his wedding suit. He had saved it during all these years, though he never wore it. Of course, when he tried it on, it was too small. He had put on a good thirty or forty pounds since his bachelor days. I still have my parents' wedding picture, so I know the suit, and I know how trim he was then. He loved to eat, and I'm sure the beer helped too, so when he tried on the suit he was barely able to pull the pants up to his knees, and shove one hand all the way through the sleeve, letting the rest of the jacket hang slovenly on the side. Looking like that, and wearing his giant white boxer shorts, he came into the dining room.

Sammy and I burst into screams of delight. My mother, not finding the situation at all humorous, began screeching like a hyena, and shoved him out the door. She followed that with a barrage of invectives, that were generally reserved for bazaar days back in Ghimeş when women started fighting over one thing or another, but usually about a man, a man who was one woman's husband and the other's lover. My father didn't mind. He was having a good time.

We realized, though, that we could not show up in the clothes we owned, as they were just a notch above dust rags. So we spent the following week worrying about how best to handle the situation; after all, on one hand we very much wanted to go; it would have given us an entrée into the Bucharest Jewish community; yet on the other, we didn't want to look like a bunch of homeless tramps.

Two days before the dreaded day of our invitation, my father showed up with a huge package and a grin so big that if it hadn't been for his ears lying in the way, it would have gone clear around his head. He laid the package on the table and told my mother to open it. It contained all kinds of fabric, a vision that verged on the miraculous, as we were in the middle of a war, and everything was scarce. There was a small roll of gray worsted and some beige gabardine for two new suits; there was enough white cotton cloth for a couple of shirts, enough navy blue chiffon to make a dress for my mother, and even a wonderfully gay piece in calico for a dress for me.

Once our excitement tempered, my mother, Sammy, and I started staring at each other, and then back at the fabric. What were we going to do with all that fabric? Wrap it around us like togas and say we just came from visiting Julius Caesar? My father laughed – I used to love his laughter; he laughed with his whole face, and he laughed so hard that tears would roll down his cheeks – as he informed my mother, "I hunt'em, you cook'em!"

"What the Hell is that supposed to mean?" my mother asked in Yiddish, capping it off with a curse.

My father walked into Sammy's room and brought out a Singer sewing machine. "There," he said with a look that suggested he had just discovered Plutonium.

"You expect me to sew two suits, two dresses and two shirts in two days? Are you crazy?" responded my mother.

"Sure," said my father calmly. "We'll all help you. What else do we have to do?"

My mother had done a lot of sewing in Ghimeş for another twenty years for another twenty years , but never on an electric sewing machine. We had a Pfaff sewing machine with a hand crank on its side with which my mother had made practically everything we wore, but that didn't guarantee success with this new machine, which kept confounding her. After the first few times the thread got snagged on itself, my mother accused the machine of being possessed and refused to continue. My father, with his gentle, cheerful manner, finally managed to convince her that she'd soon have it conquered. And she did, and after that she was flying.

For the next forty-eight hours, our apartment was turned into a garment factory, but I have to admit that throughout that whole time my mother never once complained about her ailments, and didn't sleep very much, as none of us did. But miraculously, and I can only account for this as an act of divine intervention, at three o'clock on the appointed day, my mother finished stitching Sammy's coat sleeve, and she was all done.

We had taken turns bathing that morning, so all we had left to do was put our wonderful new clothes on over our old undergarments, but those no one would see. Suddenly, in unison, staring at our bare feet, we all screamed: "Shoes!" The only shoes we had were the ones we traveled with from Galați. My parents and Sammy had leather shoes, granted the leather was cracked and the soles had worn off to the point where they were practically walking on their bare feet, but my father cut out cardboard insoles and stuck inside the shoes and my mother buffed them to a terrific shine. I only had a pair of open-back canvas sandals that Mrs. Balter had taken out of her closet just before we left. Mrs. Balter had wanted to give me a regular pair of shoes, but I had big feet.

At three-thirty, looking like movie stars at least from the ankles up, we left our apartment at St. Constantine Street #12. Half an hour later, as we walked slowly to avoid perspiring in our new clothes, we rang the bell of the mysterious Mrs. Schoenfeld. As we stood there, I found myself pushing my feet forward into the sandals to prevent my tough peasant heels from sticking out and giving me away.

III

When the door opened, I, for the first time in my life, breathed in the smell of wealth. Since then, over the years, I confirmed to myself again and again: affluence has a very pleasant, distinctive scent. The house was full of people, classy, elegant people, who spoke with great elocution, so we said as little as possible: 'thank you; thank you very much; no, thank you.'

I sat the whole time on a beautiful white brocade sofa, with my legs crossed, and a stupid smile on my face. I nervously kept rearranging the short puffy sleeves on my dress, and glancing over my body, as this was the first time I had a chance to see that I had really developed into an attractive young woman. The sight of me in a nicely fitted dress kept me so busy that I hardly had any time to notice what else was going on in the room. I am sure I would have been perfectly content to look at myself for a long time without feeling the least bit bored.

My mother sat at the other end of the ornate sofa, looking stern and indomitable as a sphinx. She probably figured that with that look there was less of a chance of anyone approaching her.

About an hour after our arrival, when most people seemed to have tired of staring at us the way one might at a diorama of prehistoric life in an anthropology museum, Mrs. Schoenfeld came to sit between us. She began talking to my mother with great verve. I remember trying to figure out her age, as there seemed to be some inconsistency between her mannerisms, which were those of a very young, excitable woman, and the condition of her facial skin, which, though concealed under layers of pasty makeup, attested to a more than insignificant sequence of harsh, demanding seasons. Her long, black hair, which she wore in a bun that resembled a birthday cake, was concealed behind a bejeweled black netting which glittered to distraction. She wore a black silk dress with a v-shaped décolleté that followed the long string of pearls cradled between her ample breasts. And she exuded a forceful aroma of fresh roses.

She spoke to my mother in Yiddish, but not before apologizing for having lost her fluency, a condition that didn't seem at all apparent to me. She was born in Satu Mare but, as she put it, mercifully left with her parents at a very young age, and really didn't know how things were back in the *shtetl*, which is why, as soon as she heard we were in town – she never said how she found out, but the Jewish community of Bucharest, though quite small, was fueled by potent gossip, so nothing stayed a secret for long – she wasted no time to have us over. Then she smiled and fleeted away, leaving my mother with a frozen smile on her face.

I divided the half hour after Mrs. Schoenfeld's abrupt departure between looking at my dress and looking at the crowd of affected people standing in small clusters, arguing with great conviction the merits of shorter hems. I occasionally turned to my mother who was still carrying the faint smile she had on when Mrs. Schoenfeld walked away. Every once in a while I would catch a glimpse of my father and Sammy who seemed to have parked themselves next to the hors d'oeuvres table and, except for the occasional exchange between them confirmed by one of them leaning towards the other, kept stuffing their faces.

Just as I was getting bored with my observations, someone sat next to me. I quickly turned to spot a gangly, slightly stooped, intense looking man with a thin spiky moustache and oversized ears. He introduced himself as Benvenuto Feingold, and he began talking to me very politely, and making sure that I understood that he was very rich and very well educated. He told me about his fancy cars, and his many travels abroad, especially Paris, and about his many leather-bound books in his private library, of which he had read all. I felt intimidated.

Mr. Feingold seemed overly eager to ingratiate himself with me. He was clearly much older than me, and I thought his display of attention was probably one of his obligations as prescribed by good manners: he didn't want one of the guests to be bored. He kept jabbering on and on about himself, like the fact that he was a polo player and his team just won a tournament. As I didn't even know what polo was, I thought best to paste a sweet smile on my face and continue thinking about how well my dress fit me; my mother had done a wonderful job. Every once in a while, when I thought his recitation was becoming more animated, I would chime in with an 'oh, wow', which seemed to energize his monologue for at least another five or even ten minutes.

Then, out of the blue, Mrs. Schoenfeld, carrying a small stool, sat down right in front of us, and asked, rather oddly, "What are you kids talking about?" and before either one of us had a chance to answer, she turned to me and gave me a detailed list of Mr. Feingold's accomplishments, least of which was the fact that he and his father owned the largest kitchenware factory in Bucharest, along with a lot of real estate.

Not understanding much of what was being said, and probably also out of nervousness, I began giggling. My unconventional response was mistakenly taken to mean that I wasn't sufficiently impressed, since Mrs. Schoenfeld quickly set me straight that Mr. Feingold's business produced some of the finest pots and pans in Europe. Upon hearing that, my giggling intensified into an all out laughter, which I tried to conceal behind my open palm, as I imagined Mr. Feingold wearing the dirty leather apron my father used to wear whenever he went out to fix pots and pans, and walking knee deep in one of Ghimeş's muddy streets next to his tinker's cart as it was being pulled by lame, old Alborak. I finally got a grip on myself and gave them my best 'oh, wow' of the evening, which surprisingly seemed to please both of these very important people.

I couldn't understand it: I was this simple country girl with not a pot to piss in, and these fancy people took all this time to impress me. I was already more impressed than they could imagine. But anyway, there they were falling over themselves trying to make sure that I understood what an accomplished man Mr. Feingold was. I was trying to figure out why they took all this trouble on my account.

First I thought that they wanted me to pass on this information to my father, but my father was an unemployed tinker without money or connections. What could he do for these fancy people? I then concluded that Mr. Feingold was looking for someone to clean his house, and he thought I would be right for the job. He could see that I was young and strong, but if he wanted a cleaning woman, why didn't he just come out and ask. It would stand to reason that with a war going on, there might have been a shortage of maids, since most of them were country girls, and with the German Army parked just outside Bucharest, they couldn't get in. I probably would have said yes, after asking my mother, of course, but I'm sure she too would have said yes, because we really needed the money; besides with me working during the day there would have been one less mouth to feed. The money we had when we first arrived in Bucharest was draining at a much faster rate than any of us expected.

Once I realized that Mr. Feingold was looking for a maid, I became friendlier – I smiled at lot more and even asked Mr. Feingold how big his house was, and whether he had a family. I was preparing myself for the question of salary, so the size of the house and the number of people I would have to clean after were essential. To my amazement, my questions elicited great amounts of chortling from both of them, followed by displays of greater excitement, as each was trying to shut the other one up with information about the size of his apartment, which was, according to Mrs. Schoenfeld, quite large and in one of the most fashionable parts of the city, and that Mr. Feingold had no family. As their information session was winding down, Mrs. Schoenfeld added that Mr. Feingold's apartment came with a cook and a maid, which confused me at first, but I understood that they were concerned that my credentials only qualified me to work as a maid's assistant. I quickly assured them that I was a fast learner and in time I would be able to manage the whole place by myself, thus saving Mr. Feingold a lot of money, as I knew that domestics could be quite expensive, especially in time of war. This led them to another round of hysterical chortling.

On the way home, I heard my parents discuss me in connection with Mr. Feingold: Do you think he liked her? Do you think she's smart enough for him? (my mother); Don't you think he's too old for her? Do you think she'll be happy with him? (my father). I couldn't understand why there was so much fuss being made just to arrange the hiring of a maid. My parents' conversation suddenly abandoned Mr. Feingold and brought up another name; this one I had never heard of: David Schoenfeld, and the same questions came up in connection with him. Later that evening, I found out that David Schoenfeld was Mrs. Schoenfeld's brother-in-law. I couldn't believe my luck: two respectable gentlemen interested in my housecleaning services.

IV

The next morning, my mother told me to take a bath and dress nicely and be ready by ten o'clock. Taking a bath was torture as it had to be done with cold tap water and dressing nicely meant putting on the same clothes I had on the previous day. At 10:15, we were off: destination unknown, but I didn't dare ask my mother; she always interpreted my queries as signs of insubordination. After a brisk, silent walk through the City – my mother was an incredibly fast walker – we entered Mrs. Schoenfeld's apartment building, but we rang the bell to a different apartment. A man I vaguely remembered from the party opened the door. "David Schoenfeld," he said, and gently grabbed my hand. He was round-faced with a shock of blond hair, and his entire demeanor seemed to scream, "Please like me." He must have just finished shaving, as he reeked from aftershave, and I could still see the ironing crease in the white shirt that he wore unbuttoned down to the middle of his chest. I guessed he wanted people to notice the tuft of tightly coiled hair peaking out of his shirt.

During the next hour, in which he had my mother and me sit on a narrow, armless sofa, Mr. Schoenfeld recited a list of personal attributes, of which the most essential seemed to be his close relationship with his very successful older brother. Mr. Schoenfeld was conducting his pronouncements from a chair that he had placed right in front of me so close that his knees kept touching mine. Every time that happened, his round face took on the appearance of a ripe tomato, followed by a breathless recitation of apologies. After the third or fourth time it happened, I burst out laughing. It reminded me of a clown act I had seen in Ghimeş, where two clowns tried to sit down at the same time, but their knees kept knocking into each other, sending them flying backwards. Suddenly, a stiff jab to my ribs reminded me that my mother was still there. She was sitting stiffly, perched at the edge of the sofa, one arm behind me, while the other crushing her pocketbook. That only intensified my laughter, but that wasn't going to be tolerated for long.

My giggling completely unraveled what was left of Mr. Schoenfeld's frayed ego to the point that his speech was reduced to one continuous stammer, while his face manufactured large beads of sweat that ran down to the tip of his chin from where they plunged to his lap, creating a large humiliating wet spot on his canary-colored pants. In my effort not to stare at his crotch, I rolled my head back and, closing one eye at the time, viewed Mr. Schoenfeld's jiggling mouth dancing from one side to the other of my nose. At that moment, my mother, spewing Yiddish curses I had never heard of before, grabbed my arm and flung me out of Mr. Schoenfeld's apartment and slammed the door behind me. Relieved, I spent the time admiring the fanciful designs on the hallway wallpaper. When the door opened again, my mother and Mr. Schoenfeld were in the process of shaking hands and wishing each other good luck. I also noticed that the spot on Mr. Schoenfeld's pants had gotten bigger.

As soon as we were on the street, my mother slapped me hard across the face, followed by a barrage of names she had for me: stupid, useless, brainless. It seemed I had really screwed up the deal. When I asked her if I lost the job with Mr. Schoenfeld, she didn't answer. That evening, during dinner, my father asked me whom I liked better, Mr. Schoenfeld or Mr. Feingold. It didn't take me long to answer. I preferred to work for Mr. Schoenfeld; he seemed friendlier, less arrogant, and younger. My father thanked me and turned to my mother, who just nodded.

The next day, I woke up to my mother's wailing about my peasant manners. Evidently, I was supposed to contact Mrs. Schoenfeld to thank her for the great hospitality she has shown us, her lowly relations. We didn't have a phone at the time, so I got dressed and went down to our landlady's apartment. The widow was home and happy to see me. When I asked her how much for the call, she just waved her hand.

On the phone, I asked Mrs. Schoenfeld if I could pay her a brief visit. I explained that I never had a chance to properly thank her for inviting me and my family to her house. She seemed delighted to hear from me, though she sounded as if she had been crying. When I asked her if there was anything wrong, she answered that life was designed to disappoint. I couldn't imagine what this wealthy, pampered woman had to be unhappy about. She insisted that, if I didn't have any plans that afternoon, to come right over. I didn't, so an hour later I was sitting on her sofa sipping the obligatory tea with milk, something I never learned to enjoy.

I told Mrs. Schoenfeld – Regina was her first name, but the few times I called her by that name, it felt awkward – that I didn't have any girlfriends my age. She thought about it and suddenly her eyes lit up. She told me that a young woman whom she thought I would like very much lived in her building with her parents and two brothers. They were an offshoot of the Rothschild clan – the right lineage but without all the insinuated wealth. She told me that the young woman's name was Coty and that she had two older brothers, one a brilliant attorney, whose name was Jacob, and the other an electrical engineer named Sallo.

Coty was very smart, Mrs. Schoenfeld continued, a graduate of the Bucharest Conservatory of Music, and a gifted concert pianist. I held my breath. Why did Mrs. Schoenfeld think this highly accomplished young woman would want to have anything to do with me? Mrs. Schoenfeld smiled, gazed at me as if she knew something I didn't, and said that beneath the surface Coty and I were really very much alike. I realized that I had just been taught a great life lesson: success in life has nothing to do with intelligence – many very intelligent people can trash their lives every bit as well as the dumbest people; it is that very rare quality called common sense or street-smarts that separates life's victors from life's victims, and I knew I had plenty of that.

Mrs. Schoenfeld phoned the Rothschilds and ten minutes later Coty was standing in front of me. She was tall and dark and elegant and carried an air of complete indifference to the world around her. Her ready smile showed off two magnificent rows of teeth carved out of pure alabaster, suggesting that rare mix of virtues: instant, absolute trust in a stranger combined with an equally swift, accurate assessment of that stranger's character. I immediately adored her. I was soon to benefit from Coty's spiritual gifts. Within a few minutes, we knew we loved each other and that we would love each other until the end of time, even though we were basically very different people. I often dream of her. She's laughing, and the room fills with the sound of chimes set off by the flutter of angels' wings.

Coty and I sat down and, holding each other's hands, we poured out the few noteworthy events of our otherwise unlived lives. I told her about my horse Alborak and how free I always felt riding him, and she told me about the drudgery of daily piano practices and the practical jokes she often played on her humorless brothers.

Something made me look at Mrs. Schoenfeld's wall clock. When I saw how late it had gotten, I kissed Coty, wished Mrs. Schoenfeld 'good evening', and left for home. I sang all the way home, and, as I walked through Chishmigiu Park, I picked a whole bunch of wild flowers which I brought home and put into a tall water glass. I still remember that day as one of the happiest of my life.

When I walked in, my mother, without asking me about my visit, shoved a mop and pail into my hands and ordered me to wash the kitchen floor. I smiled at her; she growled back and walked away.

V

The next few days were pretty interesting. One evening my parents sat me between them on the sofa and stared at each other. Finally, my father began by explaining to me our financial situation and how important it would be for a beautiful girl like me to get married to a rich man. I nodded. My father continued. There were two extremely suitable men interested in marrying me: Mr. Schoenfeld and Mr. Feingold, but since it seemed that I preferred Mr. Schoenfeld, my mother had informed him that he could begin the courtship. I thought about it and decided that Mr. Schoenfeld was nice enough looking and I would be living in Coty's building and see her every day. I imagined that should be enough of a reason to get married.

Several days later, we were again invited to David Schoenfeld's apartment; this time all of us were there. The question of what to wear was no longer an issue, and my mother even allowed me to put on a drop of cologne from a bottle she had been saving since before I was born.

A manservant opened the door to David Schoenfeld's apartment, and showed us into the same room my mother and I had been in days earlier. The room was set up differently: five elegant arm chairs had been arranged around a table on which there was a wide assortment of expensive foods that gave off a potpourri of enticing aromas. David, as that's how he wanted me to refer to him, greeted us at the door and urged us to sit down. The manservant came in with a tray of wine glasses, which he passed around. I don't think that was the first time I had wine, but it's the first time I remember; it was a delicious white wine and, when asked, I accepted a refill, but my mother, eyes blazing at the poor man, warned the manservant to keep away from me. Soon, the men got involved in some heated conversation, which I knew was of no consequence to me, so I made believe I was listening and kept smiling. My mother, as was her usual practice, sat stiffly in her chair, an unyielding, forbidding figure.

There was suddenly a loud pounding on the door. Everyone froze. It was the middle of the war, and, as Jews, we had an added reason to be nervous. The pounding resumed, only more violently. David, visibly shaken, asked the manservant to check the door. The manservant, equally frightened, tiptoed to the door and looked through the peephole. "It's only Mrs. Schoenfeld!" he roared in between bursts of laughter, opening the door wide. Mrs. Schoenfeld, her usual exacting appearance nowhere in sight, ran into the apartment holding a big butcher knife in her hand. Her face, a disturbing palette of lipstick and mascara, seemed to convey emotions of both dread and pity.

"I am going to kill myself right here in front of you David. Is that what you want?" shouted Mrs. Schoenfeld.

Sammy, my parents, and I immediately stood up and edged our way towards the front door. David, apparently not entirely surprised by the spectacle, stepped towards Mrs. Schoenfeld.

"Please give me that, darling," said David, pointing to the knife.

A somewhat pacified Mrs. Schoenfeld allowed Mr. Schoenfeld to put his arm around her, while he used his other hand to take the knife away.

"Not until you tell these people to go home and you stop this nonsense about getting married. Do you understand or do you want me to kill myself?" Mrs. Schoenfeld asked, although from her improved disposition, I suspect she already knew the answer.

My mother, unfazed by the spectacle, turned, and ordered us to follow her as she quickly made her way out of the apartment. As the door was closing, I looked back at David and Mrs. Schoenfeld and saw them embracing. When we got to the street, Sammy threw his arms in the air and asked exactly what I wanted to know, "What the hell happened there?"

My parents looked at each other, and finally my father began the sordid story. Mrs. Schoenfeld, though married to Isaac Schoenfeld, was having an affair with David, Isaac's younger brother. It seemed that everyone in the Bucharest Jewish community knew about it, but it didn't seem to bother Mrs. Schoenfeld. I turned to my mother and asked why should Mrs. Schoenfeld be allowed to have two husbands when other people don't even have one. My mother looked past me and, with her lips puckered up as if she was swallowing something very bitter, announced that I was the stupidest girl in the world, and it would be a miracle if she could ever arrange for me to have a husband. I laughed, which resulted in a quick slap on the face, but it only increased my giddiness.

VI

Things were fairly quiet over the next couple of weeks, which gave my mother the opportunity to enroll me in a dressmaking school. My mother, her confidence in my ability to secure a husband badly shaken, was determined to have me learn a trade, as she was beginning to accept that my looks might not be enough to overcome my stupidity. The detail that exceeded even my mother's tolerance for uselessness was a report from the woman who ran the dressmaking school that informed her that it would be unfair to take her money, as I was monumentally inept, and that in her 40 years of teaching dressmaking she had never encountered a clumsier girl, even among the severely retarded. My mother's ever-growing feelings of despair concerning my future seemed to further aggravate her already gloomy disposition.

One afternoon, as I was coming home from food shopping, my mother handed me a note that had been hand delivered earlier in the day. It was from Coty. She apologized for not reaching out to me earlier. I knew not having a phone made it very difficult for people to keep in touch with me. Coty was inviting me to join her the following afternoon at Capşa where I would get to meet other friends of hers. I had no idea what Capşa was, and neither did anyone else in my family. I asked our landlady, but she had never heard of Capşa either. I was getting desperate, but just as I was about to run out in the middle of the street and yell out the question, my father, who had gotten hold of a phone book, told me that it was a commercial establishment on Calea Victoriei, which was a short walking distance from where we lived.

The following afternoon at four, I walked into Capşa. It was the most elegant place I had ever seen, even more so than Mrs. Schoenfeld's apartment. There were dozens of crystal chandeliers hanging from the frescoed ceiling high above the palatial room. Dark mahogany tables with matching armchairs were strewn in a seemingly haphazard way across the shimmering light blue marble floors. White liveried waiters speedily navigated their stations like practiced roller skaters. I was entranced, and I must have looked it too, as Coty grabbed my arm and brought me to a table where four other people, two boys and two girls, were sitting sipping coffee out of tiny porcelain cups.

"Is this a restaurant?" I asked Coty.

"It's a café. The finest in Bucharest."

I could believe that.

"They serve hors d'oeuvres too. Won't you try some?" she added.

I nodded timidly. A waiter appeared and Coty gave him some instructions, and then just as quickly he disappeared. Coty turned and began introducing me to the others. I don't remember their names, but they all seemed pleased to make my acquaintance. A tall dark boy with intense blue eyes sitting next to me asked me a flood of questions: "What school are you going to? What I do you think of war? What books are you reading? I turned red and gasped. Coty quickly intervened and told them that I arrived in Bucharest a few days earlier and was very shy and preferred to just listen. I endorsed her apology with a smile. They all laughed and nodded sympathetically, then turned to a conversation that seemed to have already been in progress.

They were discussing music or more specifically who was the better musician. They were tossing around names I had never heard, but they repeated them enough times that I ended up memorizing them. The biggest disagreement seemed to be over whether someone named Enescu, who was Romanian, was a greater composer than Tchaikovsky, who was Russian. The boy who had addressed me earlier was of the opinion that Enescu was by far the better musician, and he offered what seemed to be convincing evidence; he used a lot of terms that I knew had to be part of a musician's vocabulary. The others, though equally at ease with the terminology, were of the opposite opinion, and accused Andrei, as that was the name I remember they kept calling him, of being xenophobic.

I was thrilled when the waiter lowered a plate of bite-size foods in front of me. I was getting tired of the conversation. Coty pointed to what looked like a wedge of hard-boiled egg wrapped in bacon mounted on top of cone-shaped piece of soft cheese, which was itself resting on a thin crust of bread.

"Put the whole thing in your mouth," Coty ordered.

I did. It was divine. I had never tasted anything like it. I went on to the second piece of hors d'oeuvres, and then the rest, relishing each one, but unable to recognize any of the wonderful tastes. The waiter brought me a tiny cup of coffee, just like what the others were having. The tiny cup was made of beautiful white china painted with pink and black dots. It was like nothing I had seen before, certainly not like the set of chipped Rosenthal plates my mother was so smug about back in Ghimeș. The coffee was sweet and smooth, not like the bitter, muddy coffee I had had before. Coty told me it was espresso.

I would have preferred to spend time alone with Coty. I liked her friends, but they seemed a bit affected and overly concerned with sounding smart. They were probably very good in school, but not street smart, and in life street smarts are all that matter. After listening to their silly argument over who's the best musician for another half an hour, I turned to Coty.

"How much do I owe for the food and the coffee?" I asked with great trepidations.

"It's my parents' treat for passing my finals at the conservatory," answered Coty. "You're all my guests," she said with a big smile.

"Are you sure?" I persisted.

"I am, my dearest Greta."

After another few awkward moments, I stood up. "I have to go, but I had a wonderful time. Thank you very much." I said, avoiding her eyes for fear she might see that I was fibbing. "I wish I could stay longer," I added, "but I have to run an errand for my mother."

"Oh!" she said, her smile quickly disappearing from her lips. "I was planning to spend the afternoon together, just the two of us."

I didn't know how to take my words back without sounding like a big phony.

"How about tomorrow afternoon?" I asked. "I can meet you anytime."

Her face lit up at once. "Two o'clock, is that good for you? I can meet you at your place. I don't mind coming over."

I wasn't ready to have Coty see my dilapidated apartment. "I don't mind coming over to you," I answered.

"Excellent. I'll see you tomorrow at 2," and she waved to me as I was walking away. I offered a group 'Goodbye' to the others and left the café. I never saw Coty's friends again. From the moment I got back on the street all I could think about was how do I make two o'clock tomorrow come quicker.

By one o'clock the next day, I was already on the street walking to Coty, even though at my most leisurely pace it would have taken me no more than twenty minutes to get there. But I was too antsy to sit around, besides my mother was making me crazy with all her questions about Coty: "Is her family a real Rothschild? What does her father do? What kind of people let their daughter become a pianist? Don't they know that it'll condemn the stupid girl to a life of poverty, unless, of course, she finds a rich husband?" On the way, I stopped in front of every store window, even very exclusive men's stores that displayed an absurd number of matching bowties and suspenders. I kept checking the time, which seemed annoyingly slow. Finally, at a quarter to two, I decided that I would just wait in front of Coty's building. When I turned the corner, to my surprise, Coty was already there, anxiously waiting for me. We ran to each other and kissed on each cheek.

"Oh, I'm so glad you came early. Did you have lunch?"

"Yes," I told her, although I couldn't remember if I had.

"It's such a beautiful day. Let's go to Chishmigiu. It's so romantic." She grabbed my arm. "Have you ever been there?"

"Yes, in fact that's where I spent my first day in Bucharest, " I said without offering details. "I love that park."

We talked as we walked arm-in-arm along a narrow gravel path lined with primroses. I don't know how many times we circled Chishmigiu Lake, but I kept seeing the same giant oak tree with its trunk split by lightning though still alive, again and again. Coty wanted to sit, so we sat on the very bench my parents slept on our first night in Bucharest. I told her the story, and when I finished she kissed me. She had tears in her eyes, and I hugged her and I told her that I was a tough country girl and I could survive through anything and if she were ever in trouble, I would always be there for her. It was dark and the park was deserted, and we held each other tight as we found our way to the park gate. We said 'goodbye' and hugged again and sniffled shamelessly between giggles and promised that as long as we live we'll never be more than a holler away from each other.

VII

That evening, while we were sitting at dinner, my father informed us that he had run into Mrs. Schoenfeld on the street who was exuding joy and self-confidence from every pore. She told him that he had saved her the trouble of sending us an invitation to tea the following day for the opportunity to be reacquainted with Mr. Feingold. It seemed that Mr. Feingold, in an effort to display tact in connection with the events that punctuated our bizarre evening at David Schoenfeld's, had kept his intentions in check, but now felt that enough time had passed. As soon as she heard the news, my mother was back at the helm, planning and conniving. When I got home later that afternoon and asked what all the commotion was about, my mother cryptically answered, "You will see." As far as I could see, Mrs. Schoenfeld was having us over as a way of apologizing for her psychotic behavior.

The next day, *oysgeputst* as usual, we headed for Mrs. Schoenfeld's. Back in her role as the most gracious hostess in Bucharest, Mrs. Schoenfeld prepared beautiful hors d'oeuvre platters, and she kept encouraging us to 'dig in.' My father and Sammy seemed to be having a terrific time just sampling the food, while my mother, finding no reason to allow Mrs. Schoenfeld's deranged tendencies to interfere with their friendship, informed Mrs. Schoenfeld that she had something very important to share with her. When Mrs. Schoenfeld finally sat next to her, my mother confessed that I had been going to dressmaking school and that I was the best one in the class. I looked at my mother in horror. My mother went on to tell Mrs. Schoenfeld that, as a way of thanking her for all her help, I was going to make her any outfit she wanted, provided she supplied the fabric. Mrs. Schoenfeld seemed delighted at the offer, especially since her husband had had several yards of pure silk smuggled past the German Army and she had a particular style of dress in mind. She dashed out of the room, only to reappear a minute later holding a French magazine in one hand and a small box in the other. She tore out one of the pages of the magazine and handed it to me. "This is what I want," she said, pointing to a dress that was all ruffles and lace. "No problem," my mother quickly countered. Mrs. Schoenfeld removed from the box a most exquisite piece of purple silk and handed it to me. My mother repeated, "No problem."

As I was sitting there with a magazine page in one hand and piece of silk in the other, Mr. Feingold walked in. From everyone else's reaction, including my parents, he seemed to have been expected. When he came around to kiss my hand, as was the custom, though I never liked it, I looked away. I knew of his earlier intentions, and I wanted to make sure that nothing in my conduct would allow any misunderstanding of my feelings towards him. His macabre appearance, with those long spidery fingers and his slinky movements repulsed me.

Unlike the first time when it was I who suffered through a nauseating litany of his great wealth and God-given gifts, Mr. Feingold chose my mother as his audience. But since my mother didn't understand Romanian and Mr. Feingold didn't speak Yiddish, Mrs. Schoenfeld volunteered to act as interpreter. Even though I couldn't actually see them as there were people standing between us, I could hear his every word.

"*I*, Mr. Feingold began, was educated in Paris at a world-renown university; *I* own an apartment on Boulevard Bratianu, containing original period furniture, Persian rugs, and museum-quality oil paintings; *I* am a member of the Automobile Club of Bucharest, an exclusive group that doesn't accept Jews, but they made an exception in my case; *I* won the Athens touring car race twice…that's twice; *I* am exceedingly well-read in Classical and Romantic literature, having just finished all ten volumes of Jean-Christophe; *I* speak fluent German, *Hochdeutsche*, and French, in addition to classical Romanian, the language of Alecsandri and Eminescu; *I* was twice invited to the Royal Palace where *I* met the Queen Mother; *I* have preferred subscriptions to both the National Theater and the Philharmonic Orchestra; and *I* don't smoke or drink, never have. All in all, I am as close to a perfect man as one can get, and still be human." Mr. Feingold ended his performance with a nervous laugh that developed into a cough, which he quickly subdued. "Ha, ha, ha… I was just being humorous."

After a long silence, Mrs. Schoenfeld turned to my mother and offered the following translation, "Trust me my dear Mrs. Sobel, Mr. Feingold is loaded." This was the only time I felt like walking over and giving Mrs. Schoenfeld a hug. My mother, who throughout Mr. Feingold's recitation kept blotting her mouth with a handkerchief to keep herself from drooling, replied in a voice laced with honey, "*Herr Feingold, Zie zint ein groysse mensch. Mein tochter ist nicht tzeklig, aber shverye arbiter.*" My mother assured Mr. Feingold that although I wasn't smart, I was a hard worker. I didn't care. My thoughts went mostly to the sewing of the silk dress for Mrs. Schoenfeld, a task destined for disaster. When my mother finally announced we were leaving, I nodded to Mrs. Schoenfeld, but made a point of ignoring Mr. Feingold. I was convinced I had accomplished my goal of permanently discouraging Mr. Feingold from pursuing me.

On the way home no one said anything until we were just about to enter our building, when Sammy blurted out in a voice laced with sarcasm, "So you got yourself hitched to that middle-aged, cadaverous bourgeois, that…that cut-rate imitation of Don Quixote. The only thing he's missing is the rusty armor and a lance. If Alborak was still around, it would have made him a terrific Rosinante."

I had no idea who Don Quixote or Rosinante were, but I remember grabbing my brother's arm and nodding my head in full agreement. My mother cast a rare angry glare at Sammy and told him that if he didn't shut his mouth he'd end up blowing everyone's chances at a good life.

I was looking, in turn, at each of their faces hoping to find out what everyone was talking about, when suddenly my mother turned to me and, in a voice laced with contempt, pronounced that it was the best thing that could have happened to me. I still didn't know what was going on, but I started to sob. My father put his arms around me, trying to calm me down. My mother looked at me with disdain and matter-of-factly stated that it was decided: I was to marry Mr. Feingold. My sobbing turned into hysterical bawling interrupted by severe hiccupping. People on the street were staring at me, wondering, I'm sure, which one of my parents had died. My father squeezed me tighter in his arms and assured me that if I didn't want to I didn't have to marry Mr. Feingold, which greatly relieved me. He said he would go by Mrs. Schoenfeld's place the next day to straighten everything out, and he was sure that everyone would have a good laugh about it. At that moment, my mother, her face red with rage, pushed my father aside and said to me:

"If we renege on the promise, we would become pariahs of the Jewish community, and everyone would avoid us like the plague. And you, by refusing to marry Mr. Feingold, are showing how stupid and ignorant you are. He could offer you a life full of privilege and comfort, which I promise you you will never have otherwise. And you are not only stupid and ignorant, but also selfish. This marriage could also help us out too. You owe us for all we sacrificed for you."

My father put his hand on my mother's shoulder, "Enough, enough."

I again began bawling, begging my mother, between hiccups, not to make me marry Mr. Feingold because I didn't like him. I was a young girl who had never even been kissed and my mother wanted me to give up all my girlish fantasies in order to marry a man I could never see myself with, and who was closer to my parents' age than to mine.

After I went to bed that night I could hear my parents arguing in the next room, with my father trying to defend my romantic ideals, while my mother calling him a useless vagabond, who could never manage to support his family, and that God has granted them a once-in-a-lifetime wish by getting Mr. Feingold to like their simple-minded daughter, which will not only assure her of a wonderful lifestyle, but will be good for them too. She was sure that Mr. Feingold would not allow his in-laws to go hungry and would make arrangements to get his father-in-law a good job and help Sammy get into the university. To pass up an opportunity like that would be criminal, and God would rightly never look our way again.

I stared into the darkness and decided that I was strong and adaptable and I could learn to endure Mr. Feingold. Looks are not everything. Besides he must have some good qualities, everyone does, like kindness, generosity, a good sense of humor. After all, my mother was right; I was a stupid, ignorant girl, who was lucky enough to be favored by someone like Mr. Feingold, who could have any girl, and that I should be grateful for landing a lifestyle I could otherwise spend the rest of my miserable existence only dreaming of. I kept tossing and turning for most of the night hoping for a sign, then I remembered – if I married Mr. Feingold I would not have to sew Mrs. Schoenfeld's dress. But was that enough of a sign? I kept thinking there must be more and then the clincher came to me: if I married Mr. Feingold, I could call Coty on the phone and invite her to come visit me everyday in my luxurious apartment while Mr. Feingold was away making money.

The next day, my father paid an official visit to Mrs. Schoenfeld to inform her that I had accepted Mr. Feingold's proposal of marriage. The following week was irritatingly uneventful. I didn't hear from anybody, not even Coty, and my mother was in a state of full-blown anxiety that Mr. Feingold had changed his mind, and it probably had to do with my crass stupidity. I must have said something that evening that irritated him, and he subsequently decided that I wasn't right for him: too dim-witted, too uneducated, too unaware of the ways of the world – all things that I knew she was right about. But what could I do; that's who I was.

Later that week a boy in a livery suit rang our doorbell and handed my mother a note. It was addressed to me and signed by a Mrs. Anna Feingold. From the text of the note I understood that was Mr. Feingold's mother. The note simply said that she requested the company of Miss Greta Sobel, alone, at her residence at 4 pm the following Tuesday. In parenthesis at the bottom of the page it read that tea would be served. By now I knew that when they said tea, they meant finger food too.

VIII

I nervously waited for my Tuesday interview. On Saturday, my father told me to get out of the house and take a walk in the park. I put on my calico dress and was ready to run out the door when my mother stopped me with a scream, and angrily asked me what I would wear on Tuesday if I got the dress dirty in the park. I obediently changed, while disregarding my mother's constant refrain '*khokhem, khokhem, khokhem.*'

I left the house dressed in a frayed, discolored cotton dress Mrs. Balter had made for me out of some old kitchen drapes. My mother couldn't argue about what I was putting on my feet, as I only had the canvas sandals, even though that was the pair I already wore at Mrs. Schoenfeld's party, and, unless another miracle happened, they would be the pair I would wear next Tuesday at Mrs. Feingold's.

It was a beautiful June afternoon, and it seemed that Bucharest had been lifted off the map of the world, as there was no hint of the horrors that were going on just beyond its gates.

In Chishmigiu, I walked to the same bench where I had spent that first night in Bucharest, sat down, and closed my eyes. The sun was slapping my face with bursts of warm exhilaration. I had never been so hopeful of the future. Suddenly, I was awakened by the sound of a man's voice who, surprisingly, was sitting right next to me. I shifted as far as I could to the other end of the bench, but he seemed undeterred. I squinted to look at him. He was very young, no more than twenty or twenty-one, and even though he was sitting, I could tell that he had a nice physique. He had finely chiseled features, a small thin nose, a narrow clean-shaven face, and a Kirk Douglas-like dimple in his chin, which, at that moment, had pretty much disappeared because of the big grin on his face.

His name was Daniel Bernhardt and he was a student at the Bucharest School of Medicine. He continued to talk to me even though I didn't show the least bit of interest. He told me that one day he would be a doctor and have a lot of money, although now he was struggling financially. He lived with two other young men in a small basement apartment, and he worked in a pharmacy, which provided him with just about enough money to pay for his school and all his other expenses. He said he had worked a few more hours than usual at the pharmacy during the past week and he had enough extra money to take me to the movies. I suddenly developed this hollow sensation in my stomach, but I knew it wasn't hunger because I had just had lunch before I left the apartment. I couldn't say a word, which seemed just fine with him because he had enough to say for both of us. He put his arm around me, looked straight into my eyes, and told me that we were going together to the movies the following afternoon. He explained that would be best because the movie theater had a policy of selling tickets at half-price every Sunday at 4 pm. His fast, breathless delivery and my raging emotions kept me from saying anything.

He asked me if I liked Bette Davis. I finally opened my mouth and said that I had never seen her, but that my father had and he liked her; in fact he liked her so much that he named our goat after her. Daniel thought that was very funny, and he asked me if the goat was currently living with us. I told him that would be impossible since we now lived in an apartment. He told me that goats make great apartment pets, like cats and dogs. I told him that if he thought that he would make a terrible doctor, but I knew he was just teasing me.

He then pointed to a place just beyond the park trees, and said that was where the theater was and that his heart told him that he had to see me again, particularly since I hadn't told him my name. I asked him whether he would leave me alone if I told him my name. He said that depended on the name. I asked him how could my name make any difference. He said it did. If, for instance, my name was Roberta he would go away and never talk to me again. But, on the other hand, if my name was Greta, he would want to be with me for the rest of his life. When I heard that I fell off the bench and landed on the grass. He quickly came around, put his hands around my waist, and picked me up like I was a child. For a second, I felt trapped inside his muscular arms. I inhaled his body scent; it was a paralyzing blend of coffee aroma and iodine. I gasped.

When he got me to stand up, I realized how tall Daniel was. I had to bend my neck straight back to look into his dark, determined eyes. He looked straight into mine, and said that such beautiful azure eyes should never look so confused. He was the only man who ever referred to my eyes as "azure." That's when he pointed to the name embroidered on the chest pocket of my dress: G-R-E-T-A. When I regained my composure, I told him that he was behaving in a very silly manner, not at all fitting with what was expected of a future doctor. He told me that he wanted to specialize in pediatrics, so being silly would be an asset.

After he put me back down on the bench, he sat right next to me, and we didn't talk for a while, which was fine with me. Then suddenly I remembered that I had to go home to help my mother with supper, so I got up ready to run off, but he grabbed me by the hand and told me that he wouldn't let go until I promised that I would be in front of the theater tomorrow afternoon at a quarter to four. I kept trying to pull my hand out of his grip pleading with him that I couldn't, but he just refused to let go. Finally I said that I would, but before he let go of my hand he made me swear it on my goat Bette. So I swore, even though the goat had been dead for years. And I ran off, but I did look back once and saw his radiant eyes following me.

That night at dinner I was so jumpy that my mother kept yelling at me to calm down. My father offered that it was probably related to all the coming excitement, but I could see in his eyes that he wasn't convinced. I think my father and I always knew each other's soul. Just the two of us; no one else did.

The next day I got up early, washed, and got dressed before anyone else in the house was even awake. It was Sunday, so normally we all lingered in bed a little longer, but I was so antsy that I felt I had to do something, although there was nothing for me to do. I sat at the table and, seeing that Sammy had left one of his books there, I picked it up and started reading it, but I couldn't concentrate at all; there was no connection between my eyes and my brain. My eyes were following the lines on the page, but my brain was trying to decide how to handle the things that were about to come crushing down on me within the next few hours.

I knew I couldn't tell anyone about Daniel, and the rest was a big question mark. I very much wanted to go, but I knew that I was engaged to Mr. Feingold, and I even had a meeting scheduled with his mother, which I was sure would decide whether I was suited for her son. When that thought flashed into my head, I felt relieved. I rationalized that it was all right to go to the movies with Daniel, since I would most likely fail the mother-in-law test, and that would be the end of Mr. Feingold. Then I could spend all my time with Daniel. And even though he didn't have any money at the time, someday he would and we'd live happily together in a big house and love each other.

By three o'clock I was all ready, pacing up and down between the kitchen and the front foyer, ready to run out even though there was only a five-minute walk to the movie theater. This time I just put on my G-R-E-T-A dress without even asking my mother. I wasn't about to risk arousing her suspicions. My mother might not have been book smart, but she saw everything; she was like a witch. I avoided her eyes all day as I was convinced that she could read my mind. She was having one of her bad days so she wasn't too interested in me.

After breakfast she went back to bed and lay there, periodically complaining about different parts of the body that were causing her pain. Sammy and I didn't have to deal with her; my father did, but he was a master at placating her. I never understood what this wonderful, cheerful, vibrant man ever saw in this cranky woman, who started acting like an old person when she was still in her thirties.

Now that I'm an old woman I probably understand my parents' relationship better than ever: she was stable and practical and gave him the comfort that if he overdid anything she'd be there to moderate him; he, on the other hand, was always happy and optimistic about life, and she always knew that if we were ever in a difficult situation, he'd have the courage and savvy to get us all safely out of it. Too bad his joy for life was not contagious enough for her to catch it.

By three thirty, I was standing with my back pressed against the outside door, constantly peaking at the kitchen clock. I didn't want to be there early because that would show that I was too eager, but, on the other hand, I didn't want to be late for the movie. All these thoughts were racing through my head at such speeds they were making me dizzy. Finally, at three thirty-five I decided that it was the right time to leave. As I was walking out the door, I heard my father's voice warble behind me, "You only live once, so enjoy it." I knew from the way he had said that that he must have figured out what I was doing. Thank God he was the only one, because I didn't trust Sammy. He would have done anything in his power to prevent me from putting his college opportunities at risk.

Once on the street, I tried to walk at a normal pace, I even tried counting my steps, but as soon as I turned the corner onto Boulevard Magureanu, I broke into a full run. When I got to Boulevard Queen Elisabeta, I ordered myself to slow down and breathe deeply; I wanted to look cool and poised and grown-up.

Daniel was standing there in front of the theater. As soon as he saw me, he rushed over and grabbed me in his arms. I told him to put me down right away, and that he was making a spectacle of both of us. He put me down gently, but not before he gave me a tiny kiss on the cheek. It was the first time some boy had kissed me, although I knew this did not qualify as a proper kiss. I thought of reprimanding him, but I saw his face. His dark green eyes, the color of an angry ocean, were beset by a band of deep purple, while his dirty blond hair, though evidently subjected to rigorous brushing, was marred by frequent disobedient tufts that waxed alone, and he hadn't shaved. He looked troubled. I thought of asking him if there was anything the matter, but we were running late for the movie, so I just made a mental note to say something to him later after the show.

The movie was *Now, Voyager* with Bette Davis and Paul Henried. I had never seen a movie before, but as I think back at perhaps thousands of movies I have seen since then, not one has touched me so much. I cried throughout the whole movie. After the house lights when on, I kept sobbing, with hiccups and all, and I realized my arms were wrapped tightly around Daniel's arm, and I was not about to let go.

He gently lifted me out of my seat and, with me still hanging onto his arm, we got out of the theater. It was still light out, as the sun was floating just above the horizon. He asked me if I was hungry, and I said 'yes,' although I knew I should have had better manners and said 'no.'

Next door to the movie theater was a typical neighborhood pub of the kind I had seen on almost every street corner, but never actually been in before. We walked in and Daniel had me sit down at an old wooden table set apart from the rest in the back of the pub. He then went to the bar to order. The other tables were full of young people drinking beer. I felt so grown-up. Daniel returned carrying a plate in one hand and two mugs of beer in the other. I was about to scold him for his extravagance, when he handed me a greasy slip of paper that had 80 *bani*, a paltry sum even for those days, written in pencil on it, so I smiled instead.

In the middle of the plate, there were four *mititei* still sizzling surrounded by a wall of hefty French fries. I had never had *mititei*, though I knew from Sammy that you couldn't call yourself Romanian until you tasted one of those spicy plump meat sausages.

I had only one *mititel*, and insisted that Daniel have the other three. It was the best thing I ever tasted – I never knew meat could be so delicious – and one was definitely enough for me. I took a sip of beer. It was bitter and the carbonation scratched my nose. I pushed the mug across the table towards Daniel and watched him devour the *mititei*. Then I looked at his coat sleeve and noticed the big wet spot I had made with my tears during the movie. I grabbed my handkerchief and tried to damp out the wetness by rubbing the sleeve. Daniel didn't seem to mind my hopeless efforts until I actually started putting a hole in the fabric. That's when he told me that if I kept going he'd end up with a sleeveless vest instead of a jacket. I laughed, although my eyes were still swollen from all that crying.

Daniel took out two cigarettes and lit them both, and gave me one. I told him I didn't smoke. He told me to just wrap my lips around the cigarette. When I did, my lips felt the wetness of his lips, and a surge of passion ran from my lips down to my groin that left me immobilized and giddy. I then threw the cigarette away. I never became a smoker maybe because I never wanted to lose the memory of that moment. We sat there absorbing each other with our eyes. I knew I had to distract us.

"Why do you look so tired?" I asked.

Daniel shook his head as if he hadn't heard me right, but I repeated the question.

"I haven't slept well since I met you," Daniel answered, a sad smile on his face.

"Why?" I asked, anticipating the answer.

"I've been thinking of you the whole time." Daniel slid his chair next to mine. "I'm so happy we're alone."

I looked around. There were people at other tables, but clearly not interested in us. "Why do you want us to be alone?" I persisted.

"Because I want to kiss you." Having said that, Daniel cupped my chin in his hand and gently guided my face so that our lips would meet. I didn't fight him off. I wanted him to kiss me, at least at the beginning. Then after a while my head started spinning so I pushed him away, and breathlessly pleaded that he stop.

"Greta, I don't want to stop," he said.

"But I'm getting married," I replied. That's when he stopped. He never touched me again. After several minutes of awkward silence, he looked at me as if trying to figure me out. I thought of Coty and wished she was there to counsel me.

"Do you love him?" he asked.

"Who?"

"What do you mean who, your fiancé?" he said.

"I don't even know him. It's an arranged marriage." I explained the whole situation: how poor my family was, and how rich my future husband was.

"You're making a terrible mistake, one that you will always regret: not to marry for love is a life sentence in the most pitiless jail in the world." He got down on his knees, sandwiched my hands between his hands, and begged me to elope with him that night. I told him I couldn't do that. He fell silent, but then his face lit up and he told me that he wanted to tell me a story.

"There is an old Greek myth that says that in the beginning humans were these powerful, invulnerable creatures with four arms and four legs, and the gods were intimidated by them. Zeus then decided to split them in half, which would make them weaker and perpetually miserable, always roaming the world searching for their other half. In those extremely rare cases, when the two halves found each other, they would immediately fuse themselves together becoming whole again. They would regain their old strength and courage, and nothing could ever stand in their way. But of course, since there is only one unique half in the whole world that perfectly matches another half, the chances of finding it are miniscule. I've only known you for a short time, Greta, but I am certain that you are my other half. Some people spend lifetimes looking for it, but you and I chanced upon each other now while we are still young and able to enjoy a lifetime together, and we must never let go. If you leave me, we'll both be miserable for the rest of our lives." His voice was filled with burning desperation and I knew there was no way to stop him.

"If you leave me, you'll spend the rest of your life feeling that something is lacking every time you try to fuse yourself to men who don't fit you, always wondering, always pining, never knowing what's missing in your life." Daniel stopped and looked up at me as if he was waiting for his sentence.

I gave him a short fleeting kiss on his eager lips, and got up and walked away. When I got to the front door, I turned and glanced at him. He was staring back at me motionless, his eyes sparkling pools of despair. I never saw him again, although every once in a while I would hear news about him: he finished medical school, got married, had three kids, got divorced, ended up as head of pediatrics at the Bucharest Medical Center. Then he left for Paris where I heard he remarried. I also heard that he was unhappy and drinking too much, and that he named his eldest daughter Greta.

IX

The day after I saw Daniel, I kept aimlessly staring out of the dining room window and ignoring my mother's constant barrage of criticism; apparently she found my idleness more irritating than ever. Sammy sat next to me; he had become very secretive, constantly running off without ever telling anyone where, and he seemed to have little time for me, so his sudden interest in me was most surprising. My parents were very worried about him.

"How would you like to come with me to a meeting?" Sammy asked.

"Sure," I quickly answered, afraid that he might change his mind.

"You seem to be pretty unhappy. Maybe that's because of all the injustices you see around you," he continued. "I think you'll be able to connect with the people at the meeting much more than with the likes of Mr. Feingold or Mrs. Schoenfeld and all their so-called friends."

I kept nodding in agreement without understanding what Sammy was so energized about. He walked away waving his finger and muttering, "You'll see, you'll see."

Around five o'clock, Sammy came over and whispered, "We need to go now."

On the street, Sammy began walking at an urgent pace, while warning me that if I couldn't keep up I should go home.

Fortunately, I was a good walker. After about three-quarters of an hour of walking down streets I had never been on before, he abruptly stopped, looked both ways, as if to make sure no one was following us, and rang a doorbell next to a metal-frame door. An eye appeared in the peephole cut into the door; it carefully scanned Sammy then me. The door swung opened and Sammy quickly disappeared beyond it. I was still trying to figure out what was going on when Sammy's voice lashed out, "Get the hell in here you ignorant peasant girl." I was stunned. "Who, me?" I asked. "Yes, you," and Sammy's arm reached out from beyond the dark and pulled me inside.

I followed Sammy down a dark hallway that led to a wooden staircase. At the bottom of the stairs there was a large dimly lit room that smelled of dampness and mud. There were maybe twenty young people standing silently in groups of three or four, watching an older man, wearing a worn-out black leather jacket, clear his throat.

"As you all know, we're living through terrible times, maybe the worst our people have ever been through," the man in the leather jacket began. "Two years ago, a fascist government under Ion Antonescu and his band of hooligans seized power and had this country join Germany in its murderous war against the peace-loving people of the Soviet Union. Early last year, Antonescu's Iron Guard thugs picked up dozens of Bucharest Jews and transported them to the Bucharest slaughterhouse where they were killed like animals. Afterwards, they hung their bodies on meat hooks and mutilated them in a mock process of koshering. In June of last year, thousands of Jews were murdered just outside of Iasi, and several more thousands were packed into cattle cars and deported. Since the invasion of the Soviet Union, Antonescu's army, with the support of German SS troops, massacred thousands of Jews in Bessarabia, and deported all who survived. Last December, thousands of Jews were herded into camps in Moghilev in Transnistria where a typhus epidemic denied these butchers the opportunity to kill. Thousands died.

•

"The most monstrous incident occurred in Odessa in October of last year. Romanian soldiers, under orders from Antonescu, forced thousands of Jews, men, women and children, to march out of the city where they were shot. Seeing that it was taking too long to kill the Jews, they herded the Jews into barns, which were then set on fire. There were no survivors. Thousands of other Jews have been killed since Antonescu's fascist government took control of the country and worse times are ahead. And these are just a few incidents that show that to Antonescu Jewish life is cheap. The only course of action for us Jews is to fight against Antonescu and his thugs, and that means doing whatever we can to help the Soviet counteroffensive."

The man stopped and grabbed a glass of water that was sitting on the muddy floor, and took a short sip.

"In this…our existential struggle, there are a few brave men who have distinguished themselves as fearless warriors. Two of these men are with us now. Let us show our appreciation with a round of hardy applause for Dan Atias and Samuel Sobel."

I heard the name, but I thought the man was referring to someone else, when people turned to face my brother. Everyone wanted to slap Sammy's back and shake his hand. I thought I was going to faint. The only type of hero I knew was a dead one. I did not want my brother to be a hero, regardless how weird he had gotten lately. I started thinking back at his frequent absences since we've been in Bucharest, and my parents' belief that it was because of a girl.

I remembered the time about a month back when he came home one morning, his face covered with dirt and dragging his leg. It was very early, maybe five or six in the morning, but I was up. I asked him what happened to which he looked at me with wild eyes and told me to shut up and go back to sleep. I didn't see him for two days after that, but when I saw him again his face, except for a small bandage behind his ear, looked good, and he walked just fine. In fact, I noticed that he looked healthier than before and more muscular, and he carried a fresh air of confidence about him. My parents took those signs as evidence of his being with a woman. Now I understood what Sammy was doing. He picked up where he left off in Galaţi: he was probably dynamiting bridges and railroads – a sure way to get killed.

When we got back on the street, we walked side by side in silence. But when we got far enough away from the place where that terrible meeting took place, I told him that I was going to tell on him. I said I didn't want him to die. I said the only way to keep him alive is to tell my father; he would know what to do like he knew back in Galaţi.

He grabbed the sleeve of my dress and violently pulled it towards him, "If you tell anybody," he said, staring at me with vicious eyes, "I will kill you. You understand Greta. I am not joking. I have killed many people; one more won't matter."

I have never said a word about my brother's war exploits until now. First I was afraid, then it didn't seem to matter anymore.

X

Once I was done being distracted by the episode with Daniel, I was ready to devote all my attention to the wedding preparations to Mr. Feingold.

That Tuesday I got to meet Mr. Feingold's mother. She was very polite and, though somewhat patronizing, genuinely interested in knowing who I really was. She was a large, imposing woman with hair pulled up in a tight bun and a kind, pleasant face, though marred by an enormous hooked nose, the type one sees in anti-Semitic cartoons that grossly overemphasize Jewish features. As soon as I walked in, she guided me to a large room, which she called a parlor that could easily have belonged in a palace. I followed right behind her. Her slow, deliberate movements, her firm, straight back, her long, sinewy neck – everything about her seemed to confirm her natural elegance. I liked her from the first. She showed me to an armchair that, when I sat down on it, I felt like Thumbelina.

Mrs. Feingold rang a bell that was sitting on a low round table covered with an embroidered red damask tablecloth. I thought the bell was meant to snap me out of my daydreams as I was always drifting off. I soon realized that it was rung to summon a servant girl to bring in a large tray covered with plates of different kinds of tiny sandwiches and a teapot with two dainty little cups. As she poured the tea, Mrs. Feingold urged me to help myself to as many things as I saw. She assured me, in her beautifully modulated voice, followed by a big smile, that I needed nourishment because our conversation will most surely make me hungry. I could quickly see that she was an extremely bright and insightful woman, and, most surprisingly, that she wasn't at all concerned about the possibility that I might be a gold digger solely interested in their money. She asked me a lot of questions that reflected more on my ability to tolerate a difficult personality:

"How would you react if your husband told you he wasn't going to come home one night and failed to give you an explanation?" she asked.

"I would assume he had important things to do," I answered.

"What would you do if your husband appeared arrogant and sarcastic?

"I would try to make him feel better." I wasn't sure what arrogant and sarcastic meant, but they sounded to me like ailments that required a wife's care and attention.

"What would you do if your husband was often silent and brooding, indifferent to you?"

"I would assume he was preoccupied with important matters."

"How would you, so young and inexperienced, be able to handle a husband's bad habits, like drinking and gambling?"

"I may be young, but I am quite mature for my age. I understand that a man needs an outlet every now an then from his stressful life."

I couldn't decide whether she had her son in mind when asking those questions or whether she was just trying to find out if I had a sweet, gentle personality and likely to make her son happy.

I remembered the story of the Princess and the Pea, and thought that I too, though poor and shabbily dressed, was being tested to reveal my true, beautiful character.

She never explained her reasons for asking me those questions, but she made it clear that, although I would live very comfortably, surrounded by creature comforts, waited on hand and foot by maids and chauffeurs and cooks, it would nonetheless not be an easy life. Having already convinced myself that this was to be my course, I again assured her that I was a very hardy girl and that I could put up with anything. She smiled faintly, told me that she liked me, and wished me luck. She said that she didn't believe in long engagements, and asked me what I thought of a November wedding. She had already picked the date: November 12 – a Saturday. It would be held at one of their suburban cottages, on the outskirts of Bucharest. She apologized that, if it hadn't been for the wretched war, we could have had our wedding at their country house, thirty-five kilometers outside of Bucharest, but with the German army just outside the City, it would be impossible.

Mrs. Feingold asked me to give her a list of names of people my family wanted invited, to which I answered that there were none. She politely asked me if I would mind letting her assume all the responsibilities for arranging the wedding, to which I responded by shaking my head from side to side. She informed me that she thought a small wedding would be more advisable again given the circumstances, to which I nodded. She went on to ask me a dozen other questions, which I stopped listening to, and just nodded when she looked at me. Then she suddenly got up, gave me a kiss on each cheek, and politely showed me to the door. As she said good-bye, she told me to expect a note from her son within the next few days requesting that we meet, as he planned to see me several times before the wedding. I again nodded, and thanked her for her kindness as the door swiftly closed behind me.

The following day, a livery boy delivered a note from Mr. Feingold requesting my company that Sunday afternoon for tea at Mrs. Schoenfeld's apartment.

I told my mother that I couldn't keep showing up with the same dress, and that I needed something new. Within two days, my father again showed up with some dress fabric. This time it was a white linen, which my mother finished sewing in less than a day. I later found out that the reason my father was spending so much time out of the house was because he was working as a stevedore at a loading dock, and they preferred to pay him in goods instead of money; if it wasn't fabric, it was cans of stewed eggplants or small drums of cheese or a few bars of soap.

There isn't much I remember about the few meetings I had with Mr. Feingold before the wedding, or I guess I should start referring to him as Benno. They were all held at Mrs. Schoenfeld's apartment under Mrs. Schoenfeld's watchful gaze lest I squander my virtue. I remember heading for Mrs. Schoenfeld's apartment for one of my meetings with Mr. Feingold and getting progressively angrier at the thought that someone actually conceived of me being touched by that giant insect.

Mrs. Schoenfeld would do most of the talking, and she would generally talk about the problems with her *kalta toches* husband, a topic I thought rather inappropriate in front of two people who were about to enter matrimony. But tact was not one of Mrs. Schoenfeld's strengths. I actually got to know her a lot better after the wedding, and I found out that her outburst at David Schoenfeld's was much closer to her true personality, and that beneath that surface of polish and self-assurance lived a very frightened, insecure woman.

During these meetings, Benno showed little interest in me or my life, which was fine with me, as I didn't have much to brag about, while at the same time he was not interested in revealing anything about himself. One time, as Mrs. Schoenfeld was carrying on about her private martyrdom, he cut her off to announce that he had just received delivery of a white Nash convertible which he had shipped from America, despite the fact there was a war on. He drove me in it once right before the wedding. It was a beautiful car, about the size of the apartment I was sharing with my parents and brother. It had an enormous hood painted a light shade of yellow, as were the side panels, and it had soft leather upholstery that made me feel like I was being embraced, as I slowly sank into the bucket seat.

He mentioned at least twice that he belonged to an exclusive men's club, and where, on occasion, he would have to spend whole days and even nights. All I cared about, though, was that I got through the wedding without any mishaps.

A couple of weeks before the wedding I received a note from Mrs. Feingold asking me to meet her in a French boutique called *A Votre Plaisir*, on Calea Victoriei. I was already familiar with that street. On the way to meet Mrs. Feingold, I passed Capşa Café where I had met Coty and had my first espresso. It was where Bucharest's swankiest shops were located. When I got to her apartment, Mrs. Feingold was already waiting for me.

"I'm not taking no for an answer," Mrs. Feingold said as she greeted me. She didn't wait to see my reaction, which was largely one of bewilderment, and turned to one of the salesgirls and announced, "This is my future daughter-in-law." The salesgirl noticed my face and informed me that I would be fitted for one of the best wedding gowns they had, a dazzling number in white satin and lace. I wondered why Mrs. Feingold thought that I would say 'no' to her offer. Once I was done with the wedding dress, they had me try on wedding shoes, stockings, above-the-elbow leather gloves, and even lacy undergarments. Before we parted, Mrs. Feingold told me that we were going to be good friends and I should call her Stefania and that the shopping spree was going to be our secret. Benno never knew about it, nor did he ever wonder or care how a poor girl like me ended up dressed like a princess.

While I was standing on a small platform and being pinned by the young salesgirl, Stefania asked me if I minded, and before I knew what she was talking about, she grabbed my lower lip and pulled it down. I felt violated, but I didn't have the courage to say anything. She then proceeded to lift my upper lip, all along gaping at my teeth. Next, she asked me to say "aaa", to which I promptly complied. While she was staring at my whole mouth, she kept saying "aha, aha." After she told me that I could close my mouth, she scribbled something on the back of her calling card and handed it to me. She had written the name and address of a dentist. She informed me that she was going to make an appointment for me with that dentist for the following week and I should be there on time. I felt like some cheap filly; before being traded, my new owners wanted to make sure they weren't saddled with some major dental bills.

I showed up at the dentist's office on time. There was no one else in the waiting room, so I sat there clenching my teeth as if that would conceal whatever dental problems I might have had. I felt the outcome of this visit would decide the future of the marriage.

I had only been to a dentist once before in my life, and that was when I was about ten or eleven and I had a toothache. My father took me to a bazaar in a nearby town, and inside one of the tents, there was a combined barbershop and dentist's office. After I sat in the barber's chair, the dentist, who looked like someone I had seen the year before in Ghimeş pushing a cart filled with bottles that contained miracle remedies, grabbed a rusty drill that he operated with a foot peddle. After he was done drilling, which had me screaming at the top of my lungs, the pain stopped. He then gave me a lollipop and we left.

A young woman, wearing a highly starched white coat, opened the door, beamed a scary smile that allowed me to see all one hundred, or so it seemed, of her gleaming white teeth, and asked me to follow her. She had me sit in a chair covered in shiny red leather on a highly polished metal frame that gave off a lemony scent. I was again alone when the door opened and a man wearing a white coat and thick glasses appeared. He was about thirty, had dense red hair, and his eyebrows were lifted, imparting a look of permanent surprise on his face. His name was Koch, but I was to always refer to him as The Dentist. He smiled and asked me to open my mouth. When his fingers touched my lips, they felt warm and delicate. After a few minutes, he told me that my teeth were in perfect condition and that he would convey his findings to Mrs. Feingold. The Dentist remained in my life until I left Romania.

The Feingolds knew they were getting a poor girl, and no one ever brought up the question of a dowry. Stefania advised me if anyone asked about my dowry to say that it was a matter between them and my parents, and I didn't know anything more about it. It seemed that everyone else would interpret the lack of dowry as Mr. and Mrs. Feingold Sr.'s acknowledgment of their hopeless dissatisfaction with their son, and their tacit admission that he could do no better. During the ensuing years, Benno would often remind me that he hadn't been paid a penny for marrying me. He had no idea how expensive it had really been.

Stefania was aware of the gossip that was swirling around this peculiar union. She understood that the best way to defuse it was by treating my parents and me with the dignity she would afford anyone of her class. On the day of the wedding, she sent a car with a chauffeur to pick us all up, and when I arrived she told me that it was bad luck for me to be seen by the bridegroom before the wedding, so she had this lovely room waiting for me. Not surprisingly, Benno came down the steps just as I was entering the room, and we caught a glimpse of each other. I made believe I didn't see him and quickly closed the door behind me, but I was still able to hear him call out to me in a voice dipped in bile, "So you're going through with it after all."

Between Benno's comment and Coty's refusal to be at my wedding, despite my assurances that she wouldn't even have to say hello to Benno, I should have walked out right then and there. But I didn't.

XI

On November 12, 1942 at 2:00 pm, at the ripe age of eighteen, I, Greta Sobel, a virgin, became Mrs. Benvenuto Feingold. Benno was thirty-eight at the time.

The wedding was quite beautiful and Stefania was always by my side to make sure that I did and said the right things. The wedding took place in the main parlor of Feingolds' "cottage", which was the size of an English manor. The parlor had been emptied of all furniture to accommodate the guests, and all that was left was the pink wallpaper covered with little Cupids pointing their bows and arrows at various naked couples stealing an innocent embrace. There was also a small piano, which someone played during the ceremony. As Mrs. Feingold promised, everything had been arranged beautifully.

The ceremony was very elegant. They had set up a *chuppah* at one end of the room, under which stood Rabbi Codreanu, whose long, sour face made me wonder if he may have thought that he was called to officiate a funeral. I had not met him before, but Mrs. Feingold had told me that he was a great rabbi and that she would give him all the information he needed for the wedding. He had blond hair that was cut short and brushed back very tightly against his scalp, and he wore a white silk chiffon robe lavishly decorated with gold thread. As I was standing there under the *chuppah* staring at this man who looked like no rabbi I had ever seen, he turned his head and winked at me, then whispered conspiratorially that Mrs. Feingold had spoken to him. The only thing that looked Jewish on the man was a tiny yarmulke that perfectly matched his robe. All the while this gentrified rabbi was speaking, I thought back to Rabbi Gotnick back in Ghimeş: out-of-shape and gray bearded, wearing threadbare black robes and a *shtreimel* the size of a flying saucer. But he had these wild eyes that constantly darted probing glances as if trying to reach inside people's souls and, based on what he gleaned, rendered judgment, which would then be passed directly onto God. I was sure Rabbi

Codreanu had no such relationship.

Once the ceremony was over, the entire company was asked to vacate the parlor as it was being prepared for the wedding dinner. I ended up alone in one of the adjoining sitting rooms, where I was mobbed by women I had never seen before who tripped over themselves to tell me how lucky I was to marry into the Feingold family. When we were finally allowed to return to the parlor, it was set up with tables and chairs, and, in addition to the piano player, there was also a violinist.

During dinner, they played these wonderful pieces of music that took my breath away. I asked Benno if he knew the composer. He stared blankly into my eyes, hesitated for a second, and then answered Beethoven. At that moment I envied him. Benno, I was convinced, was probably the most cultured man I would ever know, and I decided that when one deals with someone with such vast knowledge one overlooks character flaws. Many years later, I was attending a concert at the New York Philharmonic, and I heard the same wonderful piece of music. I looked at the program and it was one of Felix Mendelssohn's lieder. I realized that he had lied to me on my wedding day, and only because he was too insecure to admit that he didn't know something. I would have killed him if he hadn't been dead already for years.

After dinner, the musicians played beautiful dance music, and I loved to dance. After they served what turned out to be a magnificent meal – I still remember the main course: rolls of beef or veal covered with a caramel glaze - most people got up and started dancing. Benno and I sat alone at a separate table, and said nothing to each other throughout the entire time. I just kept waiting for him to ask me to dance. After about an hour, I turned to him and asked him to dance. It was the first time I took a whiff of his body odor. He smelled like damp mold. He sneered and told me he didn't dance, that he hated dancing, and that it made people look foolish. So I didn't dance at my own wedding.

After the ceremony a photographer came over to take pictures. Benno, who was not very photogenic, with his gaunt face, sunken eyes, and narrow frame, told the photographer that one picture would be enough. I still have that picture. It shows a girl standing next to the Grim Reaper.

While the musicians were playing Johann Strauss's Blue Danube Waltz, Benno got up from his chair. My heart froze; I thought he changed his mind and was going to ask me to dance after all. He started walking away, but he turned and told me, "I have an important appointment," and he left. At that moment, I knew I hated him. I sat alone until the music stopped. Then people came over to wish me "Good luck" and "Happiness," but I could see the words were getting stuck in their throats. Stefania avoided me; she was probably ashamed of her son. After everybody left, I went back to my parents' apartment.

The next day, I moved into Benno's apartment, which was in the same building his parents lived, and owned. It was on *Trei Scaune Street*, not far from Boulevard King Carol, in one of Bucharest's swankiest neighborhoods. Boulevard King Carol, with all its fancy restaurants and boutiques, was where everything happened, and where people took strolls when they wanted to be seen. So being close to it was truly a sign of status.

Benno's apartment was what one would call a one bedroom, although the rooms were enormous. Not unexpectedly, as it had been a bachelor pad, it was decorated very austerely, with a lot of polished wood and leather furniture, and very few wall hangings. The only thing I remember, just inside the apartment, was a large painting of Piazza San Marco with the Doge's Palace in the background. The walls were painted white, unlike the custom of the day of ornate wallpaper. The bed, which was narrower than I would have liked – something between a twin and a full-size – was a four-poster with a headboard sloping away from the bed at a steep angle so that one could rest his head on it, something Benno made constant use of when he was reading in bed. There was also a night table with a lamp on it on his side of the bed. During the three years that we lived there, he never bothered to add a second night table on my side, not that I would have used it much, as I was not a reader. Once I got to bed all I wanted to do was fall asleep as soon as possible, before Benno had a chance to lay his hands on me, not that he would often show much interest. I knew why and it suited me just fine.

XII

From the beginning, married life seemed like a prison sentence. I had no friends, except for Coty, who couldn't stand Benno. My new social position, as the wife of Benvenuto Feingold, created an unyielding awkwardness between me and my family; even my father, who soon after the wedding started working for Mr. Feingold Sr., crushed my heart when once, during one of my parents' rare visits, reverentially addressed me as the young Mrs. Feingold. The only other person I saw relatively often was Mrs. Schoenfeld.

During one of her mid-day visits about a month after my wedding, Mrs. Schoenfeld asked me, "So did you find out yet that Benno has a mistress?" I had suspected it ever since Mrs. Feingold alluded to it during our first meeting, and there have been other signs along the way, which I chose to ignore. I answered her "Yes," shrugging my shoulders, "but I've heard different stories."

Mrs. Schoenfeld jumped at the opportunity to set me straight: "Benno has been with her for many years. She is an opera singer, and, years earlier in her youth, a well-known soprano with the Bucharest Opera House. She had leading roles in *Carmen, La Boheme, La Traviata*, and other big operas. She had always been a heavy drinker and chain smoker, but since her career went into decline she has gotten a lot worse. She hasn't had a decent role in over ten years, as she has lost her voice. Nevertheless, Benno keeps throwing his money at any producer who merely promises to think about considering her in his next production. She has many debts – she is a gambler to boot – yet Benno, the quintessential cavalier, settles them all. She was beautiful in her youth, but now she's old and fat and a drunk, and Greta darling, I shouldn't worry about her. Her name is Lydia Sherban."

When it seemed that Mrs. Schoenfeld was running out of ammunition, I said that was pretty much what I had heard. I later reminded myself that Benno never bought me anything, but I didn't care. The less he did for me the less obligated I felt.

A few years later, I actually met Lydia Sherban. I was at the beauty parlor having my hair done, when the hairdresser pretentiously informed me that someone I didn't know wanted to meet me. Suddenly, this vision of Marie Dressler in "Dinner at Eight" leaned over, shook the tips of my fingers, and said that she was delighted to have finally met Benvenuto's bride. Before I had a chance to ask her anything, she theatrically waved her gloved hand high in the air and swiftly strode away. She looked tired and walked with difficulty, but I could see she must have been quite beautiful in her heyday. When I later questioned the hairdresser about her, he told me, with great solemnity that I had been in the presence of operatic royalty.

Even after Benno stopped sleeping with Madame Sherban, he continued to visit her, keeping up the pathetic archetype of the aging lovers still drawn to each other by the strength of their former passion. Years later, in a display of monumental bad taste, he once took our three-year old son with him, who most predictably informed me as soon as his father walked him through the door, "Mamica, a very big lady with big white hair gave me chocolate, and Taticu told me to wait outside and be quiet." I grabbed Benno by the pleat of his shirt and told him that if he ever took my son to his whore again, I would kill him. I thought about this incident afterwards and I felt proud of myself; I knew I was becoming a force to be reckoned with.

XIII

Without any advanced notice, about eight months after the wedding, I decided to visit Stefania. It was a beautiful summer day. I felt I owed her a greater effort on my part to prove I was a good daughter-in-law. It was around ten thirty in the morning. When I rang her door, she appeared immediately. She was perfectly made up and unusually well dressed for the morning, so I asked her if I was intruding. She said, "No. Come in Greta. I'll introduce you to someone. Don't be alarmed. Just act naturally."

In the living room, sitting in the armchair, I thought, solely reserved for use of her husband Martin, there was a man in a German uniform, an officer's uniform. My breathing stopped. Stefania smiled and pointed to me, as she looked at the man in the German uniform.

"Herr Doppler, das ist meine Schwiegertochter Greta. Ist sie nicht wunderschön?"

The man stood up and bowed slightly, without looking at me.

"Entzückende," I heard him say.

I could not separate myself from the wall. Stefania turned to me and smiled in a patronizing manner.

"Major Doppler is a German officer assigned to one of the apartments I own in this building. He is the best tenant I ever had. He comes to me at least once a week to discuss literature and music. Today we're discussing the German Romantic poet Novalis, Georg von Hardenberg."

I looked at the German officer. He was tall and thin and very aristocratic looking, with a long chin that made him look like a sad vision of Stan Laurel, the American clown I had seen at the movies in the *Stan și Bran* series. He seemed to hang on Stefania's every word, although I knew he didn't understand any of them.

"We were discussing Novalis's *Hymnen an die Nacht*. Would you like to sit and listen? We will be speaking *Hochdeutsch*."

I thought I was in the middle of a nightmare. I thanked

Stefania for her kind invitation and ran out as fast as I could. As I was passing the outside doorway, I heard the German officer call out, *"Es war so schön, Sie kennenzulernen, Fräulein."*

A few weeks later I found out that it was not uncommon to have a German officer assigned to an apartment. It was not discretionary; Stefania had no choice in the matter, but I thought she went beyond her required courtesy. I understood that this highly educated woman, surrounded by people who did not arouse her intellectual juices, would be tempted to find culture wherever she could find it, even in a tête-à-tête with a German officer of the Third Reich. While Stefania and I remained close during the years after the war, we never talked about this incident, but I did read a few poems by Novalis and I must admit they were indeed beautiful.

XIV

My mind wanders; suddenly long-forgotten memories flood my mind. It's a sign of age. When Mrs. Schoenfeld first came to Bucharest, she was an attractive, innocent country girl just like me, and just like me she was soon introduced to Isaac Schoenfeld, a banker who, like most bankers, was a quiet, introverted man. But he fell in love with her and did everything for her. He too was quite a bit older than her, but she seemed to welcome the disparity.

After they had been married for a number of years, she decided to take up with David, Isaac's younger brother. That happened about a year before I met Mrs. Schoenfeld. Her barrage of artful flattery, down to the greater size of his penis, ensnared the unfortunate dunce to the point of turning against the only person who ever stood by him – both emotionally and economically – his older brother. Mrs. Schoenfeld didn't realize or care how destructive her affair was going to be.

Shortly after the affair became public, and I mean public, as the whole community seemed to know about it, Mr. Schoenfeld, the husband, jumped out the window of their eighth floor apartment, leaving behind a long letter filled with bitter recriminations, particularly of the brother whom he had loved without judgment. This happened about a year after my marriage.

A few weeks after Mr. Schoenfeld's pathetic death, Mrs. Schoenfeld married the second Mr. Schoenfeld. David was a shallow, conceited narcissist, and an utter failure at everything he ever undertook. Not surprisingly, he had none of the business acumen of his dead brother, and when his wealth started shrinking, he decided to gamble it on an illicit roulette game that was being run by some of the most notorious gangsters in Bucharest. Despite the fact that everyone in the Jewish community opposed his harebrained idea, David remained convinced that playing roulette was an effective method of restoring his wealth.

Within three years David lost everything and, in a dismal display of brotherly atonement, jumped to his death from the same window his brother did. Mrs. Schoenfeld, ever the survivor, converted to the Christian Orthodox faith, and, as the Soviet Army was terrorizing Romania, joined the Communist Party, and married the Communist mayor of Bucharest, with whom she had three children. Over the years, she came to be regarded as a shrewd political advisor, and one of Elena Ceaușescu's closest confidants.

XV

In the months following my wedding, I began feeling a desperate need to be with people. Benno's idea of a pleasant evening was either to disappear, which I knew was evidence of his continued infatuation with Madame Sherban, or sit in bed reading a book. He never discussed the books he read with me, as he evidently thought I was too stupid. The evenings Benno didn't come home, I would eat by myself, and then sit by the window and watch the street traffic outside. Once or twice, I took a book out of Benno's library and started reading it, but my eyes would get tired and I would lose my place on the page.

Benno's only so called friends were washed-up actors who spent their time getting drunk and mourning their illustrious careers, which, whenever I had the patience to look into, proved to be nothing more than the product of their overactive imagination. After a while, I refused to be with these has-beens again, and even Benno realized they were not appropriate for me. These hideous characters with loud voices would take turns standing in the middle of the floor and bemoan, between torrents of tears, their past glory. The only moments of entertainment came when two of them would start a fight – usually of words only, but once or twice, of arms swinging as well – over stolen roles or lies or other discourtesies, but most often over stolen lovers.

My only bright memory of that time was my friendship with Coty, but after my wedding she was so angry with me for marrying Benno that she didn't want to see me for over to a month. After a while though, she relented and agreed to see me again, but only after I promised her that I would never put her in the position of having to meet Benno.

Once Coty decided that we were friends again, I visited her almost every day. I would go to her apartment before lunch and stay until early evening when I would grudgingly go home to wait for Benno, though I knew he wouldn't come. His manservant would prepare dinner, so all I had to do was sit alone at a long table and eat, while staring at myself in the mirror at the opposite end of the room examining my table manners.

Coty's apartment was paradise. Her room was on the other side of a large windowless living room, lit only by an ornate chandelier shaped like an inverted tree made of sinewy tubes of clear and blue glass braided together. In order to reach Coty's room, I would have to navigate a narrow passageway bound by curious items of furniture: armchairs with arms and legs that looked like lion's claws, two vast armoires standing across from each other with palm trees along the front in mother-of-pearl, a couple of oval tables whose thick tops were girthed by snakes, and a massive brass telescope perched precariously on a wispy elegant stand.

Before I had a chance to kiss Coty, her mother, a lean, graceful, sylph-like woman, would enter and announce lunch, which was always comprised of some sort of pie: cheese, meat, or vegetable. Lunch was served in the family dining room, which also included Coty's piano. After lunch, I would sit next to Coty on her piano stool while she practiced. I felt like I had gone to heaven and Coty was an angel. After she finished practicing, we would go to her room where we would just chatter like giddy schoolgirls.

About a month and a half after I was married, Coty seemed especially excited when I came in. She cut her practicing short and rushed me into her room, where she made sure the door was closed. She whispered to me that she had fallen in love, madly, desperately in love, and that his name was Benjamin. Since it had only been two or three days since I had seen her last, I asked her why she didn't mention Benjamin earlier. She answered that she didn't know him until two days ago. She had met him in Chishmigiu Park. She said she owed it all to me, because that was a day I couldn't come over. She had gone there in the afternoon after piano practice and sat on a bench, when suddenly this beautiful young man sat next to her and told her that she was the most enchanting creature he'd ever seen. They spoke the whole afternoon, and he loved Chopin and Debussy and Liszt. They arranged to meet the next day to see a movie. It was *Intermezzo*, in which Ingrid Bergman played a young concert pianist. By the end of the afternoon, he had proposed to her and she had accepted. That was the only time I felt jealous of Coty. I had met Daniel and he was young and handsome and he fell in love with me, but I had to marry Benno, because I was poor and uneducated and I had a family to think of.

Coty and Benjamin were married three months later. I was the matron of honor. Benno allowed me to buy a brand new dress, but he didn't show up at the wedding, which was okay with me and perfect for Coty. The wedding was held in Coty's apartment; the ceremony took place in the living room. The armchairs were stacked three high and pushed against the wall and the oval tables were placed atop the armoires, opening the room for guest chairs. There were about twenty-five people, most of whom I had met.

Everyone was delighted to be there. A lovely *chuppah*, made of a slender wooden frame wrapped in fresh-cut flowers, stood in the middle right under the striking chandelier. Coty, radiant in a plain white dress, giggled shamelessly the whole time, but especially while the rabbi, a skinny, self-effacing man in an ill-fitting suit who seemed to have known her since birth, talked generously about her.

After the ceremony, the oval tables replaced the *chuppah* and everyone sat down to eat what was unmistakably Mrs. Rothschild's cooking; the center of each table was dominated by her pies. Coty and Benjamin sat at my table, and they couldn't keep their hands off each other. Two classmates of Coty's from the Conservatory played romantic tunes in the next room: a piano and a clarinet. Coty and Benjamin were constantly on their feet dancing. Benjamin was a head taller than Coty with broad masculine shoulders and his slight stoop was accentuated when he danced; it looked like he was trying to wrap himself around her, and Coty, her wistful face barely visible, looked like a well-swathed baby.

It didn't take long before Coty's friends started asking me to dance. I didn't miss one dance; I was on my feet the whole evening. I had a great time. That wouldn't have happened if Benno had been there.

Three years later, Coty met Mircea, a talented young violinist. She was giving a concert, her concert debut with the Bucharest Philharmonic, when this gaunt, delicate gypsy boy stole her heart. Apparently all he had to do was walk up to her after the concert and press his lips against her hand. She said she felt as if someone had branded her with a hot iron. Four months later, she was rid of Benjamin, and two months after that she married Mircea. I never liked Mircea.

Coty and Mircea have been married over sixty years and have no children; whenever someone asks them about children, they answer that each is the other one's child. To this day she fears that whenever he leaves her, even if it is only to step into the next room, she may never see him again. It's an obsession that has fueled her divine soul, or maybe it is the other way around.

Right after she married Mircea, she gave up playing the piano and reinvented herself as Mircea's appendage, a role that she has played gloriously, ecstatically, ceaselessly all these years.

We remained very close throughout our lives, until very recently, when she inexplicably decided to discard me, the same way she discarded Benjamin, without an explanation and seemingly without regrets. I have tried desperately to find out her reasons for treating me as if I never existed, but whichever way I turn, I hit an impregnable wall, but that's all I'll say about Coty for now. The details of probably the greatest disappointment of my life I will keep for another time, another tale.

XVI

Once the Communists took over, and Benno's wealth was whittled away by a steady succession of Communist reforms, he, a grim latter-day Candide, became less and less welcome at Madame Sherban's house. That's when I began to respect this woman. Although old and with no means of support and ultimately forgotten by the world that once gushed at the sight of her, she wasn't interested in continuing the charade of the kept courtesan unless the rewards remained substantial.

Benno was quite upset at first, as I heard him whine to his mother that he still brought her things, whatever he could get his hands on – food stamps, black-market cigarettes, kerosene, just to be with her, and she still reduced his visits to only those times when he had something she actually needed. Apparently, what Madame Sherban "needed" was French cognac and American cigarettes and they were nonexistent. But Benno, like a madman, stalked foreign embassies on the absurd hope that they would throw something at him. The only thing he accomplished was to waste countless hours outside some of the embassies and to be subsequently arrested as a possible seeker of political asylum, a very serious crime. But after the *Securitate* men heard his story they released him; they figured no one could make up such an idiotic story.

The cutback of Benno's visits to Madame Sherban increased the pressure on me to fulfill my wifely obligations. He was an unpleasant lover, with his long spidery fingers that made my skin crawl whenever he touched me. Benno's idea of lovemaking was to creep on top of me like a giant insect, and ten seconds later when he was done, slide off and fall immediately asleep. Those sessions gave me the regrettable opportunity to observe his long, thin carcass covered with reddish fuzz.

I spent days thinking of ways to discourage him from crawling on me. As he wasn't one to be deterred by a headache, or even by clear signs of sleep, I had to become more inventive. I discovered that he found any kind of oral or nasal emission repugnant, so every time he started creeping towards me, I would either sneeze or burp right in his face. These maneuvers would temporarily cut his appetite, but not long enough to prevent him from squirming on top of me later that night while I was asleep.

All my subterfuges ended with my first clash with Stefania. Apparently he complained to her about my lack of availability, and she agreed to talk to me. She was very polite, yet quite blunt. She didn't insult me by denying that Benno had been having an affair with Madame Sherban and the reason he suddenly showed a heightened interest in me was because she refused to continue to put up with his repellent mating practices. Even at her age, Madame Sherban thought she deserved better. I, on the other hand, did not have this luxury. Stefania reminded me that because of our families' union, my parents were doing well, and my brother was a graduating senior in Civil Engineering at the University of Bucharest. Therefore, I had a responsibility to keep my husband pacified. I told her that I didn't know what she meant, and that I had been a good wife to her son, but she knew I understood. From then on, I learned to occupy my mind with memories of my happy childhood in Ghimeş particularly the times I was on Alborak's back, while Benno was ludicrously bouncing on top of me.

XVII

During the first couple of years of my marriage, I ended up making an unlikely new friend. It was Benno's father. I hadn't met him, except in passing, before the wedding, but a week after the wedding, my doorbell rang and there stood this tiny jolly figure of a man with pleading blue eyes and ruddy cheeks. He had been instructed by his wife to transport his son's gold-plated safety razor, which he had left at their house on the day of the wedding. I invited him in. At first, he thanked me and told me that he had to get back right away, but I insisted and he smiled and sauntered in.

"I was about to make myself a cup of coffee. Could I make you one too?" I asked

"Oh sure, sure…coffee…thank you," he answered. But his eyes were scanning the shelves of the large china cabinet.

"Can I get you something else?" I asked with a smile. "Perhaps a little schnapps."

"That would be great," he said, expelling all the air out of his lungs.

I grabbed a bottle out of the china cabinet and a small glass and placed them in front of him. "Treat yourself," I said. He nodded and quickly poured the clear liquid into the glass, stared at it for a second, then drained it down his throat.

"This is perfect," he said, lifting the sides of his mouth into an impish smile. I continued to sip from the cup of coffee that I had made myself earlier.

Mr. Feingold looked like a hairless leprechaun; his iridescent bald head was made remarkable by huge washed-out blue eyes that stared with the innocence of a child, and his diminutive body was bound by a pair of chubby little hands that were constantly in motion.

"I like a drink once in while, but I'm not allowed to have it at home."

"You're not at home, Mr. Feingold," I said.

"Call me Martin and I'll call you Greta, okay. Did you know I was born in Galați?"

"I lived in Galați for three years," I responded.

"I know. My father was also a tinker. We don't have very different backgrounds, you and I, Greta. He used to go door-to-door and fix people's pots and pans, but at about the time I was born, he became a minor partner in a small pot-making factory. Within ten years, he had bought out all his partners. He was a workaholic and I only saw him on Shabbat and holidays, but when he died at fifty-two, he owned the largest kitchenware factory in Romania – over one hundred workers. Now I own it. We have over 200 workers, and we export to seven different countries; Greece is our biggest client."

Martin poured himself another drink and tossed it down his throat just as rapidly as the first.

"Benno works for me," he said.

"I know," I answered with a smile. "He's your son." Martin restored his earlier impish grin and poured himself another drink.

"I'm not allowed to smoke cigars either," said Martin scratching his bald pate.

"Light yourself a cigar, Martin."

"You don't mind?"

"I like the smell of a good cigar," I lied. Martin pulled out a cigar the size of a large sausage from inside the lining of his jacket and looked at me joyfully. I placed a box of matches in front of him.

"I shouldn't be telling you this, you're just a girl, but I have a lot of vices," Martin continued after taking a deep drag out of his cigar.

"You don't seem like a bad person," I said.

"I'm a gambler," said Martin, looking at me for a reaction.

"My father loves to gamble. I still think you're a good man."

"Seven years ago I lost everything...everything," he said staring into my eyes. "I was playing poker for crazy stakes and I kept losing all night. I was down millions, but I was sure I would win the next hand, so I bet the factory, everything, the lease on the land, my entire inventory, the trucks. I lost with four jacks. Can you believe that, four jacks to four kings? I got home at six o'clock in the morning and I told Stefania that I lost everything, that we were poor. All we had left was the building and a few odds and ends.

"I know that's not the end of the story," I said.

Martin smiled and downed another drink.

"Stefania deserves all the credit. I was a beaten man. She told me to visit Mr. Rudich, that's the man I lost to, first thing in the morning and offer to run his factory. Stefania knew he would otherwise run it into the ground. I was there at eight o'clock, shaved and ready to go, and so was Rudich. He was waiting for me. He told me I was an idiot and I agreed. He told me he didn't know anything about running a factory. He told me that if I wanted the factory back I had to pay him ten million, that's a lot of money…that's our gross profit over five very good years. That was seven years ago and I paid Rudich up after the first three – that was before the war. Now things are slow."

"That's a great story Martin," I said, meeting his eyes. "I bet that cured your gambling."

"I wouldn't say that, but I don't own anything anymore. Everything is in Stefania's name, and everybody knows that. But what's strange is that now since I don't have any money to gamble, I've been winning. Couple of weeks ago I won a thousand, but Stefania made me give it to her."

Martin stopped talking and lifted the glass of schnapps towards his lips, but didn't drink from it.

"Do you still think I'm a good man?"

"Yes. I like gamblers; they're usually people who love life. Is Benno a gambler?"

"No, you don't have to worry about that. Stefania raised him to hate gambling. She didn't want him to become another me."

Martin took another drink. "I think I can trust you Greta."

"Of course you can. What are you thinking?"

"I don't know if I should ask this of you. You're a young woman, my son's wife."

"I may be young, but I know about life. What's going on?"

"Okay. Would you be able to keep some money safe for me?"

"Sure. What sort of money are we talking about?"

"My winnings. Stefania goes through my pockets and she knows all my hiding places. I'm only allowed to have a 100 lei with me. She confiscates anything above that. When I have a good night at the casino, I need to hide my winnings before she finds them."

"How would you get them to me?"

"I'll drop them in your mail box on my way home. I can't imagine Benno checking the mailbox as he leaves in the morning. So when you get a chance, go downstairs, take the money, and hide it. What do you think?"

"No problem," I said, thinking this was going to be my first adventure.

"On the nights I go gambling, I'll call you and I'll tell you how much money I need and you'll put it in the mailbox. Just make sure nobody sees you."

"Sounds great. This will be our secret."

"Greta, you're great. My son doesn't deserve you."

"Don't worry Martin, I will be fine," I answered, though I knew then that I was just fooling myself.

Over the next couple of years, Martin and I had a good system going. Early on Martin decided that I should get 5% of his winnings, which amounted to enough money to buy nice presents for Coty and my parents, and pretty hats for myself. Benno never noticed anything, even though I would wear the hats in front of him. But from that day on I felt that, with people in my life like Martin and my father, I was going to be all right no matter what happened.

CHAPTER 4
Postwar Bucharest
1945-1953

Pushing hard with both hands against the side handles, Greta lifts *herself slowly out of the bathtub. Once standing, she takes a deep breath, while tiny rivulets form all across her body and then cascade into the awaiting water below. Without urgency, she cautiously steps out of the tub, uses a hand towel to soak up excess water, and wraps herself in a bathrobe. Once her feet are securely set into her high-heeled house slippers, she trudges into the bedroom. She slowly lowers herself onto an armchair and, after a moment of indecision, pushes the recorder's ON button. She coughs demurely into her fist and begins talking, slowly, purposefully.*

I

In August of 1945, the victorious Soviet Army took over the country. There were Soviet soldiers everywhere, simple-minded, uneducated country boys who had never been in a city. They didn't know anything except they could have anything they wanted. If they saw someone on the street wearing a pair of shoes they liked, they would point their rifle at the person's head and use their other hand to point at the shoes. It was not unusual to see frightened people running barefoot away from a hysterically laughing Russian soldier.

After the first few months of Russian occupation, the soldiers' behavior became a bit more civilized – they must've been reprimanded – except maybe when they happened to see wristwatches. They would walk up to anyone wearing a wristwatch, grab the person's arm, and yell out, *"Davai chass."* At first, most people interpreted the Russians' crude gesture as asking for the correct time. I remember a tall, scrawny man, shaking like a leaf, trying to scratch number 3, as that was the time, on a dirty windowpane, while a Russian soldier was furiously yanking his watch hand. I quickly yelled at the man, "Just give him the watch." Quite a few people got badly beaten up until everyone learned that "*Davai chass*" was Russian for "Give me your watch." For most Romanians, these were the only Russian words they ever learned.

There were rumors of young women being raped, but the truth was that many of them willingly gave themselves to the gun-toting Russian soldiers. There were posters everywhere urging people to show their gratitude to their liberators. I remember one of them read, "They risked their lives for us. The least we can do is show them our gratitude." The picture next to the text showed a Romanian girl, dressed in a flimsy button-down dress, happily hanging on the neck of a Russian soldier. A doctor friend of mine who, at that time, worked in one of the largest hospitals in Bucharest told me that within a year of the occupation a lot of babies were born whose fathers were listed as 'Unknown Soviet soldier.'

The new Communist regime could have chosen to ignore these shameful facts, but instead they cleverly seized on the situation and proudly labeled these babies as "Solidarity Fruits." There were pictures of plump, smiling Solidarity Fruits everywhere, with red bandanas on their bald heads. It was the beginning of the perverse relationship between the Soviet Union and the new Communist Romania.

In subsequent years, many of the girls who gave birth to Solidarity Fruits were inducted into the Romanian Communist Party and molded into champions of the indissoluble Soviet-Romanian friendship. These coarse, shameless girls, whose only accomplishment was to have allowed a bunch of dirty, toothless soldiers to pounce on top of them for nothing, not even a crust of bread, were later taken all around the country to speak at Party functions. They were accorded all the creature comforts available in Romania at the time, including their own private townhouses in some of Bucharest's most exclusive neighborhoods, a car, a big American television set, an ultra modern kitchen, and, of course, their pick of the *Securitate* men for their enjoyment. However, like the Vestal Virgins of antiquity, they were expected to remain unmarried as high priestesses of the Communist temple.

When I first arrived in Bucharest, I got to know this short, fat Jewish woman – she must have been in her forties at the time – who lived across the street with an elderly aunt. I would often see her walking slowly around the neighborhood, bundled up in rags, and staring with wild eyes at passersby. Everyone knew she was crazy. A few months after the war ended, she seemed to have gotten worse: every morning she would be out on the street, standing on a pile of bricks, shouting that everyone should defer to her because she had done her duty to the country. Nobody knew what she was talking about until she began to show. She gave birth to a big blond baby: a Solidarity Fruit. This crazy woman became a member of the Communist Party, moved to the most elegant section of Bucharest, and it was rumored that she served as a confidential advisor to some of the most powerful members of the Romanian Communist Party.

II

Within a year, the Soviets set up a Communist government made up of Romanian resistance fighters. Ana Pauker became the head of the government. She was a smart practical woman, who, had she stayed in power, might have been able to set up a system of government that took the best of Communism - equal opportunity for all, full employment, compensation according to need – and used it to rebuild the country. But shortly after she assumed control, a power struggle developed between her faction, which included a number of Jewish intellectuals, and another led by Gheorghe Gheorghiu-Dej.

Dej went to Moscow to ask for Stalin's help, and Stalin gave it to him. Stalin decreed that although Ana was a reliable comrade, a Jewess had no business running a Communist country. Ana Pauker was arrested and charged with *Cosmopolitanism*, which was code for having committed the crime of being born Jewish. If it hadn't been for Lavrentiy Beria, the infamous head of the NKVD, who happened to like Ana, she would have been executed. As it was, she lived out her days holding menial jobs under the constant watch of *Securitate*, knowing that she could be murdered at any moment. She died of breast cancer without ever receiving any treatment, because the hateful, uneducated peasants who were assigned to watch her dismissed her request for medical attention as the whining of a Jewess. After Ana's fall, no Jews were ever allowed to assume a significant role in the Communist Party.

A new crop of Romanian Communists emerged under Gheorghe Gheorghiu-Dej, a smart peasant who quickly learned the prerogatives of absolute power. They took over the country, banished King Michael and his family, and nationalized all private property. Very methodically, the new Communist regime dispatched its henchmen to property and business owners, and presented them with an official-looking document that stated that the former owner willingly transfers ownership of all assets to the Government. Anyone who refused to sign was promptly arrested and the property was commandeered on the grounds that the previous owner was an anti-Communist collaborator. Those arrested were never heard from again.

Of Benno's friends, there was only one I actually liked. His name was Nicu Badescu; he was a prominent architect. I had met him on a few occasions and even spoken to him. He always treated me kindly and with respect, which is more than I can say about any of Benno's other friends. What impressed me most about the man was his unvarnished intelligence, stripped of conceit and artifice. He had a small private consultancy that he operated out of his apartment; there was no one working for him. One day – it must have been in the Fall of 1948 – two men showed up at his door who demanded, in the name of the Popular Republic of Romania, that they take over his office. He explained that it was his home. First they beat him up, then they took him away. Years later his wife received an unsigned typed letter that read, "This is to inform you that the location of your husband's remains are unknown."

The Government also issued new currency. The exile of King Michael and the dissolution of the monarchy at the end of 1947 was followed by what was called *stabilizare*, an euphemism for one of the darkest times of anyone who had no more than the proverbial pissing pot. Suddenly, without warning, the old money, money that people just the day before had used to buy the staples of daily living – bread, lard, sugar – became worthless. People had to go to designated distribution centers where they had to wait for sometimes days on insanely long lines to be handed a few new lei. I remember Martin saying that had the old paper bills been just a bit softer, they would have made excellent toilet paper. His comment was particularly appropriate since people had not seen toilet paper since before the war, and the only newspaper, *Scinteia*, a Communist rag that only printed Dej's speeches, had the peculiar property of having all its ink run onto people's asses, making the process of wiping counterproductive.

The mighty Feingolds became destitute. The change of currency left them with closets full of worthless banknotes. Benno and I kept a roaring fire going in his parents' fireplace for an entire afternoon, just by feeding it millions of old *lei*, mostly in large denominations, while his parents, barely breathing, sat frozen in their velvet-covered armchairs staring at the flames that were devouring their identity.

The Communist government was particularly harsh on the Feingolds: bourgeois oppressors and Jews to boot. They kept them on as employees at their old kitchenware factory, but that was only until the new managers, young, practically illiterate Communists assigned to run it convinced themselves that they knew enough to run a factory. Stupid pride played the deciding role in getting rid of the Feingolds after only two weeks; they weren't going to let the Feingolds think that Communists were stupid.

Benno had to look for a job. The Government assigned him to the position of assistant bookkeeper in a factory that made wooden drums for soft cheese.

One of the nicest things that Stefania did after we got married was to tell Martin to give my father a job. He ended up working in one of Feingolds' repair shops doing exactly what he had done for thirty years: fix pots and pans. My father loved the work, and after the Communists took over Feingold's factory, he couldn't stop laughing - they made him manager of the repair shop; his working class background was far more desirable than the Feingolds', and that was the only thing that mattered in those days. In fact, the less educated someone was, the better his chances for getting some powerful position with the Government, provided of course that he joined the Communist Party. When my father kindly refused the honor of joining the Party, he was fired.

III

One of the very few things that was available in abundance in Communist Romania was condoms. Benno, however, was unwilling to protect me from getting pregnant, despite the fact that neither one of us wanted children. And as my luck would have it, I was the most fertile woman in the world. It seemed that after every mating episode, I ended up pregnant.

As soon as I knew I was pregnant I went to Dr. Schneider, my gynecologist, and got an abortion, which was legal in Romania in those days. During the years prior to Poldy's birth I had nine abortions, which gradually turned Dr. Schneider's initial sympathy for me into full-blown rage. In fact, it would have been ten if I had kept better records of my menstrual cycle. To my dismay, by the time I realized that I might be pregnant and made an appointment with Dr. Schneider, I was already in my fourth month. Dr. Schneider flatly objected to aborting the fetus. He claimed it was too late, and dangerous, and he adamantly refused to do it. I thought of taking a chance on another gynecologist, but in the end, I just accepted my fate. That's how Poldy got through.

During the months I was pregnant, I looked like I was carrying triplets and I developed cravings for the strangest foods. I never liked watermelons, but suddenly I couldn't get enough of them. One time, while I was alone in Stefania's apartment, I saw a huge watermelon on the kitchen table, so I decided to cut myself a small piece. It was the sweetest and juiciest piece of watermelon I had ever had, so I thought another small piece would be in order. Half an hour later, when Stefania returned, all that was left of the giant watermelon were the rinds, and even those were scraped clean of any evidence of the red eatable core. Stefania looked at my belly and decided that I needed to be immediately taken to the hospital or else I would probably burst.

During those nine months, I never felt better; I didn't have morning sickness; I was never nauseous; I hardly had any discomfort; and the birth was a breeze. It was Yom Kippur day around nine in the morning when my water broke. I was very calm. I told Benno, who was reading in bed as usual, to bring the car around. He asked me why. I told him, "Just do it." He threw me an unkind stare, but obeyed. Ten minutes later we were on the way to the hospital. When we got there, the nurse showed me into a private room with fresh cut wild flowers everywhere –reds and blues and yellows. She then examined me and said that I probably won't be ready for hours and I should get into bed and relax. I told Benno to fetch my mother. He nodded. I could see he was thrilled to get out of there.

As the nurse came around with lunch my mother arrived, with Benno skulking behind her. I told my mother in Yiddish to tell him that I didn't want him or anyone else around until after I delivered my baby. My mother turned to him and, in broken Romanian, warned him in a harsh voice, "Keep away you and everybody. *Farshtaist!?*" I knew she was the right person to have with me at that moment. My mother bent over the plate of food the nurse had brought, uttered a dismissive "Feh," and moved it to a table on the far side of the room. She reached into the enormous canvas bag she always carried with her and unveiled several bundles wrapped in wax paper. There was a whole boiled chicken, a hunk of boiled beef with the marrowbone still attached, several large boiled potatoes, and a jar of my mother's homemade horseradish.

I was famished and my mother was in her element. She emptied the hospital food in the trashcan and proudly placed a chicken leg, a piece of beef that she ripped with her bare ands, and a potato on the plate. I got through it in no time and looked up at my mother. Without hesitation, she quickly filled up the plate again: another chicken leg, a piece of beef, a potato, and plenty of horseradish. That disappeared just as fast. This time she cocked her head and raised her eyebrows. I gave her a big grin. She filled up the plate again. Then I felt good.

Over the next few hours my mother talked nonstop, mostly complaining about my father, while I kept staring at my enormous belly. The nurse stuck her head in the door every half hour, looked at me with probing eyes, then smiled as she turned away. By early evening – it must have been around six o'clock – the pains started coming more and more frequently and I told the nurse. She placed an alarm clock on the cabinet opposite the bed and told me to time the contractions. When she came back, I told her they were about twelve minutes apart. She said she needed to give me another exam. When she finished, she gave me a big grin and announced that I won't have much longer to wait.

I stopped looking at the clock, but I knew the pains were coming even more frequently. I heard the nurse talk to someone on the phone; she seemed agitated. Moments later she came in the room with a syringe and a long needle. My mother jumped, "What's that for?" The nurse hesitated, "The doctor is not here yet and we need to delay the delivery." "We're not delaying anything," my mother bellowed. "If the doctor is not here when the baby comes, I'll deliver it. *Gai shoen!*" The nurse ran out of the room and I heard her back on the phone. I heard her shriek, "Doctor, please, she refuses...You need to be here...There'll be food left."

My mother lunged out of the room, and then I heard her yell at the nurse, "You tell him I'll give him plenty food when he delivers my grandchild."

Twenty minutes later, Dr. Schneider was wheeling me into the delivery room. As soon as he put my feet in the stirrups, he ordered me to start pushing as hard as I could. I kept looking up and asking, "Do you see the head? Do you see the head?" The doctor snapped back, "Just keep pushing." Then I heard the sound of my baby. It was a boy; the most beautiful boy in the world. He was big and long and he was smiling at me, a great big toothless smile.

After I gave birth, the hospital staff came around and they all told me that my boy was the most beautiful baby they had ever seen. When Dr. Bercovici, the pediatrician recommended by Dr. Schneider, came to the hospital the next day to check on my baby, he turned to me and said, "Madame, you told me that I'd be seeing a newborn. Don't waste my time. This baby must be at least three weeks old." I knew they were saying these things just to make me happy and it worked. I was twenty-one, and I felt I had finally accomplished something.

In the recovery room I met Lena. She was there delivering her son Sergiu. Afterwards, Lena and I remained the best of friends; she was always there for me, especially during my darkest moments, and I often wonder how much better I would have felt over the last twenty-five years; it's so hard for me to accept it, but that's how long she's been dead. It was she who made me see that I didn't have anything to blame myself for, not even for the incident that always seemed to fuel Poldy's spiteful ridiculing of my, in his opinion, nonexistent maternal instincts.

Over the years, I told the story of Poldy's uninvited arrival into this world to many of my friends, as I thought it to be an amusing tale. So by the time Poldy was six or seven, I had told that story a hundred times and I never envisioned its consequences as I began telling it again one night at my house.

Poldy happened to be sitting among my guests, and, with all eyes fixed on me, I recounted the whole incident, chuckling how this obstinate embryo, pointing to Poldy, miraculously got through. I then added that after the Poldy episode I became more vigilant and made sure that his three younger siblings didn't make it.

I told the story to only amuse my guests, and they all seemed to enjoy it. Yet, Poldy didn't share their merriment, and suddenly got up and ran away. I spent four anxious days searching for him. The militia finally found him living with a gypsy family in a Roma camp on the outskirts of the City. They had him dressed in gypsy clothes, and they swore up and down that he was their son. When one of the militiamen asked him directly whose son he was, he told them the gypsies', which should have given me a glimpse into the man he would turn out to be.

A few days later, a gypsy woman came to my door and told me that I could buy my son back. She wanted five hundred *lei*, an enormous amount of money, which we simply didn't have. She added that she and her family were leaving by caravan the next day and once they left it would be impossible to find them. I was furious; no six-year old snotnose was going to manipulate me.

After the gypsy woman left, I called Benno and told him that he had to get the money out of his mother, as I was sure that she still had plenty of valuable things stashed away. We went together to his parents' dark basement apartment in the building they once owned. Benno told her what happened and asked her for the money. I told her it was urgent, but the old fox made us wait. Later she reappeared holding a string of natural pearls probably worth ten times as much. Clutching the pearls, I ran out the door, leaving Benno behind.

First I thought of running all the way, but it was too far, so I waited for the streetcar that seemed like it would never come. I rode to the last stop and then I had to walk at least another two kilometers up a steep hill. I was panting, but I couldn't decide whether it was from exhaustion or just repressed anger for letting Poldy put me through that ordeal.

After examining the pearls, the gypsy woman called out a strange name and a man wearing long metal earrings appeared from behind the tent, holding Poldy in his arms. The man handed Poldy back to me, but I think the gypsies kept his soul.   For months, I couldn't stop thinking how much that string of pearls would have otherwise helped supplement our meager rations, if only Poldy hadn't been so pigheaded.

But as God is my witness, despite all his cruel shenanigans, I never stopped loving him, even though I wanted a girl; I even planned on naming her Claudette, after Claudette Colbert, my favorite actress who I had seen in *It Happened One Night* with Clark Gable – they were wonderful. But he grew on me. Maybe it was because he was the only thing that was ever really mine. The day after he was born, Benno came into my room and told me that he was about to fill out the birth certificate and, as a courtesy, he wondered if I thought of a name. I hadn't, but I knew that if I left it up to Benno, it would be something unfriendly and pretentious that would condemn my son to a sad and lonely life. I asked him to let me think about it and closed my eyes to prevent Benno's merciless countenance from invading me. He was standing by the door motionless, except for his fingers slowly tapping against the doorframe, blinking occasionally, dripping disdain.

I didn't want my son to have a name that would mark him as Jewish, like Isaac or Yehuda, but I believed that names said something about the person, so I wanted to give him a smart name. My mind was racing against the annoying rhythmic tapping of Benno's fingers.

"Tomas or Nicholas or Adam," I called out. "I like them all. You pick one, the one you like the best. Okay?"

Benno sneered and left the room. Soon after, my parents showed up. My father looked so happy. He kissed me and told me that with a boy we have added obligations: there had to be a *bris*. He told me he would be proud to arrange everything. I told him to go ahead. I knew he wanted to infuse a bit more Hashem into the occasion than had been at my wedding.

As my parents were about to leave, Stefania and Martin showed up. As if knowing what my father and I had just discussed,

Stefania announced that she had already arranged for a *mohel*, and what a difficult time she had finding one. The *bris* was going to be held at her place and she had already contacted everyone she thought should be there. My father looked at me with a Stan Laurel face – long and sad, yet humorous – yet accepted the disappointment with his usual grace.

The next day, as I was about to leave the hospital with my son in my arms, a nurse stopped me and wished me and Apollo good luck. *Apollo!?* I asked the nurse to repeat the name. I was in agony. I stared at my beautiful baby boy. Apollo? I felt like smashing him against the pavement. Benno had won, but, although I felt defeated at the time, I soon knew that it was just a battle, a minor one at that.

Benno came around with his car and dropped us off at the apartment; he then drove straight back to the factory. As soon as I walked in, I called Coty and asked her to come over. She was there in twenty minutes, especially after I assured her that Benno wouldn't be there. I opened the door with the baby in my arms. She went crazy when she saw him. She grabbed him out of my hand and began twirling around and trilling like a bird. I first thought she would hurt him, but he looked delighted.

When she was finally ready to return my baby, I grabbed him and held him; this was the longest I had been without him since he was born. I asked her to sit down, and then I began crying. I told her about Benno's treachery: how he deceived me with the baby naming, how he ignored all my suggestions, especially after he asked for them, and how he went ahead and named the baby Apollo, knowing full well how much that would upset me. On hearing the baby's name, Coty rolled her eyes and let out a deep moan. We sat in silence for a long time.

"A good nickname for Apollo is Poldy," Coty spouted. "Poldy is a nice name. We will call him Poldy. Everyone will call him Poldy. If Benno ever calls him Apollo, you have my permission to crack his head open." And he became Poldy.

IV

The *bris* was beautiful; it was intimate and unpretentious, nothing like the wedding. The *mohel* looked like a *mohel* should. He was short and scrawny and his face was covered by a scraggy black beard. When he asked who would hold the baby while he performs the ritual of circumcision, he didn't wait for an answer; he just walked up to my father and said, "You! You hold the baby. Come." My father was ecstatic. I handed him the baby. Then the *mohel* asked us, all the women, to leave the room. Stefania, not used to be bossed around in her house, stared down at the little man, but obeyed.

A long time passed with me pressed tightly against the closed door. Then suddenly, a primal scream emerged; it was my baby's. My heart sunk, and I was about to rush into the room if not for the clicking of glasses and laughter that quickly followed; I could distinctly make out my father's voice roar majestically above all the others.

After the ceremony, the women were allowed back in the room. I was the first one there; I had to retrieve my baby. I walked up to my father, who was sitting in an armchair with my baby asleep across his lap, and lifted him into my arms. As I was standing there, immune to the goings on around me, the *mohel* approached me.

"Did you find out your baby's name?" he asked in a friendly voice.

I gasped. How did he find out that ghastly name Benno had given him?

"Ap...Ap..." I stuttered, unable to articulate further.

"You are correct Mrs. Feingold. How did you find out? It is Abram Ben Benyamin. It's a beautiful name. Your father was very helpful in setting it right."

"Thank you so much. You conducted a wonderful *bris*," I answered.

"Did you know I was a Kohen?" he asked me.

"No I didn't," I answered having no idea what he meant.

"Well, I understand that this is your first born and we know it's a boy. I've conducted many *Pidyon Ha'Bens*. It's a wonderful ceremony. So what do you say?

"Sure," I said, again clueless as to what I was agreeing to.

"Wonderful," uttered the little man. "Avram was born eight days ago, right?"

I nodded faintly. The little man reached into his coat pocket and retrieved a small booklet. It was a calendar, a Jewish calendar. "Let me see, " he went on as if talking to himself. "That would be the twenty-first of Tishrei. Let everyone know that you're having your son's *Pidyon Ha'Ben* on the eighteenth of October. It's a Tuesday, so we'll do it right here after work. Let's say six o'clock. This is a big mitzvah. You know why? Your son was born on Yom Kippur. He's blessed. Goodbye. I'll see you on October eighteenth. I'm always punctual," and he left.

Over the next three weeks, I asked around, "What is a *Pidyon Ha'Ben*?" No one knew, not even my father.

I don't remember much about the Pidyon Ha'Ben other than the little man who had performed the *bris* three weeks earlier took off Poldy's diaper and placed him naked on one of Stefania's prettiest silver trays. Then everyone dumped whatever coins they had in their pockets around his legs and tush. It had something to do with buying him back from God. The *moyel* said a few prayers in Hebrew and put Poldy's diaper back on. We didn't have any wine, so everybody drank *tzuica*, and Benno got drunk and told Sammy that he was an uncouth, simpleminded peasant. Sammy wanted to hit him, but I stopped him; he wasn't worth it.

V

By 1945, Benno's bachelor pad, where I had spent three unpleasant years as a reluctant trespasser, was no longer adequate. We needed a two-bedroom apartment; I made it clear that the baby had to have his own room. But this was not a good time to look for a new apartment: sloppy American bombing had turned whole streets into rubble, and many of the buildings that survived were left heavily scarred. The war was over but its ravages were visible everywhere. There was no way to advertise, "Young couple with newborn looking for two-bedroom apartment," just word of mouth. Benno's butler told us that his sister's married boyfriend lived in a building where an apartment had just become available: there had been a double suicide.

The next day, we went to see the new apartment. It was in one of the oldest, shabbiest parts of the City and the building had a crack, running diagonally across its side from street level all the way up to the roof, wide enough for local boys to stuff a football into it while they were playing on the street. We didn't know if the crack had occurred as a result of the building's advanced age, but most likely it was caused by an American bomb. The building was surrounded by vacant lots that were covered by the rubble of the buildings that once stood on them; when I left Romania 16 years later the only change to the street landscape was the ever presence of tall grass and weeds.

The building was a two-story walk-up with two apartments per floor. The only light along the white marble spiral staircase came from a tiny window on each of the floors; the light fixtures mounted on the ceiling were broken and seemed to have been that way for a long time.

Apartment 2A was on the far side of the top floor. There were no electric bulbs there either, but enough light came through the windows to see that the apartment had been left exactly the way it was when the bodies were taken away. The little entrance foyer opened into a good-size living room that, by its state of utter devastation, with broken chairs lying sideways and shards of china strewn everywhere, looked like the site of the couple's final battle. There was a bedroom on either side of the living room; the one to the left was smaller but had a beautiful semicircular terrace that looked out onto a vacant lot lined with apple trees; the one on the right, the master bedroom, led to the only bathroom, a large white-tiled sanctuary that, with an oversized faïence tub and double bidets, hinted of better days. Just to the right of the foyer, a squeaky swinging door opened to a long hallway that itself opened onto a dark, windowless kitchen shrouded in the pungent odor of sour cabbage. On the far side of the kitchen, there was a solid door that gave out onto a narrow balcony. As I walked through it, I made a mental note that as soon as I moved in I would have it replaced with a glass door.

The entrance to the super's apartment was in the back of the building, at the end of a narrow alley lined with broken stoves and toilets. As I knocked on the door, the super opened it and asked me to come in. He stood a head shorter than me and reminded me of an egg. He stared at me with panic-stricken eyes and a toothless mouth. I raised my eyes and scanned his miserable living quarters. It was a cell, a windowless cell. A small electric bulb hanging from the low ceiling exposed a large mattress that seemed to occupy most of the space. The super's wife and two small children, a boy and a girl, were sitting on the mattress with their backs against the wall. Throughout the minute and a half I stood in the doorway, they didn't make a move. I asked the super – I later learned that his name was Ion - where they cooked their meals and he pointed to one of the stoves outside. I then wanted to ask him where they went to the bathroom, but I was afraid of what he would answer.

I asked Benno to give him some money. Benno sneered at me, then reached into his wallet, sifted through a wad of bank notes, and handed him 10 lei, not even enough to buy a pack of cigarettes. I grabbed his arm and hissed, "Give him a hundred." Benno jerked his arm away from my grip and fingered a few more notes. The super reached for the threadbare banknotes as he scanned the air over his shoulder.

"Madam, I will have the place spic-and-span for you. Don't worry."

I stared at Ion with stubborn eyes. "I don't want anything. Throw everything out. And get rid of the smell. Wash the floors twice and don't forget the windows."

"Yes madam. I know you'll be very pleased." Ion pulled back his lips as he looked down at his open palm. I turned to Benno without looking at him.

"Give him another fifty. Do it."

VI

Once we settled in the new apartment, I devoted myself to Poldy. He was my companion and my toy. I spent the whole day with him; he was such a good baby. He let me do anything I wanted to him, clip all the barrettes I could find in his sparse, soft hair, draw funny faces on his belly with my lipstick, or pull on his tiny peepee and go "Weeee". He always laughed; I knew he adored me. All he wanted to do was to be with me. I was Mamica to him and he was my big boy. Benno didn't matter any more. I could have handled anything if only the world had stayed still.

Benno went away every morning, and I had the whole day to spend with my boy. We went shopping together; when he was very little I had him in this big stroller, but as he got to be about three, he followed me on foot everywhere. I was a very fast walker, but he always managed to keep up with me. Maybe those were the happiest days of my life, or at least the most carefree. And he was growing into a beautiful boy. I was still in my twenties and I had this great child who loved me, and that seemed to be enough. I wish it could have lasted forever.

On hot summer days, we went to the city's only public pool club located at the terminus of the #2 tram. It was a large concrete affair with three separate pools, one of them dedicated to a water slide. I would pack a lunch of black bread and marmalade for Poldy and me and spend the day in the sun. He would play in the pool the whole day, while I lay motionless for hours on a slab of concrete, indifferent to the world around me. But these wonderful days didn't last long. Within two years of the end of the war, my life, and I'm sure most everyone else's, was quickly reduced to a primitive struggle for survival. The Communists, always doubting their own legitimacy to govern the country, made what would probably have been an already difficult post-war period into a living hell.

One of the worst shortages was clothing; the few items available - shirts, pants, skirts, and coats - were made in one size, large enough to accommodate even those who seemed to have managed to retain an ample corporeality. The majority of the people had to have their clothes taken in, which made tailoring one of the most lucrative non-governmental occupations. Maybe if I had learned something at that dressmaking school my mother sent me to when we first arrived in Bucharest, I might have had an easier time in later years making ends meet. Shoes were the only items of clothing that came in sizes, small, medium and large, so people always bought the larger size and stuffed the tips with newspaper. Those who had particularly large feet had to convert their shoes into open-toed sandals, which worked well enough, even in winter, with several layers of woolen socks.

This reminds me of a funny incident, one of the very few of this period, although I didn't think so at the time. I had learned from a woman who worked in a shoe store that the next day they would be selling boys' sneakers. I had previously not been able to find any shoes for Poldy, so I had him wear Benno's old polo boots. Poldy was about four. I cut the upper part of the boots, so he could bend his legs, and then I stuffed several issues of *Scinteia*, the Communist Party's daily newspaper, into the boots. But that still didn't keep the boots from falling off. I didn't know what to do, but then I came up with a bright idea. I drilled two holes on either side of each boot and tied a string that ran around Poldy's neck. When he walked he looked like baby Frankenstein. Every time I looked at him, I would start laughing hysterically. He didn't seem to mind; he loved the attention. Anyway, Poldy needed shoes, so I asked Benno to leave me enough money, which, after feigning a sudden case of deafness, he did.

In order to go on with the story, I need to digress for a moment. There were very few grocery stores, and even those that were still around didn't carry daily staples like milk or bread. Since the

Communists arrested everyone involved in the distribution of farm products to the City on suspicion of anti-Communist activities, a few enterprising farmers loaded up their little donkey-drawn carts and became street vendors. Twice or three times a week, one of these framers passed our window, shouting, "Fresh milk, fresh cheese." Whenever I heard their calls, I would yell down my order, which I would follow by lowering a small basket with the money. To keep the money from blowing away, I would put it in a small metal can. After the vendor replaced the money with my order of milk or cheese, I would raise the basket. Poldy always sat with his nose pressed against the window as he seemed fascinated by my aerial transactions.

The morning when Poldy's sneakers were to go on sale, Benno left a 20-*lei* banknote on a side table next to the window and left for work. I went into the kitchen to make breakfast. While Poldy was alone in the living room, a street vendor passed by peddling little rubber balls at 1 leu a ball. Poldy, overwhelmed with excitement, stuffed the 20-*lei* banknote in the metal can and lowered the basket. I don't know how long Poldy waited before he came rushing into the kitchen screaming, "No ball! No ball!" As soon as I realized what had happened, I ran downstairs looking for the ball vendor. Needless to say, I never found him, and Poldy never got his new sneakers.

That evening, when Benno got home and found out what happened, he wanted to thrash Poldy, but I wouldn't let him. Seeing, however, that Benno was angry with him, Poldy ran up to one of the corners of the room and stood there, his nose pressed against the wall. Since we had never asked him to do that before, we could only assume that he'd seen another boy do it. I think he would have still be standing in that corner if I hadn't told him that he had stood there long enough. I am sure to this day, he had no idea what he had done wrong. Afterwards, the only thing that preoccupied Poldy was the whereabouts of the missing ball. For the next week, every morning he would post himself by the window and wait for hours for the appearance of the ball vendor.

VII

Buying food was the adventure from hell. I tried it once or twice, but then I had to stop; I hated it so much. By the time Poldy was seven or eight, he became my food shopper, and he didn't mind it. If we wanted bread, he had to go to a bread distribution center. He had to be on line by five am, even though the place didn't open until seven am, or else the bread would run out. Each person on line was entitled to a one-kilogram loaf of black bread. That bread had to last us for a week.

I never knew in advance which distribution center would be selling food on any particular day and, if so, what specifically –flour, margarine, cooking oil, beef bones, prune marmalade, chicken parts or salami – so I had to be very creative. I would wake up Poldy around three am, get him dressed while he was still half-asleep, and give him ten   , enough money to buy most anything in those days, though he rarely spent even half that. The Government controlled prices, so even though there were great food shortages, people, whenever lucky enough to find something, anything to buy, didn't have to spend much.

People got on line outside food distribution centers without any idea of what they would be buying that day. It wasn't until eight am when the doors opened, and a man came out and announced what had been delivered overnight. They never had more than one food item to sell, but many times they had nothing, and all those people who waited on line for over three hours had to leave empty-handed, knowing they'd be without anything to eat for another day. Like I said, one day it was margarine, another day it was marmalade, and another day it was flour. On rare occasions they had salami or bologna. My standing order to Poldy was, "Buy a kilo of anything they have." Cooking oil, whenever they had it, came in big metal drums, so Poldy had to always carry an empty bottle. They siphoned the oil out of the drums with their mouths, so whenever the guy ended up with a mouth full of oil, he would spit it into someone's bottle.

When Poldy got home around eight am, I quietly got out of bed so as not to awaken Benno's foul morning urges, closed the bedroom door behind me, and went into the kitchen to make Poldy a cup of hot chocolate. While I was getting him ready for school, he breathlessly shared his shopping adventures with me. By then he was already stuttering pretty badly, so, instead, he ended up doing a nervous pantomime of what happened on line. I made sure the bedroom door was closed; I was in no mood to put up with Benno's foul morning urges.

Once in a while we got lucky and Poldy brought home a chicken, a live chicken. That reminded me of Ghimeş before some big Jewish holiday, when my mother would hand my father a big knife and point him towards the chicken house. As soon as I knew what was happening, I ran into my room and hid under my blanket. My father was so brave. Later he would tell me that it was safe to come out from under my blanket; by then the chicken had not only been decapitated, but plucked as well.

Whenever Poldy came home with a live chicken, I would tell him to take the chicken onto the balcony behind the kitchen and cut off its head. I usually wasn't there when it happened, but once I opened the door a few minutes earlier than usual and I saw that the chicken wasn't quite dead. It was a frightful sight as the headless chicken, blood still gushing from its neck, kept bouncing around for what seemed like an eternity. Poldy would always be gone by the time I looked in; I knew he didn't like doing it, but I also knew that in order to succeed in life we sometimes have to do things we don't like. Maybe he wasn't meant to be like my father, although I had hoped he would.

Food preparation required great ingenuity. I used to stretch one fat chicken into five or even six dinners. I made a meal out of every part of that chicken, including the gizzard, the neck, the heart, the liver, the feet, the neck and the ever-savory *pupik*. Four boiled potatoes, a *pupik*, and a chicken neck made a good dinner for the three of us. Sometimes, I would fill a huge pot with water, and throw in chicken pieces, vegetables, and a big beef bone, if I could find one, and let it boil: that was chicken soup. With the help of a large loaf of black bread, we had food for a week.

VIII

I was never religious, though my father was. When the Communists first came to power, they proclaimed that, even though they thought it was idiotic and a waste of time, everyone had the right to practice his religion. They reasoned that a true socialist society could not be built in a day and that people had to be carefully educated to abandon their obsolete, irrational ways. At first, they started holding mandatory "reality" seminars. One day I found a note in Poldy's bag; it was an invitation. It said that the parents of the child whose bag the note was in had to attend a brief lecture. Benno and I went; we had heard that parents who had ignored the invitation had been arrested. It was summertime, so we were told that the lecture was to be held outdoors.

We arrived early, so we got to sit in the front row. A table and a footstool had been placed at the far end of the playground. Behind the table there were two men standing; one short and fat and dark-skinned, the other even shorter and emaciated and sickly pale. After a short wait culminated by a long shhhh from the principal, the short, fat man stared angrily at the collection of frightened parents, then took a quick one-two step from the foot stool onto the table, where he began speaking in accented Romanian. He sounded like a Hungarian peasant from Transylvania. I knew the type: for a loaf of bread he would sell his mother; for two he would also deliver her.

He said he was born Catholic and he went to Catholic school as a youngster, but he realized early on that Catholicism was all lies. Jesus Christ was a myth created by rich people to subjugate people like him, honest working folk. He went on to remind us that Karl Marx said that religion was the opium of the masses and the only thing religion has done during the course of history was to fool honest working people into believing that their suffering in this world was a guarantee for happiness in the next world. As he stepped off the table, the principal and one of the parents briefly applauded and then stopped. While still angrily staring at the audience, the short, fat man snapped his fingers at the emaciated, sickly man.

As the emaciated man approached the table, the short, fat man grabbed a hold of him and helped him step onto the footstool. He was shaking wildly, and if not for the short, fat man he would have fallen. He rested on the footstool and then, after taking several labored breaths, he finally stepped onto the table, all the time being steadied by the muscular arms of the short, fat man. Once on the table, he seemed frozen by fear, his eyes glued to his feet. After another long wait, the short, fat man growled, "Get on with it Itzig."

The emaciated man finally turned to face his audience, and in an uncomfortable Jewish accent, he muttered almost to himself, "What has God ever done for us Jews. We have been persecuted and murdered for two thousand years. We're almost extinct. Another war and there'll be no one left. Communism promises to take care of us Jews, to treat us like everyone else, like human beings. Without religion there'll be no anti-Semitism, no persecution, no murders."

The emaciated man, suddenly imbued with unexpected energy, raised his fist above his head and shook it violently, such that his whole body seemed like it was about to disintegrate. "Only a fool would remain a Jew after what's been done to us. I was a religious Jew, but I'm done with Judaism; I'm done with being treated like a dog. I am a Communist now, and people respect me. They call me Comrade Frumm and they shake my hand and they wish me a good day."

Since arriving in Bucharest, my father had been going to a synagogue right across the street from his apartment on Strada St. Constantin, but one morning in December of 1947 he found a ludicrously large padlock attached to the gate. He was heartsick until his landlady later told him about another synagogue two blocks away that, for some reason, had been allowed to stay open. When Poldy got to be about six or seven, my father would take him to that synagogue for Shabbat services. Poldy loved it; he got to stand among the men, while the women were all crowded upstairs in a dilapidated balcony.

By the early 50's, the Communists' initial attitude of benign disrespect for religion was replaced with a more malignant approach: religion came to be thought of as a capitalist tool for restoring the old regime, and all houses of worship became off-limits to everyone except the clergy, who were mostly old men, as all theological schools had been closed since the war. Not long after, local Communist Party leaders began organizing "demolition festivals," where school children, equipped with axes and sledgehammers, were assigned to tear down a church or a synagogue as fulfillment of their compulsory "volunteer work" program. Soon, someone in government must have realized that these idiots were destroying buildings of great historical value, so suddenly all churches acquired national heritage status.

That protection was not extended to synagogues, so within a couple of years few were left. My father showed up unexpectedly at my door one morning in tears. He had just seen his *shul* in ruins. But as Jews have done for two thousand years, a few of the former congregants, including the old rabbi, started holding services in the basement of someone's house, and Romania surged backwards to the Middle Ages.

IX

I had as little to do with Benno as I could. He still was in the habit of crawling on me like a giant spider, but I was not a child any more, so I would just push him off; he would lunge again, and I would push him off again. Even though he was taller than me, I was stronger, so I usually won, even though the scuffles would, on occasion, get very ugly. My nighttime routine was to turn my back on him as soon as I got into bed. On those nights when he had the urge, he would start by moaning like a sick dog. That only got me to double-check that I was wearing my bra and girdle under my nightgown.

The one night I remember as a highlight of my marriage, I sensed before I even got into bed that he would start with me, so I kept on my slippers. They were made of hard leather with a spiky wooden heel capped by a metal tap. I stiffened up and waited. As I had expected, he suddenly reached over and grabbed my breast. I thrust my elbow in his face. He slapped me. I rotated my body so that my feet were pointing at him and began pounding my heels into his face and chest. He escaped screaming; he did not return that night.

I was no longer afraid of him, nor would I listen to any new lessons in marital etiquette from Stefania. I think this was the first time I realized that I had some identity, some rights. And I had my boy to give me confidence. He was all mine. Benno never played with him, never had any patience for him. To him, Poldy was too young, too ignorant, too much trouble.

Madame Sherban died when Poldy was four. I remember it because Benno, in one of his more revolting displays of sleaze, informed me that he was going to take Poldy along to the funeral. I told him that I would stab him in the mouth if he as much as repeated that insane suggestion.

From the beginning, Poldy excelled in school. He was not only one of the best students in the class, but was also as swift as a gazelle. When the state-sponsored athletic try-outs came to his school, they picked him for the pre-Olympic team. That was a rare honor. Athletes in Communist countries were treated like war heroes, and in some ways they were. The Cold War was not fought with tanks and bombers, but with propaganda, and the spoils were not land, but the hearts and minds of ignorant people across the world.

Romania, like most Communist countries, was committed to the Communist mission of spreading Communism to the world, and Communist leaders realized that one of the most effective ways of doing this was by showing the world that Communism bred healthy bodies that could outrun and outscore any athletes from Capitalist countries.

At every Olympiad, small Communist countries like Hungary, East Germany, Czechoslovakia, and Romania took a disproportionate number of medals, a testament to the superiority of the Communist way of life. Romania spent a great deal of money and effort preparing athletes to dazzle the world, and they thought Poldy had the potential of being one of them. Once on the pre-Olympic team – Poldy was about eight or nine – he got to travel, all expenses paid, to training camps all over the country. He was gone for weeks at a time and I remember feeling empty.

X

After Sammy graduated college and started working, life was very hard on him. He thought that once he had the degree, the world would roll out the red carpet for him. He was seeing Coca at the time, and wanted to marry her, but didn't have enough money to offer her the kind of lifestyle he thought she deserved and expected, having herself come from a rich family. He worked long hard hours in the field, but they were paying him beans, while his classmates were getting promotions and making much better salaries.

Sammy knew it had to do with his background: he was not only Jewish, but being related to a well-known bourgeois family like the Feingolds made matters worse. No one denied his work for the Communist underground, yet the few times he actually got an audience with one of his former comrades-in-arms, now high up in the Communist hierarchy and holder of a cushy, well-paying job, he was told that they were sorry; there were no positions available for him, yet he should not lose faith as his brave efforts during the war were their own reward and that no one could ever take that away from him.

I hadn't seen Sammy in months. After my wedding, he avoided my company except for major family affairs, like Poldy's bris. I knew he hated Benno and hated me for making what he considered the devil's deal. I only got to see him when I was visiting my parents and he also happened to be there. My father tried to plan it that way. Whenever he knew that Sammy would be visiting, he would call me and suggest that I drop by as well. As soon as I walked in, though, Sammy would give me an icy look and tell my parents that he had to go.

Once when Poldy was about four, I visited my parents, and Sammy was there. Poldy, not sensing the tension between us, ran up to Sammy and joyfully called out, "Uncle Engineer, Uncle Engineer." We were all very proud of him being a civil engineer, but it seemed none as proud as Poldy.

Sammy coolly shook one of Poldy's outstretched hands, then spin away from him, as he gravely announced that he had to get back to the construction site. I knew that was not the case; all his projects were not only out of town, but in the farthest corners of Romania where no one else wanted to be, which was the cause of much of his frustration.

It was sometime in the spring of 1950 as I remember staring out the window at the lilac trees in bloom on the street below when the doorbell rang. I was shocked to see Sammy. The first thing that came out of my mouth was "Is father okay?" He apologized but he had no one else to talk to.

"What's going on?" I asked.

"I'm getting married and I should be happy, yet I'm miserable," he answered.

"Why?"

"I'm away from Monday morning to Saturday afternoon every week and I know she doesn't want to move to Iasi, a seven-hour train ride from Bucharest. And she doesn't want to be a job widow, and even if she agreed to marry me like this, she'll end up cheating on me. What do I do, what do I do?" he whined.

I asked him about his chances of being reinstated in the Communist Party. He told me they didn't want him. They didn't want him because his sister was married to a former people exploiter, a filthy bourgeois bloodsucker and a Jew to boot.

"Why don't you tell them that you've always opposed your sister's marriage and you have no connections with the Feingolds?"

"I don't know. What I do know is that every time they look up my name, Samuel Sobel, they see Feingold right next to it."

"Then why don't you change your name?" I asked him. "Give them proof that you have broken with the past and with the family."

Sammy thought about it for a minute, then his face lit up, "This might work." The permanent crease across his handsome forehead suddenly disappeared.

I didn't hear from him again for over a year. One day there was a letter in the mailbox from Sandu Sobescu. Inside was a handwritten note that read, "Comrade Greta Sobel is invited to the wedding of Comrade Sandu Sobescu to Comrade Coca Segal at 10 am on May 23, 1951 at the Young Communist Leaders' Meeting Hall on Strada Iuliu Baras." The note, written with a thick black pen, was not in Sammy's hand, but to the side there were two words unmistakably Sammy's, "Come alone!!"

It was a Sunday, a beautiful spring Sunday. I told Benno I was taking Poldy for a long stroll and wouldn't be back until evening. Benno didn't even take his eyes of his book.

By then Poldy had become a great little walker. We covered the twenty-odd blocks in less than fifteen minutes. I had on a simple summer dress with big blue flowers and a long-sleeve white wool sweater that I was going to take off once we got there. I dressed Poldy in a pair of knitted shorts with shoulder straps that I had just bought at Romarta.

The place was teeming with people – people I had never seen in my life. At the far end, there was a small stage dominated by a long wooden table with six chairs lined up facing the room. On the table there were several loaves of black bread, chunks of feta cheese, two Sibiu salamis and a glass bowl filled with ripe tomatoes. There were also three bottles of *tuica*. *Tuica*, if I didn't mention before, is Romania's answer to Russian vodka. All I know is that it's made out of plums, it's crystal clear like vodka, and it comes in only one strength: 150-proof.

As I looked around I could see other tables, most of them round, though some were square, that carried the same assortment of foods and liquor, with the lone supplement, a large jar of mustard. I remembered that Sammy was allergic to mustard. I couldn't see Sammy, so I approached a young man, more boy than man, sitting at one of the tables dressed in the blue uniform of UTM, the Young Communists' Union.

"I'm looking for Sammy," I said.

The young man scrunched his face as if confronted with an impregnable riddle. "This is Comrade Sobescu's wedding. He's my group leader. There is no Sammy here." The young man pronounced "Sammy" as if it was something to be avoided at all cost. I sat Poldy on one of the chairs and handed him the notebook in which he scratched his wild doodles.

"There he is," said the young man jumping to his feet, as he pointed to Sammy standing in the middle of the room surrounded by other men, much shorter and darker than him. I turned, ready to walk over to him, but the young man quickly grabbed my hand, "Don't interrupt him now. Can't you see he's with his men? We are never to break in on those discussions."

"My name is Greta, and this is my son Poldy."

"P...Po...Pol...dy," the young mam mouthed with obvious contempt. "My name is Stefan Popescu. I am a student at the Polytechnic Institute of Heavy Construction," he said, pointing to a red and blue badge pinned to his shirt. "I'm graduating in six months. I've already been assigned to be a concrete worker on a dam in Suceava. It's a great job, especially for someone like me, although I don't know what reading and writing have to do with construction." The young man refilled his glass from the bottle of *tuica* and poured it down his throat. "Comrade Sobescu must like me. I probably remind him of himself when he was with the Underground."

"Ah, very impressive," I said with solemnity.

The young man suddenly recoiled. "And who invited you?" he asked, staring at me and then Poldy.

"I met Comrade Sobescu during the war," I said without hesitation.

"Were you with the Underground?"

"Yes, yes, and this is my son Pyotr. His father was a Soviet soldier."

"Oh, I see. That's excellent," he said, suddenly displaying a great smile. "But you said your son's name was…something else that sounded foreign."

"That's a nickname I gave him. I'll call him Pyotr when he gets older."

"Pyotr is a beautiful name. You should call him that now. People should know he's the son of a Soviet liberator."

Poldy, unaffected by his surroundings, was busy attacking the drawing paper with wide, aggressive hand movements. The young man, his face growing progressively more distorted, was watching him, trying, vainly it seemed, to match the image with something familiar in his memory bank. I forced a smile and reengaged the young man.

"Do you know Comrade Sobescu?"

"Of course. Who doesn't? He's dean of my school. I have him for steel construction. He's a real engineer, civil engineer. Did you know he was chief engineer for the Iasi Slaughterhouse? It's the biggest slaughterhouse in the world outside the Soviet Union."

I turned to see what the tumult was behind me. There was a man standing on one of the tables in the middle of the hall speaking in loud, hesitant tones, "Sit your asses down. We have a wedding to get through, as if you didn't know you morons, Comrade Sobescu is getting married." The man stumbled forward as someone traded him a glass filled with *tuica* for the empty one in his hand. "Then you can get drunk, but you all better be back at your posts tomorrow, otherwise I'll personally send you to the Danube Delta for reed-cutting duty. You all know what that means, you fuckin' faggots."

There were several pairs of hands trying to help the speaker off the table, though the task wasn't accomplished until someone actually got on the table and walked the speaker off while holding him in a half-nelson.

By now, Sammy was standing on the small stage with what seemed to be his bride behind him. She was short and round with sparkling eyes and a puerile grin. What could he have seen in her, I wondered. Everyone else was scrambling to find a seat at one of the tables. A few arguments broke out, some pushing and shoving, but before long everyone was sitting down. The sound of clinking glasses echoed throughout the room.

"Mamica, it stinks in here. Can we go?"

As if stung, I turned to Poldy. He had stopped drawing and was holding his nose.

"It doesn't," I snapped. "Maybe you made a cockie in your pants?"

"No Mamica. I didn't. Look," said Poldy, pointing to his partially lifted behind.

Stefan was staring at Poldy with furrowed eyebrows. I grabbed Poldy's hand and slammed it down on the notebook. This kid was going to get me in trouble. "Get back to your doodles and keep quiet," I hissed. Poldy took the pencil and stabbed the notebook.

"He's teething," I said to Stefan. "It's best to ignore him."

"Ah, yeah," responded Stefan with an idiotic smile.

"Look Stefan, look what's happening," I said, pointing to the stage.

A man standing next to Sammy grabbed his hand and shook it violently, then turned to the short thing hiding behind him and gave her a kiss on each cheek. "They are now man and wife," the man roared. "Let's eat and drink." Sammy and his new wife raised their hands and solemnly pointed to their wedding bands. Then they sat down and started eating thick slices of bread covered with feta cheese. Sammy helped himself to generous amounts of *tuica*. Every time he poured himself a drink, he tried to do the same for his pudgy wife, yet she put her hand across the glass and smiled demurely.

After several attempts, Sammy leaned over and whispered in her ear. She lifted her glass and slowly brought it to her lips. One sip was enough to bounce her head backwards, yet she persevered. Sammy, hesitantly, got back on his feet and addressed the audience. He unfolded a piece of paper, pushed his glasses back up on the bridge of his nose, and thrust his chin forward. He looked solemn and sad. I could see above his head there were black-framed pictures of Stalin, Lenin, and Marx. I wondered what happened to Engels.

"Dear comrades, I am so proud that you, my family, can all join me here for one of the happiest days of my life. Comrade Coca and I will always have you, all of you, close to our hearts, as we strive together to build this nation into a fortress of productivity and democracy in order to deserve a place of distinction next to our Soviet brothers in our struggle against America and its capitalist stooges. Thank you comrades."

Sammy waved to his wife to join him. She jumped to her feet and lurched forward. He put his arm around her shoulders and gave her a kiss on the cheek. I could see she was at least three-months pregnant. On the side of the stage, an accordionist started playing.

"Dance comrades, dance," called out Sammy. "We will join you in a moment."

People started linking arms and forming an ever-wider circle. They were dancing the hora. The man, who previously addressed the crowd from atop a table, got in the middle of the circle and started gyrating wildly. A big fat woman dressed in a cheap, low-cut dress stepped in front of him and began jumping up and down without concern for the rhythms generated by the accordion, which by now were barely audible. Her laughter echoed throughout the room.

Suddenly, one of her massive breasts popped out of her dress. The woman continued to laugh and jump, making no attempt at retrieving her breast. The man stood still, watched the bouncing breast, as the woman seemed to be laughing and jumping with even more abandon, then reached over and, with one firm hand movement, shoved the breast back inside the dress.

I could see that Sammy and his bride joined the hora circle. I looked around; there was still no one I recognized. I lifted Poldy off his seat; he was once again busy performing his wild doodles, and we left.

We walked to my parents' house. My parents knew of the wedding, but they had not been invited.

"I hope he will be happy from now on," my father said. "He's been very miserable lately. But now he's been accepted in the Communist Party, he's got a big job as the head of a trade school, and a new apartment on Strada Roma, where all his Communist cronies live." He reached over to where my mother was sitting, put his hand on her shoulder, and, watching her ashen, expressionless face, said, "We should be happy for him."

My mother stood up propping herself against the table, slowly walked towards the kitchen, making a vulgar spitting gesture, and turned. "It's a *shandah* not to invite your parents to your own wedding. God will punish him. That's what I'm afraid of."

"Shush," answered my father. "He'll be fine. I'm not worried." He then turned to Poldy, "And how is my grandson?"

"The place was stinky," Poldy answered.

"It smelled terribly, it's true," I intervened, "but this one almost got me into a lot of trouble. You can't say anything critical to those people. They'll think we're capitalist agitators. It doesn't take much nowadays to get arrested and end up cutting reeds in the Danube Delta. And then no one ever hears from you again." My father smiled, "You're a smart woman Greta, you'll be fine."

"But how did Sammy finally get into the Communist Party. It's not that easy, especially for a Jew," I asked.

My father leaned back as was his way at the start of one of his tales and cleared his throat.

"As you know, technically, our Marxist-Leninist regime has

banned all forms of religion. Religion is, as we are being told everyday, "the opium of the masses." Yet, ironically, a man is much more likely to be welcomed into the Communist Party if he has previously been a Christian. So, about nine months ago, an Eastern Orthodox priest baptized Sammy, supposedly under clandestine circumstances. This was also when he changed his name to the much more Romanian-sounding Sandu Sobescu. The fact that he was baptized was quickly acknowledged by the Communist hierarchy, as the week after, he received his first promotion, which carried a substantial monetary reward. Two months later, Sammy was invited to join the Communist Party, which he promptly accepted."

My father stopped long enough to grab Poldy who was running wildly around the table and sat him on his lap.

"From that moment on his life got much better. He began making enough to afford marrying Coca, and got a beautiful three-bedroom apartment. The apartment came with a Fram refrigerator, which, as you know, is a sign of great personal luxury, as the rest of us still have to deal with the daily delivery of ice. He was even given a second-hand Dacia car. Now he doesn't want to know from us, which I understand, and I want you and you're your mother to accept it as well, as I have."

I saw my mother squirm in her seat. I felt really angry too, but I couldn't understand why. I grabbed Poldy's arm and I went home.

After that, I didn't see Sammy for many years. I knew his wife gave birth to a girl, and they owned a Fram refrigerator, and they took frequent vacations with their second-hand Dacia – they preferred the Bulgarian to the Romanian coast, especially Varna, and they gave a lot of parties for their Communist friends.

XI

One of the oddest experiences of those years happened after Coty's parents were given their exit visas. Once Coty decided to leave Benjamin, she had to go back to live with her parents in Mrs. Schoenfeld's building. Mircea, as a violinist without a family, did not qualify for separate living accommodations, and the waiting period for a young couple to be assigned a room somewhere in Bucharest would have been months, sometimes years. But for some unexplained bureaucratic glitch, the government had never assigned anyone to Coty's childhood room, so Coty and Mircea were able to move in. But in 1952, Coty's parents got their exit visas and left for Israel, and within a week two families were assigned to the apartment, but this time, the government remembered Coty's childhood room. Coty and Mircea were now homeless.

By the time Coty came to me, she had already tried everything – begged her relatives, argued with the authorities, offered a gold brooch to the security guard at the conservatory to let them sleep on the floor of the room where they stored the instruments – but all to no avail. Without thinking, I told her to bring their stuff over; I would find a place for them.

When Benno came home that night and heard that I invited Coty and Mircea to stay over, he started howling like a madman. He knew their situation, but he didn't care. I had never done this before or since, but I got down on my knees and begged him. I didn't realize how much I cried until I looked at my sleeve; it was soaked. Benno grudgingly agreed to let them stay for a week. When I walked out of the bedroom after my screaming match with Benno, I saw Coty and Mircea, their arms intertwined, sitting silently on the tiny living room sofa; the paper-thin wall made them aware of their predicament. I watched the two of them, their blurry eyes focused somewhere beyond reality, and realized that they wouldn't survive a day on their own.

I looked around: there was absolutely no room on the floor, but smack in the middle of the living room there was the dining table and six high-back chairs that came from Benno's bachelor apartment. The table was about the size of a double bed. I turned the chairs around so their backs faced each other around the table, laid a bunch of blankets on it, and told the two lovebirds to get on the table and go to sleep right away.

Coty and Mircea lived in our apartment for six months; that's how long it took them to get assigned to a small room on the outskirts of Bucharest. During the time they stayed, they were hardly ever home and when they were, they barely said anything. At first, I was very surprised how they always came home after we were done with dinner, especially since I knew that their work at the music conservatory ended before 3. But one afternoon I noticed them walking, hand in hand, around the block, so I followed them. They would get off the tram at our stop and then spend the next three hours walking around the neighborhood, shivering in those flimsy coats, but always holding on to each other. I knew they would rather be doing that than be in our house a minute longer that they absolutely had to.

One of the incidents that I believe typified life under Communism involved Coty's brother Sallo, which, incidentally, was quite reminiscent of what had happened to Benno's friend, Nicu Badescu, the architect, a few years earlier. I didn't know Sallo very well, other than he was a well-known electrical engineer, married with a son. One day, men from *Securitate* came to his house in the middle of the night and arrested him. He had been with the Communist Underground during the war, but authorities were accusing him of having betrayed one of his comrades, who ended up being shot by the Germans. For three months they beat him daily with rope soaked in gasoline to secure a confession. Coty later found out that he had confessed to everything they wanted him to confess to within the first week, yet they kept on beating him until they killed him. Years later, when I developed a contact with someone from Securitate, I found out that Sallo was a case of mistaken identity, but I never told Coty about it. Those types of mistakes were very common.

XII

As the summer of 1953 was approaching, my friend Lena and I had had enough of the overcrowded city pool and decided that we would spend two weeks at the Black Sea shore. Without any preparation and very little money, we, with our eight-year old boys in tow, took the train from Bucharest to Constanta, a four-hour ride. When we got there, we walked through one of the working class neighborhoods of the city and asked everyone we ran into if they had a spare room. One woman – I later got to know her quite well; her name was Elena – stopped us and said that she had a room. We dragged our luggage and boys through the streets of Constanta until we arrived at Elena's apartment building. After climbing four stories up a dark, dingy staircase, we got to her apartment: a tiny one-bedroom flat, where she lived with her husband and two teenage children. They all slept in the same bedroom. She and her husband slept on the wooden bed next to the window, while the children, a boy of fifteen and a girl of twelve, slept on a narrow metal frame bed next to the door.

The apartment was extremely small and cramped, so I asked Elena where she expected to put us. Baring a wry smile, she told us that her husband had been a Black Sea fisherman, but had gotten injured, and now could only get part-time work as a night watchman, so between her job at the local cannery and his, they weren't making enough money for even just bread and cheese and the occasional kilo of lentils. I realized that as bad as we had it in Bucharest, it was still far better than people in out-of-the-way cities. Bucharest was the capital and the only place in Romania that could ever be observed by Western eyes, so the Communists were forced to give it a gloss of prosperity.

Elena offered us not only the bedroom, but also the use of the living room. When I asked her where she and her family would live, she said not to worry, the four of them would be very comfortable sleeping on the kitchen floor. I told her that I refused to allow her family to live under such inhumane conditions. She looked at me and, with a sad grin, she said, "Madame Feingold – calling someone 'Madame' under Communism was taboo; everyone was 'comrade' – the modest amount you'll be paying me for the use of my apartment is enough to keep me and my family fed for an entire year. I think that's worth two weeks of discomfort, don't you?"

The sleeping arrangements were simple. Lena and I slept in Elena's bed; Sergiu and Poldy slept in her children's bed.

Every morning we woke up at the crack of dawn, heated up some coffee-like brew made from roasted oats while making sure we didn't step on any of Elena's family members, and took the local bus from Constanta to Mamaia. At Mamaia, we walked onto the most beautiful beach in the world; the sand was fine and pearl white and it always remained cool under our feet, and the water was calm and didn't taste very salty; and as I remember, every day for the two weeks we were there we had perfect sunshine.

The two weeks we spent at the Black Sea shore were filled with simple pleasures, not the least of which was not being pawed by Benno. Once we got to the beach, Lena and I just lay on a blanket until the sun went down. The boys played in the water or built sand castles or buried themselves in the sand. They made friends and kept themselves entertained. We only heard from them when they were hungry. We brought along sandwiches that Elena had prepared for us each morning; drinking water was available in the lobby of Continental Hotel, a very fancy hotel, which was only open to foreign tourists, mostly East Germans. Our boys were able to get into the hotel after befriending the only Romanian girl staying there. Her name was Manuela; she was the daughter of Angelica Rozeanu, the seven-time world ping-pong champion and one of the mythic figures of Romanian sports. Manuela, who was the same age as the boys, had taken a liking to Poldy and the only way she knew how to show it was by humiliating him in ping-pong, but somehow he seemed to relish the losses.

Through Manuela, we met the manager of the Continental Hotel, a short, fat man with a bald head and a swarthy complexion, who enjoyed picking his nose while he was talking. I asked him if he could get us into Casino Mamaia, an equally restricted nightclub across the road from The Continental. He said sure, but it would take money, and nothing else. We didn't know what to do until smart-girl Manuela offered him a couple of ping-pong paddles autographed by her mother, something he could easily convert into cash, especially with all those East German tourists around.

Casino Mamaia was a lot of fun. I loved to dance, and there were always scores of men up to the task. We parked the boys on one of the benches in the back with a glass of *braga*, a kind of root beer, in front of them, and Lena and I sat provocatively at a table by the dance floor. Most nights, the boys would just fall asleep, so we could party on until closing time. We didn't have to worry about sleep; that's what we did the whole day on the beach. After a while the staff got to know us by name, so the male patrons thought we were local celebrities. Not only did they fight over us for a dance, but sometimes, on the way back to our table, we found eight or ten glasses of our favorite Vermouth cocktail waiting for us. We drank, but never to the point where we lost our heads. We always stayed a step ahead of our escorts; first of all we didn't know when we might be dealing with *Securitate* men; second, we were after all married women, with two young sons sleeping not twenty meters away, so whatever carnal urges might have seized us had to be tempered by discretion. That, of course, didn't mean we conducted ourselves like nuns.

I don't remember many details of our nights at Casino Mamaia, but I do remember one night, as I, playing my Queen of Sheba role, was standing in the middle of the dance floor surrounded by ravenous men, ready to do anything for me and to me, when Poldy wedged his way through them and called out in a voice louder than I thought him capable, "Mother, I want to go home now." I would have killed him on the spot, if not for all the witnesses.

XIII

I was never to repeat my wonderful summer of '53 at the Black Sea shore; maybe that's why I still remember it so vividly.

The early years of Communism are the most painful to recollect. Even though life got harder in later years, after I was without a husband and had to provide for me and my son, it was somehow not as desolate. I remember waking up in the middle of the night, breathing heavily, hearing someone pounding on the door. I would go to the door, but there was no one there, and I would spend the next ten minutes calling out through the cracked door, "Hello, hello, hello." Another night I would wake up and see shadows moving across the glass door of Poldy's room. They looked like men in uniform who had come to take my son away. I ran into Poldy's room ready to do battle, but all was quiet and Poldy was peacefully asleep. I felt I was going mad. I think if I had had the certainty that I'd be taken away and killed, I would have welcomed it.

Even during the war, as bombs were dropping all around us, I felt calmer, more fatalistic: *que sera, sera.* Even the fear that the Nazis were going to start deporting Jews from Bucharest was not as overwhelming as the Communist shroud, which was meant to slowly, grimly smother us. The relatively lower-level sense of fear that we, the Jews of Bucharest, felt during the war about deportation to a Nazi camp had something to do with a rumor that a man by the name of Axelrod had paid Hitler millions to leave the Bucharest Jews alone. In hindsight, I realize how ridiculous that story was – Hitler never honored any agreements, let alone one with a Jew – but we believed it, and that gave us some level of comfort, and what's more, the reality seemed to support it. To my knowledge, no Jews from Bucharest were taken to Nazi concentration camps. It was probably because Hitler was too busy gassing Jews from everywhere else, and the war ended before he got around to Bucharest.

Communism was different, more insidious, more unpredictable.

We knew that bombs or bullets were meant to kill us, but the Communists were people like us, people with high ideals, people whom a country girl like me wanted to see succeed; Sammy, my brother, was a Communist. These were not monsters, yet they behaved worse than monsters. The Nazis made no secret of their murderous plans. The Communists, while equally vicious, were constantly playing up their concern for people's welfare. They tried to be nice at the very beginning, but as soon as the economy started faltering, they began to worry they might be toppled just like they had done to their predecessors, so they lost their sense of humor.

The Communists never accepted that an economy based on need and not performance was doomed to fail, but they kept on trying, and getting more and more frustrated. That's when they started looking for scapegoats: American Imperialists, whom they imagined as having nothing better to do but devote all their time to sabotaging Communist efforts; or those who had belonged to the former bourgeois class; or the Jews, who most Gentiles already believed had money stashed away even when they seemed to be starving like everyone else.

The sad thing was that I always thought that Communism could have worked. An ideology that promises that everyone will have a job and the job will pay enough to make a respectable living, regardless of education or abilities, will always appeal to someone like me, a simple, uneducated woman. If I were to be allowed only one word to capture the evils of Communism I would say it's "arbitrariness." With no real laws or regulations, or at least none those in power felt bound by, everyone lived in a constant state of terror. Yes, this was the worst of time, which is probably why I have so little to say about this long eight-year period.

CHAPTER 5
The Prison Widow Years
1953-1959

A fter several frustrating attempts, Greta finally finds herself a comfortable place on the sofa. She bends her head back until it rests against the wall, and, staring at the ceiling, takes a deep breath trying to slow down the heaving of her chest. Fixing her eyes on the recorder, she begins to speak.

I

Benno was arrested in October of 1953. I wasn't all that upset when it happened. I didn't think about what I would live on, instead for the first time in a long time I felt free. Benno got caught in a crazy scheme in which he was just a pawn. Two wise guys, Carl and Philip, one Gentile, the other Jewish, recruited Benno, simply because he worked as a bookkeeper in the front office of a factory that made wooden drums for cheese. The factory wasn't very well guarded; there was nothing to guard other than flimsy, paper-thin boxes that looked like oversized, round cookie tins. Carl and Philip filled Benno's head with the wild idea he would make a lot of money, which would cancel out the indignities he suffered at the hands of the Communists, and give him back his self-esteem.

All he had to do, they told him, was sneak inside the factory at night and grab a few worthless cheese drums that he saw lying around, without waking up the night watchman. If, for some unlikely reason, the night watchman woke up and saw him, Benno was to say that he forgot his girlfriend's key in the office, and then wait until the watchman fell asleep again. The "girlfriend's key" ploy was not only highly believable, but it fit perfectly into

Benno's wounded fantasies.

The actual assignment wasn't quite as simple as Carl and Philip had originally advertised. Every night for about three weeks at a time, Benno would go to the factory, steal a few drums – he couldn't steal too many for fear of raising suspicions – stick them onto the pushcart Carl and Philip had given him, and roll it home through the deserted streets of Bucharest. I know it sounds insane, but in those days people did crazy things to survive, so the sight of a man dragging a pushcart loaded with cheese drums down the street in the middle of the night did not attract much attention, primarily because anyone who happened to see it would immediately look away and convince himself that he just imagined it – elective blindness was a great survival gift.

When Benno got home, he would park the cart inside Ion the super's alleyway, and then he was supposed to caw like a crow, though he sounded more like a tortured monkey, which would be my cue. I would then open our second-floor apartment window and lower the small shopping basket I used for transacting business with street vendors. He would tie two or three drums at a time to the basket and I would raise it back up. The drums, which were made of thin sheets of plywood, didn't weigh very much. When the cart was empty, Benno would hide it behind Ion's broken sinks. The process was reversed when Carl and Philip came to pick up the drums.

After a while, there were dozens of cheese drums all over our apartment. There were cheese drums on top of furniture, under the beds, inside closets, in the bathroom, even hanging from the living room chandelier. And when I thought there was absolutely no room left, Carl and Philip would show up with their rickety pick-up truck and move everything out. They would appear unannounced in the middle of the night, and Benno and I would have to be ready. We would stay upstairs to load the drums onto the basket, while they would be down on the street to untie the drums and load them onto the truck. It was a miracle that no one saw us or, at least, that no one reported us. Then Benno had to start all over again with his nights of plunder, punctuated by Carl and Philip's periodic visits that temporarily relieved the clutter in our apartment.

Later, much later, I found out that these two guys, Carl and Philip, drove their pick-up truck loaded with cheese drums to a city in Transylvania named Oradea, where there was a group of cheese farmers who, although working daytimes for a cheese cooperative, would stay up nights and make more of this special sweet Romanian cheese that tasted a bit like Ricotta cheese, but a bit firmer and sweeter, and, just like true Ricotta, made of unpasteurized sheep's milk. Carl and Philip filled the cheese drums with the cheese they got from the farmers and headed for the border. If not stored in these special drums, the cheese would have spoiled in a few days.

Carl and Philip found a corrupt border guard who was willing to let them drive their truck across the border into Hungary. They drove clear across Hungary, which was also a Communist country, with very tight Government control, and somehow found their way into Austria. From Austria, they drove straight to Paris where they sold the cheese. It seems the French loved this cheese. Since they had no passports, they must've bribed a lot of border guards. And this is one time when knowledge of foreign languages came in handy; it is unlikely that Carl and Philip could have pulled their crazy scheme off if they hadn't been fluent in at least the three languages they encountered along the way: Hungarian, German and French.

The French paid them in francs, and on the way back, Carl and Philip stopped in Switzerland and set up Swiss bank accounts for just the two of them, in which they deposited most of the money. With the little money left over, they bought Swiss watches, which they hid in the truck. They made four or five such trips, although they probably made enough money on one trip to retire on.

When they got back to Bucharest, they showed up with a large cardboard box with a few watches scattered at the bottom of it. They told Benno that's what they were able to buy with all the cheese money, and asked Benno to take as many watches as he thought he deserved. Benno, in an idiotic display of good breeding, grabbed a small handful of watches, looked at Carl and Philip for their reaction, and then, with an apologetic smile, threw a few back.

Carl and Philip played the same game with the cheese farmers, but after the second or third trip, the cheese farmers got wise to them. They found out how much their cheese could bring in France or some other Western country, and began to ask for more than just a few watches. Carl and Philip, two cocky city slickers, blew off the cheese farmers. The cheese farmers went to the authorities, got immunity from prosecution, and spilled everything.

Carl and Philip, as it turned out, had someone with *Securitate* on their payroll, so when they came to arrest the dynamic duo, they found nothing incriminating. Of course, they didn't bother to alert Benno.

One early morning, I woke up to the sound of angry door knocking. I, already in a panic, ran to the door in my nightgown. Three dark-suited *Securitate* men, without saying a word, pushed their way in.

"How many people in this apartment," barked the one who seemed in charge. He was taller and darker than the other two and wore a military pin on his lapel. His dark rigid eyes, which were perched way up on his face, made him look like the figure of suffering Christ I had seen on crosses as a child in Ghimeş.

"My husband and I, and our nine-year old son."

"Get everybody here now," he ordered.

"May I put on some clothes?"

He looked at me and then turned to one of his men. "Marin, go with her. Don't let her out of your sight."

Marin followed me into the bedroom. Benno was already dressed, as he must have heard everything. I grabbed a bra, a pair of underwear, and an old dress that was lying on the back of the armchair and ran into the bathroom, closing the door behind me.

Marin slammed the door open.

"Where the fuck do you think you're going?" he roared, his round face covered with his own spittle.

"I need some privacy," I pleaded. "I'm getting dressed."

"I'm not letting out of my sight," he answered. "You heard the chief."

"I need to put these on. It'll just take a second," I continued, pointing to the few items I had in my hand.

"No way. What you worried I'm gonna fuck you? Listen whore, if I want to fuck you I don't have to do it while I'm on duty. I come tomorrow and get you to make me dinner afterwards."

I got dressed with Marin watching me. I knew he was about to jump me when his chief called, "Marin, get your ass back here. We gotta bust these stinky kikes."

I went into Poldy's room and got him dressed, then the three of us sat at the dining room table with our hands in clear sight, as told. It didn't take them long to discover the box of watches at the bottom of the bedroom closet. They spent the next four hours going over the contents of every drawer and every cabinet. Every once in a while, one of them would come to me and ask me something, like where is the key for that cabinet or who's the old bitch in the picture. I gave them short polite answers, which they seemed to appreciate.

After a while, Poldy announced that he was hungry, and I asked the chief if I could give him some bread and marmalade. The chief looked at Poldy, thought for a second, and then answered, "He looks fat enough. You can feed him when we're done." Then Poldy became fidgety, so the chief warned me that if I didn't calm him down he'd crack him one across the face. I turned to Poldy and told him that we were in enough trouble without him aggravating our guests. He made one of his unpleasant faces, but then settled down. All this time, Benno sat like a stone carving on a Medieval sarcophagus, the only evidence of life suggested by rills of perspiration traversing his sallow, cadaverous cheeks.

When the three *Securitate* men were done with their

perquisition, one of them picked up the box of watches, the other took the cheese drums, and the chief, in a highly affected voice, asked Benno to accompany them.

As luck would have it, just the night before I took one of the watches out of the box, an IWC Schaffhousen, thinking that I would give it to Poldy as a Bar Mitzvah present, although there were no plans for a Bar Mitzvah. I put the watch in the pocket of my housedress and forgot about it. They never found it, and I later gave to Poldy.

Carl and Philip each got five years in jail based on the farmers' testimony, but Benno got ten years of hard labor.

After he got arrested he behaved like a coward, telling the *Securitate* men that I had helped him with the cheese drums. So they also arrested me; one afternoon a *Securitate* man showed up and nonchalantly told me that I was being arrested. When I asked him if I needed to bring any clothes, he told me, with a sickly grin, that I didn't need clothes where I was going.

I was kept in a cell for three days without any explanation, without even the sound of a human voice. A hand would appear twice a day in the small opening in the door and leave a tin bowl of hot lentil soup and a slice of bread.

After three days, a man walked into my cell. I was lying on the cot, and, without warning, he sat next to me. He told me he was going to be my interrogator and his name was Victor. He was in his late thirties, about my height, sour looking, with sunken cheeks and dirty fingernails.

Victor, in a manner that suggested that he'd been in this type of situation before, informed me that my misdeeds could easily cost me five years in jail, and my son would be placed in an orphanage. Then he changed his delivery and became unusually friendly. He leaned over me and told me that it would be a pity for a beautiful woman like me to rot in jail. He bluntly told me that if I agreed to sleep with him he would not only arrange to have me released, but he would make sure that Benno was well taken care of while in prison. And as proof of his good intentions, he would not collect on my end of the bargain until after I was released. He never worried about my reneging on my promise; he knew that I knew that he could always have me arrested again, and the next time there would be no more trading opportunities.

The next day I was released, and I remember walking home and thinking that I was only twenty-nine, but that the future was soon going to require me to behave with the wisdom of someone much older. Of course, Victor showed up a few weeks later to collect on his debt. Poldy was there at the time, so I asked Victor if he could come back another time. He looked at me with those hollow eyes and chortled, and then shoved me in the bedroom. All I could think of while this animal was using me like some ragged cushion was how this experience was going to affect Poldy who was sitting in the next room, separated from the clamor that was going on in the bedroom by a wall as thin as paper; but after a while I stopped worrying. I had no choice, yet I knew Poldy would never understand.

When I came out of the bedroom, Poldy was sitting on the floor with his back against the wall, and his face covered with tears. He was eight. He didn't say anything about it then; he never has.

II

Soon after Benno was arrested, maybe three or four months, a young man showed up at my door and informed me that he had been assigned to a room in my apartment. He showed me an official-looking paper, which read that the previous occupant of the apartment was now residing in a state prison, and would be there for ten years. What amazed me about this whole situation was that the government, this Communist government, so utterly mired in inefficiency and confusion, would be able to communicate in less than three months between the Justice Department, which was responsible for Benno's arrest, and the Housing Department that there was a vacancy. The fact that I would have to share my apartment with a stranger made me feel more violated than all the pounding that I was subjected to by the apes who during those years saw me as nothing more than a trough in which to ejaculate.

My new apartment mate was named Anton, and he came from Buzau, a small town some fifty kilometers north of Bucharest. He was in his early twenties, and this was his first time in the big city. He was small, with a tiny face and thin white lips. He looked years younger than he was, and he moved with the gracefulness of a dancer. I realized right away that there would never be anything between us; if anything, he brought out my maternal instincts. His arrival deprived Poldy of his room, the room he grew up in, so from that day on, at the age of eight, he started sleeping on a narrow sofa in the living room. After the initial feelings of personal violation and the resentment of having to share my apartment with a stranger wore off, I approached Anton. He was very polite, but extremely anxious. If I had hoped for someone I could open up to, I quickly realized that Anton was not that person.

He worked for a branch of the Romanian movie industry named Romanfilm that processed foreign films: translated them, checked them for content to make sure there was nothing subversive, and prepared the subtitles. Anton's job was to handwrite the subtitles for these films. His job title was calligraphist. He would work mostly at home at an old drafting table hunched over strips of clear film with hands covered in black ink.

The first few years living with Anton were quiet. He never went out; he didn't have any friends. The phone never rang for him, except once or twice on some work-related matter. I felt sorry for this young man with no life.

But things changed one night. He came home covered with blood and most of his front teeth knocked out. Although he had lost a lot of blood and was in a great deal of pain, he stayed very calm. I wanted to call the militia, an ambulance, a doctor, but he wouldn't let me. Despite my hysterical screaming that he might die from loss of blood, he remained adamant about not contacting anyone. I don't know where Anton found the willpower to get himself home. He asked me for some hot water and some bandages. This was the first time I actually touched him. He had the whitest skin I had ever seen on a man, and underneath there were only bones. I washed the blood off, and even managed to stop the bleeding from a large cut he had on his neck. But most of the bleeding came from his mouth, and that took longer to stop.

He fell asleep but woke up the next day and came into my bedroom, which was not unusual, since the apartment's only bathroom was off my bedroom. He wanted me to call his office and tell them that he wouldn't be able to be in that day because of a bad cold, which prevented him from calling himself. Without his front teeth, he sounded awfully strange.

After the phone call, he said he wanted to talk to me. I put on my house robe and made us coffee. Romanian coffee was like Turkish coffee. I bought coffee beans at the store, on those rare occasions when they had them for sale, roasted them in a frying pan over a low flame, and grounded the beans in an old wooden coffee grinder I found in Benno's bachelor apartment. The product of boiling the ground coffee in water was a cup of black mud, but I can still smell the wonderful aroma that lingered in the apartment for hours afterwards.

Anton and I stayed in the kitchen, because I didn't want to wake up Poldy. Although he had difficulty speaking without teeth, he made it clear that he had gotten himself in a lot of trouble. It all started with him agreeing to have a drink with someone from his office who nonetheless he didn't know very well. It turned out that this individual, whose name was Comrade Popescu, was his office's Communist Party liaison man. Every office had someone like him.

Comrade Popescu's job was to make sure that nothing subversive took place or was even discussed, but, before long, his responsibilities included running weekly propaganda meetings that celebrated the glorious accomplishments of the Communist Party. That's when he reminded everyone that we owed everything to the generosity of our Communist leaders, especially Gheorghe Gheorghiu-Dej, the Secretary of the Romanian Communist Party. At the same time, he had to preach about the spiritual and financial bankruptcy that raged in the West, a fact caused by the most corrupt form of government: American Imperialism.

During the propaganda sessions, Comrade Popescu encouraged people to publicly denounce each other for anything they saw that might be interpreted as a failure to live up to the moral and ethical standards set by the constantly virtuous Communist leadership. Of course, the public and the private denunciations served as vehicles for people to settle old scores: a man could easily end up in jail because someone else had his eyes on his wife, and this was an expedient way of getting the husband out of the way. Comrade Popescu also served as a receptive ear for anyone interested in snitching on someone for assumed crimes against the Communist state, and there were plenty of rats in Romania. Comrade Popescu was the man Anton agreed, mostly out of fear, to have a drink with.

They went to a bar and Comrade Popescu started drinking *tuica*, while all along telling Anton what a cute boy he was. After a few drinks, Comrade Popescu told him that he could arrange for Anton to get a big raise, and that all he had to do was go with him to his *garçonnière*, the equivalent of a *pied-à-terre*, which most Communist big shots had, in addition to their extravagant family homes, while most everyone else in Romania had to share overcrowded tiny apartments with two or three other families.

Anton politely refused, saying that he was happy with his current salary. As Comrade Popescu got drunker, he began shoving his hand inside Anton's pants, telling him he had to have him or else he would expire of passion. The bar was full of people, and Anton was certain they had heard him, but no one got involved. Given that Anton was not showing any signs of yielding, Comrade Popescu started calling Anton a faggot, and that he, a high ranking member of the Communist Party, must have been crazy to be interested in him.

At that moment Anton excused himself, walked out of the bar, and headed home. But Comrade Popescu caught up with him on the street, and with steel knuckles on his fist, started hitting him wildly. When it was over, Anton was lying in a pool of blood. No one stopped, though there were many who passed by, slowed down, looked, and then walked on.

The following day, Anton asked me to find him a dentist. As it turned out, the Dentist, the one who examined my teeth at Mrs. Feingold's request before my wedding and had since remained a good friend, fitted Anton with a pair of dentures that looked almost like his own teeth. From that point on, Anton and I became friends, at least for a while.

After that incident, Anton changed a lot; he suddenly began having friends over. Poldy was about ten by then, and the only thing separating the living room where he slept from Anton's room was a pair of flimsy glass doors. Anton started being visited by another young man from his office. I would hear them whisper for a short time; then the lights would go off and there would be some tumbling and the bed would squeak.

One evening, Anton's friend came early while Poldy was playing ping-pong with a friend on the dining room table. The sound of the ping-pong ball bouncing on the table was quite loud and irritating, so after a while I heard Anton's friend's voice order Poldy and his friend to stop. The boys continued to play ping-pong despite subsequent warnings from Anton's friend, each one a little more menacing than the last. Finally, Anton's friend seemed to have had it; he burst into the living room, slapped Poldy across the face, and returned to Anton's room. Afterwards, as Poldy started whimpering, I came out of the bedroom and told him that he had to be more mindful of people's feelings.

Soon after, other men came and spent a few hours with Anton on his creaky bed. Rarely would I see the same man twice. Anton became brasher, more outgoing, and definitely more concerned with his looks. In the past there was never an issue over the use of the bathroom. Both Poldy and Anton took practically no time in the bathroom, giving me all the time I needed to create the 'Greta image'. But, suddenly, I had competition in the use of the bathroom: Anton began taking baths.

There was no running hot water; in order to take a bath one needed to boil water on the stove in a crock the size of a lobster pot, and then carry it into the bathroom. One day, Anton, while wearing his usual tight shorts and carrying the lobster pot filled with boiling water, tripped as he was entering my bedroom. The lobster pot tipped over and released a cascade of scalding water onto his bare legs. To this day, I close my eyes and cringe at the vision of Anton's flesh erupting into thousands of grotesque-looking ulcers. I ran to the nearest pharmacy to buy whatever ointment they had for burns. They didn't have any, and I was told that neither would any of the other pharmacies. I checked the local hospital, but they were not equipped to treat burns. I came home and I grabbed the bit of margarine we had in the kitchen and coated as much of the burnt area as I could. It took Anton months to heal and his pretty legs were left permanently, hideously scarred.

Once Anton was well enough to walk, the male visitors started coming again. One evening, to my surprise, a middle-aged woman showed up, very distinguished, with an old-world look about her. She had a beautiful little dachshund with her that immediately stole Poldy's heart. The woman noticed that, so she asked Poldy if he wanted to play with him or even take him out for a walk. She told him the dog's name was Pic. Poldy did not wait for any other admonitions; he grabbed Pic's leash and ran out the door.

Seeing a woman in Anton's company made me curious. I waited until the woman was inside Anton's room, then sat myself, with a book in my hand, at the dining room table and listened. I never read, so I would've looked pretty funny if someone saw me. The woman's words came hissing out of her mouth. At one point, she must have lost her self-control and started shouting that Anton had stolen her husband. She stormed out of Anton's room, just as Poldy was entering the apartment, grabbed her dog and was gone. I could see, as she was walking past me, that this once very beautiful woman was shaking like a leaf, blood drained from her face. I never saw her again.

One evening, not long after that incident, a man showed up, not young, but very distinguished looking and well dressed, and he had Pic with him. He seemed disoriented and extremely nervous. He stopped in the living room unable to take another step. Poldy walked up to him and told him that he knew Pic, and he would love to take him for a walk. The man mechanically handed him the leash, and Poldy took off. The man asked if he could use the bathroom. As I nodded, he thanked me absentmindedly, and walked at a fast pace right into the doorframe of the bathroom leading with his head. His head started bleeding, and all he could do was curse under his breath. As Anton and I were working to stop the bleeding, Anton introduced him to me; his name was Silviu Baragan. As they went into Anton's room, I could hear him whispering that life at home had become hell. I didn't hear Anton respond, but after a while the man stopped talking and all was quiet. That lasted a good hour. Ultimately, Silviu reemerged from Anton's roomed, and, still disoriented, headed towards my bedroom. I smiled at him and pointed to the front door. He apologized and walked out of the apartment. Poldy had to chase after him to hand him Pic's leash.

Several days later, Silviu and Pic showed up again. Poldy opened the door and, as if they had had a previous arrangement, Silviu casually handed Poldy Pic's leash and Poldy took off. This time Silviu didn't hesitate; he turned the knob and walked into Anton's room. There were only soft whispers, and I heard Anton say that he loved him and how lonely his nights were and how he couldn't wait any longer. The man left again in a hurry, but this time he remembered to take Pic.

After another few days, Silviu showed up again with Pic. Poldy and Pic seemed to have been waiting for each other. Poldy grabbed Pic, whose short hard tail was flailing violently, and ran down the stairs.

At first, there were only whispers, but afterwards, the lights went out and the bed started clanging, maybe louder than it ever had before. This routine, which repeated itself twice a week, continued until I left Romania with Poldy five years later. Although I'm sure that by then Poldy knew exactly what was going on behind the glass doors, he never mentioned it. The only thing he ever said relating to this situation was when we were sitting on a bench waiting for the train that was going to take us out of Romania.

I asked him, "Aren't you happy you won't have to deal with Anton and his visitors?"

He started into space for a long time, then gave me one of his disgusting answers.

"I'm happy Pic is dead."

III

Poldy was never a very outgoing child, but when he turned ten he became extremely withdrawn. He used to go out on the street after school and play with the other boys of the neighborhood, but one day that stopped. I don't really know why, except that once, as I was raising my hand to slap him for being disrespectful to me, he stared at me defiantly and said, "I know you want to hit this dirty kike, just like everyone else." Those were some of the most hurtful things he ever said to me; I know I shouldn't have, but I let him have it. I ended up breaking my thumb on his bony head.

For a year afterwards, Poldy would come home, do his homework, and then sit on his bed staring into space. Until one day, out of the blue, he started painting. Stefania gave him an easel, a painter's palette, brushes, and a bunch of old dried-out tubes of paint. She had been an aspiring artist when she was young, but gave it up when she got married. She saved the painting set, and fifty years later she gave it to Poldy. He threw himself into this new activity with the frenzy that he demonstrated in every one of his other misguided ventures. He spent hours and hours splashing gobs of colored grease on bits of Benno's old shirts and the house smelled from turpentine and he looked like a clown with all that paint all over his body.

Within a couple of months he had over twenty canvases that he had lined up against the wall of the living room. But I was not happy with the fact that he was spending so much time at home. There was too much going on in my life, and I never knew in advance when someone would be visiting, and I certainly didn't want everything to play out in front of him. Yet I couldn't very well keep throwing him out of the house.

One evening, unexpectedly, Poldy asked me if I wanted to look at his paintings. I told him I didn't have time, yet he ignored my answer and started showing them to me, while at the same time explaining the composition, choice of colors, and what each one meant. He took a long time explaining, and he became very animated in the process. He was trying to make me feel that I didn't know anything about art. He told me that he had shown his canvases to his grandmother, and she thought they showed a lot of potential. So I asked him what he wanted from me. He said that he wanted my opinion. So I told him straight: I thought they weren't any good, and that he should spend more time out of the house playing with his friends. I had hoped that would be the end of the conversation, but he persisted, and asked me whether I thought he had any talent. Irritated by his selfishness, I told him that if he had any talent it would have 'screamed' out of him years earlier, and would not have suddenly appeared just because his grandmother happened to have a painting set and he had too much time on his hands. The next day Poldy returned the painting set to his grandmother and stopped painting.

IV

With Benno in prison, I was forced to confront my predicament: I was a woman without skills and the wife of a convict. Being the wife of a convict wasn't really that unusual in Communist Romania, but while the other convicts were in prison for political offenses, my husband was there because he stole a bunch of cheese drums. This was the man who only ten years earlier was one of the richest in Bucharest, and behaved like his blood was bluer than anyone else's. In the old days he would have spoken with total revulsion against anyone who had committed the most insignificant of crimes.

Once at a party at Regina Schoenfeld's house before I married Benno, Sammy mentioned, half in jest, that when he was a kid back in Ghimeş, he stole a chicken, or rather found a lost chicken in our yard and omitted to tell anyone about it, and ended up hiding it in his room.

Sammy was a wonderful storyteller, and I'm sure he embellished his chicken incident well into fiction, so everyone belly-laughed until Benno chimed in with his sanctimonious bullshit that there is no such thing as a small crime.

"Once a man commits a crime, any kind of crime, he has lost his humanity," Benno announced with that nasty voice of his. He could put a damper on people's good times, and he not only succeeded in ruining Sammy's good mood, but also offended him so deeply that Sammy never again wanted to be with him, and by association with me. I think Sammy was angry with me not so much for marrying such a man, as I am sure he remembered how much he benefited from it, but for staying married to him. Sammy couldn't deny his own meal ticket. I didn't see much of Sammy after that, and even less after he graduated from university and got a job as a construction engineer on a slaughterhouse in Iasi.

Sammy knew that he was assigned the Iasi project because no one else wanted it. What he didn't know is that most projects, like construction of dams and bridges or even building of embassies and hotels, require top security clearance, which was only given to members of the Communist Party. I learned this from Victor, my friend at *Securitate*, whose path, for better or worse, I often crossed during those years. As far as major civil projects were concerned, they were mostly built from Soviet blueprints. Embassies and hotels required even greater security clearance because their construction required the placement of listening devices in every room, at every restaurant table, along every hallway.

There were over sixty million listening devices in a country of fewer than twenty million people. The office of *Securitate* knew everything that was said by anyone in the country, and their excuse was that these listening devices were protecting people from the many agitators and troublemakers who were trying to undermine the stability of the people's democracy. Sammy was caught between a growing sense of aversion towards the things that were going on around him and his desire to succeed and lead a prosperous life. He chose success and prosperity. I am sure his decision was motivated by his craving to show the Feingolds that he can do well on his own.

Three years later, my father informed me that Sammy was assigned his own dacha, a winterized fully furnished little cabin near Sinai; that was the ultimate testament to success in Communist Romania. All Sammy had to do in return was to stay loyal to the Party and not ask too many questions, and, of course, turn in anybody who seemed the least bit suspicious.

Sammy fulfilled the role of loyal Communist with great zeal, and died at fifty-two of a heart attack brought on, at the very least, by his enormous weight gain. I was told he weighed 160 kilograms - that's more than 350 pounds - at his death. I was no longer in Romania when that happened, and I did not attend the funeral.

V

Once on my own and with no means of financial support for myself and my son, I went first to my in-laws. They had lost everything, although I suspected that the wily Stefania had stashed away many valuables, which in a pinch could have been sold for ready cash, but she turned me away, claiming she had nothing to give. The dramatic loss of her privileged position, the arrest of her son, and most tangibly, the knowledge that I was sleeping with a *Securitate* man, regardless of the circumstances that led to it, something that could never be concealed in a gossip-driven place like Bucharest, was too much even for the stoic Mrs. Feingold. An unbridgeable gap developed between Stefania and me that couldn't be spanned by all my pleas.

I may have understood why Stefania was unhelpful to me personally, but not why she was hurting her grandson, the only person she claimed she ever truly loved. I know it because this haughty, super intelligent woman wasn't bashful to proclaim her feelings: she felt little affection for her husband; she felt repelled by her son; and she felt contempt for everyone else. Yet she poured into her grandson extraordinary feelings, so I can only imagine how painful it must have been for her to deny her soul just to teach me a lesson.

Then I thought my brother would help. My father had given me the address of his fancy apartment. I hadn't seen him since his wedding. When I got there, they were in the middle of a party; his wife had just given birth to a girl. A stunning looking serving maid opened the door. She smiled and asked me to wait at the door.

When Sammy appeared, I came straight out and told him that I had no money, no food, and asked him if he could help me with a few *lei*. Through the cracked door, I could see on the foyer table platters full of every imaginable delicacy. But he said he couldn't; with the new baby, and the expense of having to furnish a new baby's room, and the cost of the car, and the holiday at Varna there was no money left. Besides, he added with a twinkle in his eye, that he also had to take care of Angelica's expenses. I knew he meant the serving maid.

In fact, these so-called serving maids were government-issue courtesans, carefully selected for their loyalty to the Party and absolute discretion. By letting me know that he had been assigned one of these serving maids, Sammy was conveying to me that he had achieved the highest echelons of the Communist Party. Of course, the Party had an ulterior motive for dispatching these serving maids: they were constantly relaying information back to their Communist Party operatives, who kept extensive files on all of their members, with special emphasis on the individual's drinking and sexual preferences. It seems that the more debauched a Party member was, the thicker the file, and, consequently, the more certain they were of the individual's loyalty.

Once I ran out of relatives, and I had no close friends to go to, I began to despair. Not only did I not have money for food, but I was getting these weepy letters from Benno imploring me to bring him Sibiu salami and cigarettes when I came to see him, which was once every other month. Apparently Sibiu salami and cigarettes were the currency of the prison. I knew Benno didn't smoke, and he wrote me that he hadn't taken it up in prison, but he said that a carton of cigarettes could be traded for a large loaf of bread, and that would augment his diet for at least a week.

I had no pride left. I took one of Benno's pathetic letters and went back to Stefania, hoping she had a change of heart. I found her aged and her once thunderous voice barely audible. When I finished my pitch, she remained still. After a long silence, she asked me if I wouldn't mind seeming myself out as she was feeling tired. In hindsight, I think she was not as angry with me as she was with her reprobate son. This smart, practical woman, who always seemed so in tune with other people's needs had suddenly changed into an insensitive, unconcerned sphinx. The shock of losing all her money, her way of life, made her bitter and apathetic. She and Martin were now living in the same apartment building they once owned, but in the basement, in the super's former residence. It was sad to see this *grande dame* reduced to a life of penury. Nevertheless, as I said before, I knew she still had stuff stashed away, but she wasn't going to share it with anyone. Her heart had turned to stone.

Yet I somehow managed. During the five and a half years that Benno was in prison, despite all the chaos and misery that was my life, I never failed to visit him as often as they allowed me to, and bring him the allowable ration of 1 kg of Sibiu salami, 1/2 kg of sugar and two cartons of cigarettes. Benno never once asked me how I got the money to buy the things that he so selfishly demanded. The Sibiu salami was mostly an export item, and not only difficult to find, but very expensive. He never inquired how I managed to get to the many out-of-the-way work camps they kept moving him to and from all the time. All he cared about was that I promptly showed up with his order.

My visits to see Benno were incredibly arduous. Every few months they transferred him to another work camp in some god-forsaken corner of the country. They had him cut reeds in the Danube Delta, where he worked the whole day in water up to his chest; pour concrete for a dam they were building in Suceava; dig a trench for a big oil pipeline outside of Timisoara, five meters down without cave-in protection. All these work camps were many miles from any train stations or bus stops, so the rest of my way had to be covered on foot with a ten-kilogram rucksack on my back that held the precious cargo of Sibiu salami and the cartons of cigarettes. Always the first thing out of Benno's mouth when he saw me was, "Do you have my salami? How about the cigarettes?"

VI

Somehow, though, all those dreadful trips to visit Benno in prison to bring him salami and sugar and cigarettes blend into a hazy memory of unrelenting wretchedness, except for one.

Benno had been in prison for close to three years, and I had been informed that he had again been transferred to a work camp near Tulcea on the Danube Delta. The year before he was assigned to reed-cutting duty, they had him work twelve hours a day immersed in freezing water up to his chest digging a new channel for one of the branches of the Danube Delta. I knew that very few people survived the disease-infested place for more than a couple months.

Saddled to a ten-kg rucksack, in the early hours of July 23, 1958, I got on the #1 tram to Gara Obor. At Gara Obor, I climbed onto a beat-up wooden train car that would take eight hours to cover the 320 km distance, approximately 200 miles. By the time I got to Tulcea, the small, rickety buses that serviced the work camp had stopped running for the night. There were no hotels or inns in the area, so I figured I would hide under a tree and wait for the next day. But as luck would have it, it began pouring like a dam had broken in the sky and bolts of lightning were striking all around me. I knew enough to run into the open field: soaking wet is better than fried by a bolt of lightening. As I was sitting there in the middle of a field covered with nothing but weeds, using my body to keep Benno's supplies dry, a priest came out to me out of nowhere and offered me to spend the night in his church. I followed him to a small wooden church at the edge of the field. The priest told me I could sleep on the floor of the church and he blessed me. After he left, I took off my clothes and wrapped myself in the embroidered tablecloth that was covering the altar. I was sure God would understand.

By morning, my clothes were dry. I returned the altar cover, got dressed and left without saying goodbye to the priest. The walk to the bus stop was not long, but the earlier downpour had turned the ground into inescapable craters of mud, so when I got to the camp, my legs caked in black sludge became a source of great amusement to the two retarded guards assigned to me.

The gated entrance to the camp led to a gravel path that ended in front of a dilapidated clapboard house. A tall, fearsome wire fence stretched on either side as far as the eyes could see, dwarfing the rusted metal gate. Signs on small sheet metal boards along the fence announced its chilling properties: ELECTRIFIED, with a stick figure of a man surrounded by crude depictions of thunderbolts in red paint. The house served as inspection room, visiting area, and living quarters for the guards. Behind the house, there was one long wooden structure that served as barracks for the inmates. The door to the barracks had gotten stuck in the open position for a few seconds, so, while one of the guards jerked it loose, I was able to see inside: there were two rows of double bunk beds as far as I could see, maybe 100, and each bed was occupied. This explained why the four grim-looking guards in charge of the camp, all wearing battle helmets and a machine gun on each shoulder, seemed so high-strung: the pressure of guarding a hundred prisoners got to them.

As soon as I walked in, two of the guards asked me to stand against the wall, while they went through the rucksack item by item; they seemed to be most worried about concealed weapons, particularly knives. They sliced the Sibiu salami in several sections and, coarsely, poked their grimy fingers into each section. Afterwards, they frisked me, both of them, running their hands across my body, one and then the other, stopping and winking at each other when they got to my breasts and crotch. Then they asked me to walk into the visiting room.

Unlike the inspection room, which was entirely empty, there was a small wooden table with two chairs on either side. I sat on one chair and waited. A few minutes later Benno arrived. He looked like he had shrunk, and his face never attractive had turned into something out of a freak show: large protruding ears, bulging dark eyes, and a nose that looked like a scythe had cleaved its way out of his skull. He was dressed in faded prison stripes that looked too clean; he must have just put them on.

As soon as he sat down, he started wailing that I needed to get him out of there, that he couldn't dig anymore, that he wouldn't last another day. I looked at his hands; I could see that they were recently washed, yet his long, unkempt nails were encrusted with black sludge and his once delicate palms were scored in blood. As I was sitting there, feeling repulsed by this sniveling, disgusting creature, I saw the other two guards carrying a stretcher with a body on it.

One of the guards casually engaged the other. "What should we do with this one? I knew it wasn't a good idea to just dump it in the ditch where the goons are digging. There's only four of us. They can ambush and massacre us."

"Don't worry about it Mitica. We got the guns. Maybe we should just shoot one, so they know we're not fuckin' around."

At that moment, Benno jumped to his feet and started yelling like he had just been shot.

"Hey, what the fuck is wrong with that one?" asked one of the guards.

"Nothing," I quickly answered. "I just told him his mother died."

As soon as I got back to Bucharest, I contacted Victor and told him that he had to get Benno out of there. He did, but it cost me about six months of visits, sometimes twice a week.

VII

While visiting Benno in prison, I had no choice but to leave Poldy alone in the house even though when I started he wasn't even ten. He knew his routine; he was a resourceful little boy. He would go to school during the day and then, on his way home, pass by his grandmother's – I mean Stefania's – where he could always mooch a meal. Once, when he was about eleven, I left him alone for about four days. Benno's work camp was at the other end of the country, and I went by bus, because it was cheaper.

When I got home after one of these visits I heard what had happened. While in school, some boy in a higher grade grabbed his books and started tossing them around to other boys, making Poldy run from one boy to another, begging for his books. The boys, finding this game of 'Monkey in the Middle' sadistically enjoyable, refused to return his books, so Poldy grabbed the arm of the boy who initially took his books and tried to reach them. The boy, who was a lot bigger, took great offense at being touched by Poldy who already had two strikes against him: he was smaller and a Jew. The older boy threw him to the ground and kicked him repeatedly, while calling him a dirty kike. One of the kicks landed in Poldy's eye, causing a serious gash right under it. The eye doctor to whom Stefania rushed him said afterwards said that it was a miracle that he didn't lose the eye. That's what I had to deal with when I got home.

A week later, the school conducted an official investigation, and concluded that it had all been Poldy's fault, since had he just waited until the boys were done playing 'Monkey in the Middle' with his books, they would have eventually given them back to him without any incident. The ruling was that Poldy gratuitously and willfully provoked the older boy, for which he was suspended for two weeks. Case closed.

VIII

Just when I thought all hope was lost, Anton came to my rescue. When he saw how difficult things had gotten for me, he told me that a Hungarian man from Transylvania, a high-up Communist Party member, had been hanging around his office trying to translate a Hungarian-language documentary that he had made about the life of farmers in Transylvania. When he saw that nothing was being down for his movie, he lost the little bit of self control that he had and threatened to bring the wrath of the Communist Party down on the entire office. But since his Romanian was so poor, no one quite understood him. So Anton, knowing that I spoke Hungarian, told his office that he knew someone who was looking for a job translating Hungarian into Romanian.

They agreed to hire that person if for no other reason than to keep the wild Hungarian off their backs. The next day I walked into Anton's office dressed for my first ever job. The Hungarian man was there. His name was Lazlo. As soon as he saw me, he insisted that I be hired on the spot, and I was. The job paid enough to help me make ends meet and, like magic, that crisis was over. I think back on my father's decision to send me to Romanian school, and I bless him for it every night in my prayers.

The only problem with that job was that as soon as that movie was translated, they didn't need me any more. There weren't any other Hungarian movies to translate. There were a lot of Russian, and, of course, American and French movies, but no Hungarian. They kept me on for a lot longer than they needed me, but after another twelve months, I was told that my services were no longer required. But by then I was an experienced woman of the world. I knew how to talk to people. I always learned quickly just by watching others, so I quickly learned the language of business, the language of social interaction.

IX

After I left Romanfilm, I got a phone call one day from a man speaking Hungarian. He told me that he was a friend of Lazlo's, and that he needed a smart woman to do business with. Since I was again without money, this call could not have come at a better time, so I said yes.

This new Hungarian was Miklosh. He wanted to raise guinea pigs, which he planned to sell to all the hospitals in the Bucharest area for lab work. I didn't know exactly what he was talking about, but once he found out that I was a farm girl, he said I was perfect for the job, and not only would I draw a salary, but I was also to share in the profits. I knew that private enterprises were *verboten* in Romania at the time, and I told him that my husband was already in prison, but he assured me that this business had gotten a special permit from the government. I checked with Victor, my friend from *Securitate*, and found out that Miklosh was legit.

Within two weeks I found a small rundown barn outside of Bucharest as a place to house the guinea pigs. My job was to feed and care for them. Miklosh brought me a small cardboard box with two guinea pigs in it and told me to put them inside the pen. I told him how desperate I was for money, so he promised he'd bring some next time he was in Bucharest. He was gone for a month, probably the hardest month I ever lived. I had told Poldy that if he wanted food he had to steal it.

Suddenly, one afternoon, Miklosh showed up at my apartment with a wad of money, and casually reacquainted me with the facts of life. He was a large, brutish man who didn't mince words; if I wanted money for food, I had to sleep with him. He was literally holding the money in one hand and his penis in the other. That was my choice, and of course Poldy was on the other side of the paper-thin bedroom wall. That's when I just stopped caring. We either ate or we didn't. I either brought Sibiu salami and cigarettes to Benno or I didn't.

The next day I looked in on the guinea pigs; there were ten. In another month there were thirty, and by the end of the year the barn that was the size of a soccer field had become too small. We were doing a terrific business, and this was the first time since Benno was arrested that I could walk into a store and buy myself something, anything.

One afternoon, after about a year of the good life, as I entered the barn to take care of my charges, my heart stopped. All the guinea pigs were dead. I was told later that it wasn't uncommon; they were very delicate animals and must have caught a virus. I was once again out of business.

Despite the demise of our business, Miklosh kept on showing up. He was even less considerate in matters of sex than Victor, or even Benno had been. The only difference was that Benno was basically harmless, while Miklosh, despite my pleas, just wanted to flatten me into a bed sheet. After one of those sessions, I felt like I had been pounded with a meat mallet. It's a miracle that old bed didn't collapse. Once he was done, he would pull up his pants, which had been straddling his ankles, throw a bunch of money on the night table, and storm out of the bedroom. On the way out, he always insisted on shaking Poldy's hand.

Miklosh grabbed Poldy's hand in his huge paw and squeezed it until I could hear bones crack from the next room. When I came out, there were tears in Poldy's eyes. It didn't take Poldy long to become acquainted with Miklosh's sadistic routine, so the next time he refused to shake hands. But Miklosh was not going to be denied the pleasure of torturing an eleven-year old boy, so he protested that to refuse to shake somebody's hand was a grave insult. Poldy would then relent, only to be subjected to another round of torture. Then one day Miklosh disappeared, without giving me the satisfaction of telling him how much he disgusted me. I can only hope he was arrested and sent to cut reeds in the Danube Delta, but not before Victor's Securitate men cut off his penis with a broken beer bottle.

X

There was one unexpected act of kindness during this time. It came from Martin. It had been years since he and I conspired to keep his gambling obsession alive. Following the end of the war, I didn't see much of him, and even when I did, he was always lurking in the background, as if ashamed to have me see what he had been reduced to. But one day he showed up at my door.

I had nothing in the house, so all I could offer him was a glass of water. I asked him to sit down. He sat down, looked at me and smiled, "I think this will help, Greta," and he pulled a heavy gold bracelet out of his pocket. I threw my arms around his neck and gave him a big kiss.

"Next to my father, you're the best man I ever met. God bless you."

I grabbed the bracelet and held it tight. "But how do I sell it?"

"Take it to the pawnshop on Edgar Quinet Street. They're the only ones who have money now."

After Martin left, I ran to my brother's house. Sammy wasn't there, but Coca answered the door with her screaming daughter in her arms. She had put on a lot of weight since her wedding. She told me that Sammy wouldn't be home for hours. Her face was ashen and she seemed to have been crying. I asked her if I could hold the baby. She uneasily handed her over and told me her name was Anca. As soon as I brought her to my chest, the baby stopped screaming. Coca's demeanor immediately changed.

"Won't you come in, Greta? I have some delicious canapés: goose liver, mushrooms, cheese, whatever you want." I could feel she desperately wanted to make friends with me.

"They sound wonderful Coca, but I don't have the time. Maybe another time."

I looked at her; I felt I could trust her. Selling jewelry to anyone other than government-approved stores like the pawnshop on Edgar Quinet Street was a serious offense punishable by many years in prison.

"I have this beautiful piece of jewelry that I badly need to sell." I showed her the bracelet. I could see her eyes light up.

"How much do you want for it?" Coca asked me.

"Two thousand lei," I said. It was an enormous amount of money, and I was expecting her to haggle with me. She walked out of the room, leaving me to stare at her luscious canapés. She returned holding a stack of bills. She counted out twenty 100-lei bills into my outstretched hands. I thanked her, gave her a hug, and ran to the nearest grocery store. Poldy and I ate like kings for a long time.

XI

Once I had a few *lei* stashed away, I stopped feeling that every day had to be a life-and-death struggle. That's when I reconnected with old friend Lena. I remember the first time we met. It was when I was in the hospital giving birth to Poldy; she was in the next bed giving birth to her son Sergiu. We gave birth two hours apart; Poldy came out first, Lena struggled for fifteen hours with Sergiu.

I hadn't seen Lena in a couple of years, and then one day I ran into her while walking down Boulevard Carol. We hugged, and then we went to Capşa for a scrumptious cup of espresso. Through Lena I later met a lot of people, and many of them remained life-long friends.

Once Lena decided that she was done taking care of her adolescent son, she abandoned all other marital commitments and began a life of delightful hedonism, and I, as her best friend, took full advantage of her zest for life and friends. Her apartment was always full of friends, and since her husband, Marcel, was one of the accountants assigned by the Romanian Government to keep track of budgets on all major construction projects all over the country, he made a good salary, which Lena knew how to turn into a good time for many who refused to accept that Communism meant a living death, and flocked to Lena's to forget.

She was always having parties with the most interesting people in Bucharest. Every other evening her apartment was full of singers, songwriters, actresses, and interesting hangers-on, and every party was lavishly catered with the best foods one could find in those difficult years when most people were starving. Maybe that's the reason why Lena's affairs were so well attended.

Lena had a piano in her living room and, with all these entertainers around, there was always at least one piano player in the bunch who could play some good dance music; I never danced so much in my life. We were all young and loved to dance.

Lena always timed her parties to coincide with Marcel's

frequent out-of-town business trips, since, she assured us, had he been there, things would have been quite awkward. As the man in charge of how the Government spent its dwindling resources in order to convince the world of the permanence of Communism, as reflected in the imposing edifices it was building all over the country, Marcel was in a constant state of anxiety that his wife's reckless lifestyle was undermining his position as the Government's financial watchdog.

As I think back at that time when fear and uncertainty were the defining attributes of life and anyone could disappear without a reason and nothing made sense, Lena's place was an oasis for all of us trying to regroup for yet another day. Nevertheless, Communism was still there, but somehow when you walked into Lena's apartment, you left its horrors at the door, and entered a world where you felt you deserved to indulge in anything because you knew that as soon as you stepped back outside, your miserable life was there waiting. Needless to say, her parties got pretty wild at times.

Despite the fun we had, the specter of death that was Communism made its presence known even there. One of the regulars was Tudor, a beautiful man who always entertained us with his piano playing. He had been a nightclub performer before the war. If he didn't play the piano and sing a song, he told a joke, and his jokes often had a subversive quality. One night, after he had a few drinks, Tudor told a joke that, considering the paranoid attitude of the Communists, he probably shouldn't have. He compared Gheorghiu-Dej, the head the government, with Bula, a character out of Romanian folklore who was always silly and foolish, but not stupid. Someone at the party heard him and must have told one of those Communist Party liaisons. The next day, Tudor was arrested. He had a beautiful wife and two young girls. They never heard from him again.

I found it interesting that soon after Tudor disappeared, this deformed, repulsive character who occasionally made an appearance at Lena's party, but always kept very much to himself, ended up moving in with Tudor's wife. It may all be a coincidence, but I don't believe in coincidences, besides I remember Lena telling me, when I first wondered about Quasimodo, that he was a member of the Party.

Lena has now been dead over twenty-five years. That's when I first had the opportunity to get to know Marcel better. He wasn't quite like Lena had described, and frankly I knew that Lena was just badmouthing him because she had been angry with him for many years, since the time she found out that he was having an affair with one of her friends. She had started out by loving him, but after his betrayal she decided to just live in the moment and spend as much of Marcel's money as possible. Marcel, probably racked with guilt, never complained, possibly hoping for the longest time that Lena would eventually forgive him. But she didn't, and the parties never stopped. Marcel hung around her for another 30 years waiting for absolution, but it never came, and then she died. Despite the fact that she was always gay and full of love, there was a core of bitterness in her heart that never healed. Marcel, like a true martyr, found his redemption through a life of constant humiliation and denial.

After Lena died, Marcel became my companion, and remained so until he died three years ago. We had been together for almost 25 years, and I cared for him. He was always considerate and attentive in every way possible, and I know he cared for me very much, but I could see that those years with Lena, when he had to keep denying his own self, his needs and desires, took an enormous emotional toll on him. Although he was always ready with a compliment and quite generous, he left me longing for something that I could never put into words, and I don't mean anything physical. There was an emotional restraint, an inability to open up and connect with those around him that might have been just a sign of timidity. Or maybe Lena had been right all along when she said that Marcel "lacked a soul."

XII

As I've mentioned earlier, Poldy had gotten involved with track and field; I don't remember exactly what events he was involved with, but he was good enough to be assigned to the pre-Olympic squad. All the Olympic athletes were picked out of the pre-Olympic squad.

I never saw him compete, but he kept coming home with trophies, which he lined up on the windowsill. I later found out from his coach that Poldy had won the national championship for boys his age in one of those events – it might have been the high jump or the long jump – one of those jumps, I think.

One day, Poldy informed me that his coach wanted to meet me. A week later this very attractive man in his late thirties rang the bell and introduced himself as Petre Vladescu. He had a mane of blond hair brushed straight back and a long muscular neck coursed by large blood vessels that got engorged every time he spoke. He was incredibly charming and his movements reminded me of a gymnast. He told me that Poldy had a lot of natural ability and he could go all the way to the Olympics. But then he dropped his courteous demeanor and started questioning me as to why I never showed up at any of the meets. He said everybody else's parents show up and cheer their kids on, and then impudently started lecturing me on the relationship between parental support and an athlete's performance. I told him that being without a husband didn't allow me that luxury, but since he seemed like such a sensitive man he would be ideally suited at playing the role of both coach and surrogate father, particularly since Poldy seemed to like him so much. Then, watching this man's beautifully sculpted body, I dropped my sarcastic tone. I told him that I would make it worth his while if he devoted more time to my son than to his other charges. He smiled approvingly and turned to Poldy and offered some encouraging remark, which made him wince. Petre stopped by a few times during school hours when he knew Poldy wasn't going to be there, and I showed him my gratitude, but ironically Poldy suddenly refused to race again.

XIII

Communism couldn't do anything right, except make people question their own senses, and even that dubious feat failed them in later years. But through the 1950's, people still desperately wanted Communism to work. The Government used basically two methods to sustain this dream: one, denying the people access to information contradictory to the Communist dogma, and two, barraging people with incessant messages brilliant in their simplicity – Communism good, Capitalism evil. The messages argued that everything invented in the last fifty years was done by their much smarter, Communism-imbued Soviet brothers, including the automobile, penicillin, and the airplane. They even had very Russian-sounding names responsible for these great deeds. The messages also maintained that life in the Soviet Union was the most prosperous on earth, with special emphasis on extravagant contrasts with the most bedeviled place on earth, the United States. The pictures that invariably accompanied these messages showed side-by-side pictures of Soviet and American homes; the Soviet homes were pictures of comfort and decency with smiling, healthy-looking people engaged in worthy activities, while the homes identified as American were dilapidated shacks suffused with naked, malnourished Black people. These messages always ended with the admonition that we, Romanians, must work hard to achieve the level of prosperity of our big brothers in the Soviet Union, but with diligence and, especially, vigilance against the continuous traps set by the evil Capitalists, we will succeed. In the fall of 1958, I went on a trip that put into question much of this information.

At one of Lena's parties, I met Kitty. I never spent much time with her; she was married to an invalid – her husband had lost a leg to diabetes a couple of years earlier, and she came to Lena's parties mostly to fill a small carrying bag with food that she would then rush to her husband. Lena always assured her that she could take as much food as she wanted, but Kitty felt terribly guilty about it and always apologized to the point of irritating anyone within earshot of her.

One time, when I got to Lena's, most of the guests hadn't arrived yet, so I ended up spending a few minutes with Kitty. It was a lovely summer evening and I was sitting alone on the small bench on Lena's balcony usually reserved for those of us who on occasion needed some privacy. Kitty hesitated into view and immediately began apologizing. She was short and plump with short black hair and bulbous green eyes, but she had a disarming smile dominated by iridescent white teeth. I told her that I had also been meaning to ask her about her husband. She told me she didn't want to talk about that. She appeared sweet and unaffected and seemingly interested, unlike most people I ever met, in whatever I might have to say.

"I heard about you, Greta," she said. "Everyone talks about you with such high regard: how you manage, a woman without skills, to keep house, to raise a son, to take care of your husband while he's in jail. You are the bravest woman in the world."

Kitty and I ended up spending the whole evening on that bench. I told her a lot about myself and my life, which only succeeded in boosting her already high regard of me. She told me about herself and her wretched life, but she didn't whine about it; she just presented facts to me in a simple, straightforward manner that made them comfortable to accept.

It was already dark outside when Lena peeked her head through the balcony door to let Kitty know that she had put fresh strawberries and whipped cream into her food package. Kitty jumped to her feet and repeatedly thanked her while rhythmically bowing. I grabbed her wrist and squeezed it, and she stopped. After Lena disappeared, Kitty threw her arms around me and began crying. I told her I understood. She stood up, told me that she had to get home before the whipped cream spoiled, and walked out, but she promised to keep in touch.

About two months later I got a call from Kitty. I was genuinely happy to hear from her. It was during one of the bleakest times I went through, and I told her that. She said she was calling me specifically to share with me a perfectly legal way to make a lot of money.

"They have these Black Sea cruises from Constanta to three Soviet cities along the coast: Odessa, Yalta and Sochi."

"I don't see how we can make money going on a cruise?"

"Trust me, Greta. My cousin just got back, and she made 740 lei, and that's after what she had to pay for the cruise. She sold all her *shmatas*, things that she hadn't worn in years; they bought everything. As soon as I heard about it I called you. You're always on my mind, Greta."

"I'm not following. Who bought your cousin's *shmatas*?"

"People there. They wait for us at the pier where the ship docks, mostly Jews, but *goyem* too. Oh, by the way, Greta, you do speak Yiddish?"

"I do, but why is that important?"

"We don't speak Russian. Yiddish is the only language to communicate with these people. They have tons of money, rubles, but empty stores with nothing to buy; they freeze their asses in the winter. They'll pay fifty rubles for an old sweater, and 150 for a coat; a winter coat in decent condition – wool- they'll pay 300, maybe 400. We think we have it bad here in Romania; they have it worse. They're ahead of us in Communism; that's where we're going to be in ten years, completely destitute."

The official price for a three-day cruise to the famed resort cities of the Soviet Riviera was 650 lei. That was a lot of money, besides I didn't believe Kitty; the story of people waiting by the pier with rubles in their hands ready to pay anything for our beat-up, old clothes seemed far-fetched even for the unreal times we were living through. But I had heard wonderful things about Yalta and the Crimean Peninsula and the beautiful beaches and the luxury hotels, and I figured that even if nothing came of our business venture, I would at least get to see something.

Kitty and I booked a cruise for the end of October on the *Transylvania*, a Romanian cruise ship; Kitty knew somebody at the booking office – I knew what that meant from personal experience – who was able to get us the tickets for only 420 lei each. We had to share an interior cabin on the lowest deck with two other women, but all the meals were included. Along with our tickets, we received a list of a permissible travel items. The list not only mentioned what toiletries or clothes were allowed, but also how many of each item: one toothbrush, one pair of stockings, one pair of shoes, one sweater, etc, etc. Anything in excess of the amount specified would be cause for invalidation of travel documents. At the bottom of the list, someone had written in block letters: NO SWEATERS.

In the days before we left, I went collecting old clothes. My mother told me she had a gray woolen skirt she hadn't worn in years and Lena promised me a closetful of sweaters and blouses. I also had a few sweaters, most of them bought before the Communists at Romarta, but which I hadn't worn in years.

The night before, I asked Ion the super if he could help me carry some stuff down Strada Popa Petre to the tram stop on Calea Mosilor the following morning. I told Poldy I'd be gone a few days and to behave himself while I was away. He gave me one of his infuriating sneers, but I was too busy to engage, though I really wanted to smack him. If he only knew I was doing it so he'd have food to eat and clothes to wear.

I met Ion at five am. He had a small rolling cart that made the process quite civilized. Getting on the tram with four large mesh bags filled with clothes was another matter, but the tram driver patiently waited until Ion loaded all the bags. There was no one else on the tram at that hour so I didn't have to tell anyone to shut up. As Gara Obor was the final stop, I had time to make several trips to get everything off the tram. A broken down dolly helped me cover the distance from the tram stop to the train platform in one trip. While I was waiting there, Kitty showed up. Like me, she had four mesh bags filled with clothes and a small suitcase, but she was carrying everything on her back: two bags tied together draped over each shoulder and the suitcase in her left hand. She looked like one of the Black children working in a South African mine I had seen in propaganda pictures. I knew I shouldn't've, but I started laughing hysterically. She stopped walking and joined me howling at the top of her lungs.

A conductor came along and helped us get our bags on the train. A few minutes later the train was in motion. Fortunately, we were alone in the cabin so we can begin our dressing process. I had my mesh bags lined up on one bench, Kitty on the other. Slowly, one by one, we took out sweaters from the bags and put them on. By the tenth sweater, Kitty looked like the Michelin man. Kitty assured me that I looked no different. We burst out laughing. It got hot, very hot; we opened the window; we continued the dressing process. When we were finished, I had twenty-two sweaters on me; Kitty had nineteen. We also each had five skirts on top of the one we were already wearing. When the conductor who helped us with our bags came to check our tickets, he took a look at the two sweaty behemoths sitting across from each other and fell back in horror.

"Anything wrong?" asked Kitty in a most nonchalant manner, while wiping her forehead with her enormous forearm.

"Are you ladies alright?" asked the conductor.

"Never better," answered Kitty, while swiping away at the unrelenting perspiration. All this time, I held a handkerchief to my face to conceal my giggles.

Once we decided on the order we needed to wear the sweaters, we returned them to the mesh bags and spent the rest of the time fantasizing what we would do with all the money we made. I would buy myself a new winter coat – black Persian lamb. I had seen one in the window of the pawnshop on Edgar Quinet; it was in mint condition and they were asking only 1,700 lei. Kitty's dreams were a bit more pedestrian: she wanted to buy her husband a prosthetic leg. When the conductor, walking past our cabin, announced that we were crossing the Danube, we began the dressing process all over again. An hour later we were in Constanta.

The train station was two blocks from the pier. Wearing

twenty-two sweaters, but no longer carrying the mesh bags, I headed for the *Transylvania*, our cruise ship, with Kitty close behind me. We must've been wobbling pretty severely as two cruise officials, whose chest tags designated them as controllers, rushed up to us, offering to help us the rest of the way. The controller who grabbed my arm, a badly groomed young man with a droopy mustache that completely covered his mouth, seemed torn between breaking into a fit of laughter and bemoaning the unfortunate sow on his arm. When we got to the line of passengers waiting to be checked in, he made eye contact with another man in like uniform and walked me to a little table on the side of the gangplank. He asked me to open my little valise. I was happy to do it: there was nothing inside except for items specifically permitted, and, of course, no sweaters. I closed the valise, thanked my mustached controller, and told him I could take it from there. He tipped his hat and walked away.

Sweat was rolling down my face at an alarming rate, and I was sure another minute inside twenty-two sweaters, I would pass out from severe dehydration. Kitty was close behind me, and looked no better. As I was walking up the gangplank, I saw other women who displayed signs of temporary obesity just like us, but none anywhere near our weight class.

We soon found our cabin. Luckily there was no one else in the room, so we quickly took off our sweaters and skirts and hid them under the bottom bunk bed. Just as we finished, two other women walked in who were obviously wearing multiple sweaters. They stopped and stared at us and the blood drained from their faces. Kitty, clearly a much nicer person than me, as I would have let them sweat it for a while, told them not to worry and that we had just taken off our sweaters. One of the women – I later learned her name was Olga – threw herself at me and gave me a hug. The four of us spent the next two hours looking for good hiding places in a cabin the size of a large closet. No one hiding place was large enough for everything, so our biggest challenge was devising a bookkeeping system that kept track of everybody's stock. We knew that they would be searching the room at least once before reaching Sochi, our first destination.

The *Transylvania* left Constanta around four pm and was soon in open water. The four us – Kitty, Olga, Marta, and I – went up on deck. We would have stayed there longer to watch the lighted pier slowly shrink in the distance if not for the sudden gusts of wind and hard pounding rain. We left and headed for the dining room, two decks below. The ship was bouncing dreadfully. On the staircase, a woman had fallen, and then other women fell on top of her. The door to a bathroom suddenly swung open just as a woman vomited all over the floor. We all saw it. We tried to walk away as fast as we could, but her frightful moans caught up with us.

By the time we reached the dining room, Kitty, Olga, and Marta looked green. I felt fine, just hungry. As I was trying to decide which table we should sit at, Olga and Marta, their bodies bent forward, ran off out of sight. I looked at Kitty's face; it was ashen and covered in perspiration. I told her to go back to our room and that I would bring her back something to eat. She bellowed, "No food," turned, and ran off.

The dining room was lined with long picnic-type wooden tables. I didn't want to sit alone, but the only occupied table seemed to be designated for the crew. I walked over and asked, and a handsome, young sailor smiled and told me to join them. As soon as I sat down, a waitress brought me a bowl of hot bean soup and a slice of black bread. She immediately warned me to always hold on to the bowl.

"You better hang on to it, honey, or we'll all be wearing beans to bed tonight."

I glanced across the table at a man I immediately recognized: it was my mustached controller who was now staring at me. He was trying to resolve the incongruity of my sudden and dramatic weight loss. I continued looking down at my soup, and after a while he stopped staring, got up and left. After the soup, they served coffee and a cookie; there was no main course. My new pals wanted me to stay longer, but I was tired and wanted to get back to the room.

The hallways, which an hour ago were teeming with people, were now empty. The ship was jerking as wildly as before, but I knew I wasn't going to get sick. As I turned the corner, there he was, my mustached controller.

"I know what you're doing, and I want half. I don't want to fuck you; I just want money," he said in a low, menacing voice.

I nodded and walked away.

When I got back to the cabin, the place stunk from vomit. I only saw Marta. She was lying in her lower bunk perfectly still, seemingly devoid of life; she must've had nothing else left in her. Olga and Kitty were not there; I had a pretty good idea were they were, but I knew there was nothing I could do to help them. I took off my clothes and climbed up to my bunk. I was about to stick my head under the cover when I noticed that I was eye-level with the sole porthole in the cabin. I stared out into the blackness; when I saw a tiny light flickering in the distance, I felt contented and went to sleep.

When I woke up, the ship was still. We were docked at a long, wooden pier, and I could see out of my porthole that many of my traveling companions had already disembarked and were milling about the pier. I got dressed quickly and joined them. The air was fresh and the sun was sweet and overwhelming. I found my three cabin mates sitting on a bench at the far end of the pier. They seemed to have regained some semblance of life. I asked them how they were feeling and if they were interested in some food. They felt better, but definitely no food.

Beyond them, I saw a white sand beach and people in bathing suits, and it looked so inviting. I went back to the ship's dining room, walking past my mustached controller who was standing in the doorway sizing me up with hateful eyes. The place was mostly empty, so I found a place to sit at a long, otherwise empty table, just as the waitress came over.

"What's for breakfast?" I asked.

"We're out of margarine," she answered.

"Bring me what you're not out of." I said.

She smirked and walked away and quickly returned carrying a cup of black coffee and a slice of black bread. As she placed the coffee in front of me, she pointed to a large ceramic jar on the table. It had once contained prune marmalade, but now it was empty. The coffee was hot and strong and the bread was fresh; I felt good.

I went back to the cabin, grabbed my bathing suit, and walked over to the beach. I was not going to sell sweaters that day. I was going to lie in the sand and make love to the sun. I always had this great skin that allowed me to sit in the sun all day and tan a perfect bronze and never burn, and that's exactly what I did that day in Sochi. On the way back to the ship, I again passed my mustached controller. I smiled and walked on. When I got back to the cabin, I met the girls. They were feverishly discussing methods of preventing a recurrence of the terrible seasickness they had the night before. Olga, whose husband was a Party member, had already explored the possibility of returning to Bucharest by train, but her visa did not allow her to do that, so they all felt they were doomed to two more days of hell. The original purpose of the trip – to sell *shmatas* - was no longer on their minds. It was now an issue of survival, nothing but survival.

The ship left port around seven o'clock, and, as soon as it did, the ferocious bouncing began. I glanced in the tiny round mirror to the side of the cabin door. I had gotten a good tan and looked nice. I was a 34-year old adventuress on the high seas.

I awoke in the middle of the night; the jolting had stopped. It was only midnight. I wondered what had happened, but not enough to check, and went back to sleep.

"We're in Yalta," I heard Kitty utter in a strange guttural voice. "Thank God. I didn't think I would make it," she added. I looked at Olga's and Marta's bunk beds. They were sleeping – probably the first decent sleep they had since leaving Constanta. One of them was generating a snoring sequence of unsettling sounds.

"Get some sleep," I offered to Kitty.

"Yes, yes," she responded, and turned to face the wall.

I got dressed and left the cabin.

"When are you going to start selling something," barked my mustached controller, who seemed to have been waiting for me.

"Can't you see, we're all sick on this ship," I answered defiantly.

"You spent the whole day on the beach when you should have been selling," he hissed at me.

"I slept on the beach, because I was exhausted from being up all night and throwing up my guts, especially after that extravagant dinner you people serve on this ship."

My mustached controller – I never learnt his name – spat at my feet and walked away. I made my way to the main deck and watched the flickering lights of Yalta. I would have gone for a walk had the gangplank been down. I sat on a long chair; there was a cool breeze in the air, and I closed my eyes, and when I opened them again, it was morning.

I walked over to the rail and I saw the city of Yalta stretching out in front of my eyes. I glimpsed Swallow's Nest in the distance – I had seen it in a Russian movie and it mesmerized me – and had a sudden urge to visit it. I was waiting for the crew to lower the gang plunk, but, to my surprise, they were raising the anchor. Twenty minutes later, we were on our way to Odessa. I walked over to a crewmember.

"What happened to Yalta?" I asked.

"That was it," he answered.

"But we were told we would be visiting Yalta," I insisted.

"You got to look at it and that's better than walking around this place," said the young sailor. "Believe me comrade, I've seen it and you're not missing anything."

I walked back to my cabin bracing myself for the next round of shaking and pounding, and I felt sorry for Kitty and the other women. When I got there, they seemed to have been prepared for the worst, as empty buckets and cut-up newspapers were everywhere. I turned around and headed for the dining room.

Luckily, as I scanned the room, I did not see my mustached controller. I sat down next to a bunch of women wearing dirty-white uniforms – they were probably kitchen staff.

"Is the sea always so rough?" I asked them.

"This is nothing comrade," answered a tall, young woman with terrible posture and eyes like a raccoon. "You should have been on the last cruise. Two women died on that one. But it's not the sea. It's this old tub; it doesn't have any stabilizers."

One of the waitresses brought me a bowl of soup with a slice of bread on the side. I grabbed the bowl, and nodded to her that I knew I had to hold it tight. It was sour cabbage soup, better known as *chiorba*. It was tasty and hot. I used the bread to help me sop up the last vestiges of matter smeared on the side of the bowl.

"I see you're doing fine," said the young woman, watching me eat.

"I guess I don't get seasick," I answered.

"You're getting you're money's worth," she added pointing to the last piece of bread that was disappearing into my mouth. She laughed heartily, and so did I, and so did the other women. It was the most fun time I had during that entire God-forsaken cruise.

I went back on deck. It was the best place to be, away from everyone retching and vomiting around me and the awful smell. I was there alone, lying on the same lounge chair I was on the night before, and I fell asleep again, but this time, when I opened my eyes the gangplank was down and we were in Odessa.

I ran to the cabin.

"This is our last chance," I told Kitty who was sitting on her bunk.

"I can't do it Greta…I can't. You go."

I put on five sweaters and two skirts and flew down the gangplank. There wasn't anyone else. I had no idea what I was doing, but this was not the first time I was in this sort of situation. There was a narrow street leading away from the pier, and I decided that if anyone were looking for sweaters, they would be on that street. I wasn't twenty steps down the street when I noticed women and men standing in doorways and staring at me. I walked up to an older man in a tattered black suit, plastic sandals and an unkempt goatee.

"*Fahshtay Yiddish?*" I asked.

The man pointed me toward a woman wearing a black babushka standing in the doorway across the street. Before I had a chance to walk up to her, she ran to me.

"*Ich fahshtay Yiddish. Mien mann,*" she added pointing back to the man in the tattered black suit, "is nicht ein Yid."

I nodded, smiling at the woman's husband. The conversation continued in Yiddish.

"Do you have sweaters?" she asked, poking me in the ribs.

I peeled back the top sweater revealing the others behind it. The husband and wife team began tugging at the sweaters, while others crowded around us. A man's voice thundered in Russian.

"What did he say?" I asked the woman wearing the babushka.

"Nothing. He's got *bubkas*. Don't listen to him," she said with contempt. "I give you a good price. How is forty rubles? I take them all, all four. 150 rubles. With the two skirts make it 200. Very good price."

"No, I want fifty rubles per sweater and I have five not four, and sixty rubles per skirt. That's 370 rubles." I said.

The woman looked at me with awe, but didn't hesitate.

"*Da.* Take them off."

I began taking the sweaters off one at a time when I felt the woman's hands pulling at them all at once. She removed the skirts off me the same impatient way. She then smelled them.

"*Da, da.* You're a tough broad," she said, smiling like a Cheshire cat. "Boris, give her the money."

The man in the black tattered suit pulled a huge roll of bills out of his pocket and quickly peeled off five of them into my hand. I looked at the bills; there were three 100's, a 50, and a twenty. I put the money in my pocket.

"I have more merchandise," I said. "I can bring it here in

five minutes."

"Hurry," the woman said. "We'll wait."

I ran back to the cabin, hid the rubles in my valise, and put on more sweaters and also two of Kitty's skirts, and ran back to my customers. They were all there.

"Can I sell them some stuff?" I asked the woman in the babushka.

"No," she answered. "I got better prices."

"We give you sixty for the sweaters and seventy for the skirts," a man's voice rang out.

"Don't listen to him," the woman in the babushka intervened. "I give you sixty for the sweaters too."

"If you want me to continue doing business with you, you need to give me ten more rubles for the five sweaters and two skirts I sold you before. Otherwise I do business with them," I said.

"*Da, da.* Boris, give her seventy more rubles."

Boris handed me the money.

"What else you got?" asked the woman, shoving her hand into my chest.

"Ten sweaters and two more skirts. That's 640 rubles. *Da?*" I said.

"*Da, da.* Boris, give her the money." Boris peeled off a few more bills from his ludicrously large roll.

"I have more," I said.

"I don't need any more," the woman answered. "Now you can do business with them."

"Can you translate for us?" I asked.

"No, I have to go home," she answered flatly.

"It'll only take a minute," I pleaded.

"No problem," someone said in broken Romanian. "You come, *da?*"

I ran back to the ship, put the new money haul next to the other in my valise, and put on the last seven of my sweaters and five of Kitty's.

When I got back to the street, the woman with the babushka

and her husband were gone, but there were still plenty of people waiting for me. I didn't want to waste time hondling, so I grabbed a piece of black tar off the sidewalk and wrote, 12 x 60 = 720.

A man pushed through the crowd and shoved a wad of rubles in my face. I counted the money: 720 rubles. I removed the sweaters in the manner of the woman with the babushka and handed them to the man. He grabbed them and ran away. The crowd gave out a loud sigh of regret. I showed them my open palm and ran back to the ship. Five minutes later, I was back wearing the last of our sweaters.

I tried to wipe off the previous sign with my sweaty fingers, but that only succeeded into turning my fingers into five black crayons. I then finger-painted 14 x 60 = 840 in stereovision. There were no offers; everyone was standing there staring at me. I peeled back the top sweater thinking that they didn't believe I was wearing fourteen of them. Suddenly, a woman gave out a loud scream, "*Da.*" I started peeling off the sweaters, when a man bent down over my scribble, picked up the piece of tar and crossed out the four in 840 and wrote a 5 instead. The woman who had screamed earlier ran over to the scribble and crossed out the whole number and replaced it with 900. The man crossed out the 900 and wrote 1000 above it. There was silence after that. I took off the sweaters and handed them to the man. The man handed me ten 100-rubles bills. He was a tall, powerfully built man with a big blond mustache and blue eyes whose image brought to my mind the pictures of Stalin that hung everywhere. As I was leaving to head back to the ship, the crowd dispersed.

Walking up the gangplank, my mustached controller appeared from behind an open door and grabbed me by the arm and pushed me down a dark corridor. He didn't ask a word, just shoved his hands in my pockets. He counted the ten Russian banknotes, folded six of them into his pocket and rammed the rest down my chest.

"That's for trying to screw me out of my money," he said as he walked away. I never saw him again.

Back in the cabin, I looked around. My three cabin mates were sleeping. I emptied my valise of the money I had put there earlier and climbed up to my bunk. I glanced out the porthole: nothing outside but the vastness of sea and air stitched together at the horizon. I shoved my fingers into my money; it was more money that I could have imagined. I counted it: 2,200 rubles. I would have had 2,800 if not for my mustached controller: that's the price of doing business I decided and smacked my lips. I had done it in a little over an hour. I climbed back down, just as I felt the ship moving again, stashed the money into the tips of two pairs of shoes I had with me and slipped the shoes inside my stockings. I went to sleep; the first peaceful sleep I had in three nights. In a few hours we would be back in Constanta.

When I woke up, the ship was still and Kitty and my other two cabin mates were standing around, their bags in hand.

"Greta, get up. We're back," said Kitty.

"What time is it?" I asked.

"It's nine thirty," answered Kitty. "It's too late to go back tonight. We'll have to find a place to sleep here tonight in Constanta. There's a train for Bucharest tomorrow at nine forty-five."

I started getting dressed when Kitty leaned over and whispered, "The sweaters are gone. They must've searched our cabin while we were sleeping and found our hiding spots. But I don't care. I would've left them here anyway. They were worth shit."

I nodded and continued getting dressed. A few minutes later, a loud horn blew.

"We can leave now," Marta announced.

We picked up our suitcases. Olga and Marta were obviously leaving their sweaters behind – maybe the next travelers will find them and have more luck with them.

After we said "goodbye" to Marta and Olga, Kitty and I began walking the streets around the train station hoping to meet someone who could put us up for the night. By eleven o'clock, the streets were empty and any chance of running into anybody, especially someone with a room, seemed less than remote.

As we were crossing the tracks to get to the other side of town, Kitty noticed a train car standing alone on a piece of track surrounded by tall grass. We climbed in; it was a sleeping car, with many of the cabins in a sad state of disrepair and badly smelling of a mixture of mildew and excrement, but, at the far end, we found one cabin that was passable or maybe we were just too tired by then. Fully clothed, wearing our coats and using our valises for pillows, we went to sleep; as on the ship, Kitty took the bottom bunk and I took the top.

When I opened my eyes next, Kitty was leaning over me. I felt the cool morning breeze coming through one of the broken windows.

"We need to go," she said. "It's 8 o'clock, and we don't want anyone finding us in here."

I nodded.

"Besides I still have a few lei left and I want to treat you to breakfast, " said Kitty, showing me the contents of her handbag. "It will be the first meal I've had in four days. I don't know what's keeping me going."

Just outside the train station there was a *carciuma*, a small pub that usually sells only beer and *mititei*, the spicy Romanian sausages that I last had years ago when I was with Daniel, but to our amazement they had coffee, which wasn't bad, and bread, fresh black bread, and butter, real butter. We each had two of each and the server, a short fat woman with kind eyes, couldn't stop smiling at us. She probably never saw two scruffier and hungrier women in her life. The bill came to one *leu*. Kitty paid, but I gave the woman another *leu* tip.

The train was mostly empty, so we found ourselves a free cabin and each of us slumped on our own bench.

"What a bust this whole trip has been," Kitty began. "What an idiot I've been; I convinced myself that the money I'd be making on this trip would justify sleeping with that filthy, dirty *jglob*. But now I'm left with nothing but this unclean feeling that I don't think I'll be able to wash off even if I scrubbed my whole skin off.

"It wasn't so bad," I said with a smile.

"It wasn't so bad?" countered Kitty, with tears in her eyes.

"It was the worst time of my life: I've been beaten, fucked and robbed." By now Kitty was sobbing uncontrollably.

A train conductor stormed into the cabin.

"What's the matter?" he yelled.

"Her husband died," I answered.

"Oh, she'll get another," said the conductor and left the cabin.

"I wish that was true," Kitty continued, as her chest kept heaving alarmingly. "I told myself that I must do this to make Eddie's life a little easier. All I've done is make myself feel like a stupid whore with nothing to show for it."

"It could have been worse," I said.

"Greta, I thought you were a smart woman. How could it've been worse? You think that if I had died, it would have been worse? The way I feel right now, that would have been better."
I picked up my valise and reached inside my shoes.

"Are you saying that if it turned out that we made some money, you wouldn't feel any better?" I asked, displaying a toothy grin.

"What are talking about?" snapped Kitty.

"I'm talking about 2,200 rubles I made selling our sweaters while you were puking your guts out. Here is your share: 1,100 rubles," I said triumphantly.

"Oh God," said Kitty, holding the money.

"Does that make you feel like you are any less of a whore?" I asked.

Kitty held the money, smiling bitterly. "No, I still feel like a big whore, but at least not as stupid. But how did you do it?"

"I did just like you told me: I went down one of the streets near the port wearing the sweaters and there they were, the Russians wearing rags, but full of money, willing to pay anything for that junk. I couldn't believe it; they were so wild they were tearing the sweaters off me."

"I can't take this; it's your money, " said Kitty.

"What are you talking about? Now you're acting like a stupid whore. We're partners: fifty-fifty. If I had gotten sick, you would have done the same."

Kitty got up and grabbed me and squeezed me tighter than I thought she was capable of. "God bless you, Greta. You are the best person I ever knew."

After that, I lost contact with Kitty. I often think of her and hope that after that Black Sea cruise her life got better, but I doubted.

XIV

A few weeks after I returned from my Black Sea excursion, I received a call from Lena.

"You must come over right away," Lena ordered. "I can't talk over the phone."

It was in the middle of the day and I had a million things to do, but I dropped everything and ran all the way. Lena was not generally an alarmist.

"What happened?" I yelled, as I walked through her door.

"Do you remember the Shapiros?"

I did. They were a quiet, middle-aged couple who lived in Lena's building. They had twin boys about our sons' age: 12 or 13.

"They were arrested this morning," Lena said breathlessly.

"But why? They seemed utterly harmless," I said.

"They were charged with conspiracy against the republic. That's a capital crime."

"What did they do?"

"Nothing, Greta. They did nothing."

"But even under this crazy regime, when people are arrested it's because they've done something, maybe not very much, but something," I said. "Benno deserved to go to jail."

"Greta believe me, these people didn't do anything," said Lena. *Securitate* men claim they found anti-Communist pamphlets in their children's pockets, and now they're accusing them of using their children to spread subversive propaganda. This is nonsense. These timid, self-effacing people would never do anything like that."

"So what do you think happened?" I asked.

"What I think happened is that *Securitate* men stuffed those papers in their children's pockets so the Shapiros can be blamed for it," said Lena passionately.

"But why, why them?"

"I don't know why. I jus know we can't risk the same thing happening to us," Lena went on.

"But what can I do?" I said, feeling hopeless.

"You must sew Poldy's pockets, stitch them shut. You must do it right away. I just did Sergiu's."

"Are you saying that if they want to hang a crime on you and your son's pockets are stitched, they'll give up?" I asked.

"Greta, don't try to be reasonable. These people are crazy. If your son's pockets are stitched, they'll stuff their shit in some other child's pockets."

I went home just as Poldy was walking up the steps. I told him to take his pants off right away. He told me they were threadbare and I wouldn't get very much for them, besides they were his only pair of pants and without them he would be arrested. I told him to save his lip and hurry up.

XV

Whenever I felt hopeless, I could always go to my father. He could never help me financially, but sometimes all I needed was a kind word.

My father had been without a job for years, and my parents' only source of money was the occasional handout from me or Sammy. Even though I only rarely experienced what I would qualify as prosperity, and Sammy's resources were infinitely greater than mine, I still helped them a lot more than Sammy.

But one day my father announced that he had been given a license to operate a soda counter, which made him pretty much his own boss. It was the only form of private enterprise the government allowed. The so-called owner of the soda counter was responsible for all expenses, such CO_2 tanks, syrups, cups, etc., but got to keep all income from the sale of soda. My father had been assigned a hole-in-the-wall storefront, big enough for him and a helper, at the corner of two very busy thoroughfares. The only thing he was allowed to sell was carbonated sodas, limited to three flavors, cherry, strawberry and banana, which he would mix right in the store according to a formula set by the government. The formula specified the required CO_2 tank pressure and the ratio of carbonated water to syrup, but the government, out of sheer stupidity or demonic amusement, though I tend to believe the former, made it impossible for an honest man to eke out the barest of incomes.

So my father, who had always been the most honest of men, began to cheat: lower CO_2 pressure and lower ratio of syrup to carbonated water. There were no inspectors, but if someone filed a grievance, my father could have ended up in jail. Poldy became my father's helper, and he often came home and told me that in the course of the day there was always at least one person complaining that the soda was flat or that there was not enough syrup, and threaten my father with a formal grievance. That's when Poldy came in handy.

My father had prepared him for these situations: he would turn to Poldy and start yelling at him for having screwed up again and warning him that one more mistake he would be out of a job. Poldy, equally up to the task, would start crying frantically and blame his mistake on his bad eyes, and, for full effect, pull out of his shirt pocket a pair of broken eyeglasses. By now the customer would have felt that he had caused enough trouble, apologize and leave. My father loved his little store; for some reason it reminded him of his days of glory as the carefree tinker everyone loved. He never made any real money running that soda counter, but he had fun finding himself useful again, talking to strangers and, probably most importantly, being away from my mother.

XVI

At another one of Lena's parties, I met Manny. I didn't like him at first. He seemed to be one of the hangers on, and he didn't say very much. One day he just showed up, and when I asked Lena who he was, she said she didn't know, but that was not unusual. People knew of Lena's parties and would show up if for no other reason than a good meal. Most of these people would never come back a second time; Lena would make sure of that by telling them, sounding very official, that only Communist Party members were allowed. Lena was so good at these pranks, and, of course, we never saw those people again.

Manny became a regular; he was always hanging around me. Whenever the music went on, he was the first to ask me to dance. I was annoyed that he monopolized so much of my time; I wasn't interested in him or anyone else at the time. Benno had been in prison about two years. And my relationship with the Dentist was going nowhere. I finally accepted what everyone else seemed to have known all along, and that is the Dentist was not going to leave his wife, and all my evidently incorrect deductions that she was old and ugly and shrewish, and I was the woman he wanted evaporated.

I still had to deal with Miklosh's occasional onslaughts and Victor, the *Securitate* guy, but those I could manage, and Manny kept insisting. He asked me out again and again. Whenever I said no, he only smiled and promised to continue asking. I told him he was wasting his time; I had more than my share of entanglements, and I was not about to complicate matters any further.

On our first date, Manny took me to an expensive restaurant, usually frequented only by high-ranking members of the Communist Party, where they were playing dance music. I knew that the bill for that night must have cost him at least a month's salary. I didn't know at the time what he did for a living, but he was being very generous. When he came to pick me up, he showed up with a bouquet of white roses, which were almost unheard of in those days, and a brass compass for Poldy. I was convinced at first that he was either a Party member or someone involved in some illegal deals, in which case he'd end up in prison just like Benno. I certainly didn't want to be in a relationship with anyone like that. There was a saying in Romania at that time that was not far from the truth. It claimed there were three types of people in Communist Romania: those who have been in prison, those who were in prison, and those who will soon end up in prison. Of course, this saying didn't account for all those people who disappeared under government orders.

I had a good time that first evening with Manny. He knew how much I liked to dance, and he was a terrific dancer. We talked a lot that night too, but not about our lives; he didn't know anything about me and I didn't know anything about him. He had such an easy comfortable way about him that I began to feel attracted to him. He thought I was smart, and witty, two compliments that I didn't often hear; most men were quick to tell me about how beautiful I was or how well I was dressed.

I felt Manny was getting to me; I mean it in a good way, but for all I knew, he could have been married. For all the attention that he paid me, he never once asked me about my life, and, more importantly, never talked about himself.

Just before the end of the meal, when he asked me out again, I said no. He seemed crushed. Tears came to his eyes; he told me he cared for me. I told him he didn't know anything about me, and I didn't know anything about him. As I was saying these things to him, I could see him getting paler and paler, almost ready to faint. I ignored his signs of distress and asked him how he could afford to take me to such an expensive restaurant and yet I never heard him mention what he did for a living. Then I told him that I was married with a son, and that my husband was in prison. Most men would not want to get involved with a woman whose husband was in prison; these women were often tailed by *Securitate* men, and no one wanted the added attention. His nonchalant reaction made me believe that he was himself from the *Securitate*, and, if that was the case, I had no intention of getting involved with a Party member.

I was foolishly bold, and told him that Communism had destroyed my life; I gave up on happiness and youth to marry a rich man so I wouldn't have to struggle, and then the Communists took over and destroyed the life style I had given up a real life for, and got nothing in return. Now all I had was misery and privation. Manny sat there grim and speechless. When I finally ran out of reasons why I didn't want to continue seeing him, he simply said that he wasn't a Communist and he wasn't involved in any shady deals, but that he couldn't tell me what he did.

At that point, my female curiosity stepped in, and I told him that I could never consider spending another moment with him unless I knew who he was. He grew paler and grimmer still, and paid the check and pulled me out of the restaurant. It must have been nine or nine thirty in the evening. The restaurant overlooked a lake, and he walked me over to a boat dock, and grabbed a small wooden boat, and pushed it into the water. There was usually an attendant there during the day as the boats were for hire, but the attendant was gone and the oars were hidden away somewhere, yet the boats were unlocked.

Manny found two rounded fence posts that could act as paddles, and asked me to step into the boat. When we got to the middle of the lake, Manny placed the wooden posts in the bottom of the boat and sat there motionless. By then it had gotten dark, and all I could see of him was the occasional glint in his eyes, reflecting the shore lights. I was sitting at the other end of the boat, stabbing him with my eyes through the darkness. I knew he wouldn't have rowed all the way to the middle of the lake if he wasn't going to tell me his secret. That was certainly no way to win my heart, so I kept still.

After about twenty minutes of dead silence, he started clearing his throat. The more time passed, the more I wondered whether he wasn't just thinking up a story to get me off his back. Suddenly, like a sonic boom, his voice drowned out the tiny splashing sounds, as the boat rocked from side to side.

"I'm about to tell you things about myself," he began, "that if the *Securitate* men ever found out, there would be no trial; they would have me shot on the spot. I'm telling you all this because the way I feel right now I would rather be dead than spend another moment without you. Since I first met you at Lena's home, I have been spending every sleeping and waking moment thinking of you. I tell you all this so you'll understand what possessed me to take this crazy risk. One word from you to anyone would get me killed." Manny's voice stopped, and only his irregular heavy breathing, whose resonance clashed with the soft creaking noises of the boat, confirmed his nervousness.

"You don't need to worry. I will not hurt you," I said simply, my mind wondering what the big secret was. After another few minutes of heavy silence, he finally began his tale.

"Five years ago," Manny began, "I was working for the Romanian Olympic Committee, and got to travel a great deal; most of the time I travelled to other Communist countries. I was attached to the men's Romanian Olympic handball team, which the coaches felt at the time had a real chance of winning the Gold medal at the Melbourne Olympics in 1956. This was right before the Helsinki games, so they figured if the Romanian team scored some important wins, they would set the tone for the next Olympics, where we could go all the way.

"The team was extremely competitive, but the coaches recognized that in order for the team to be ready for Melbourne, detailed scouting records had to be kept of all the teams they were playing against, and for that they needed a good scouting analyst. Most of the good scouts they thought they could trust had already defected. They knew of my loyalty – I had been the team's assistant coach for over ten years, with some very impressive wins to my record and I love of the team.   But I was also a major political asylum risk: I was Jewish and single, with no ties back in Romania other than my sickly old mother.

"They were in a bind, though; they had no one else. So they decided to send me to Helsinki, but not before they interrogated me about everything that I ever did from the day I was born. I must have come out all right, besides they had no choice: I was the only one who really understood the game and could help the team. As you know the Romanian team did win the Gold medal at the Melbourne Olympics, something they seemed to think that in some measure was due to the meticulous records I kept on every player from all the other teams, as well as the movements our players needed to work on."

Manny fixed his eyes on some blurry speck of light on the far shore of the lake. I felt he wanted to continue, but something was preventing him.

"Greta, do you smoke? May I have a cigarette?'

"I don't smoke; I'm sorry," I answered.

"I don't smoke either, but this is one of the few times in my life I wished I had a cigarette."

"You're safe with me," I said, reaching over and touching his arm.

At that moment, a soft breeze carried his body odor to me. It was pungent and enticing. Manny was eager to go on.

"Once in Helsinki, I had a very busy schedule, and the only thing that I had in mind was keeping the best records possible of every game our team played. And the team was very good, but we lost games out of sheer inexperience. We had no idea how to capitalize on an opponent's weaknesses or to take advantage of power play situations. But, largely due to my reports, all of our players' problems were corrected by the time we got to Melbourne.

"I sat in the front row at every game and took constant notes, oblivious of what was going on around me. This was my routine during that first week in Helsinki before we got eliminated in the quarterfinal round, which everyone saw as an impressive accomplishment. Once we were eliminated, the policy was that we all must return to Romania, including the team, on the first available train. The train would travel from Finland through the Soviet Union straight to Romania. Once in Soviet territory, they would relax their guard, as there was no place to run to any more.

"On our last day in Helsinki, after we packed our bags, we were told that we had a couple of hours left to do a bit of sightseeing. That was totally unexpected, because in the past that was when most defections happened. They told us that we would get to visit several of Helsinki's most important tourist sights. I had seen the man who was making all these announcements. He was part of the Romanian *Securitate* contingent, but he was kind of aloof and never talked to any of the athletes or any of the support staff, like myself. I heard someone call him by his first name, Ion, once.

"And off we went. We took our luggage with us. Afterwards we would head directly for the train station. I was sitting next to another staff member, someone attached to the equipment contingent. I was lucky to have the window seat. At the front of the bus, there was a bench that, unlike the rest of the bus benches, was turned around to face us. Ion and a Finish woman were sitting on it. They were communicating in French. The woman, a Finnish guide, told Ion what we were seeing and then Ion translated it for us. First we were told that we were approaching the Senate Square, where the offices of the Finnish government were located, and we were all excited that we would get to see some of those old buildings. But that was not to be. When we got to Senate Square, the bus just kept on going, and all we could do was crane our necks as the bus turned down a side street. We next passed by the National Museum that, we were again told, in addition to being an example of the best of Finnish architecture, contained some of the finest works of art found anywhere in Europe. I prayed that we would get to stop there, because according to the Finnish guide, the museum had paintings by some of the best Impressionists, including Manet, Monet, and Renoir, whom I had only seen in cheap black and white reproductions. But once again the bus just drove by.

"Next we went to the Temppeliaukio Church, and by then no one expected the bus to stop, and it didn't. Besides, I knew it wouldn't stop; it was a place where religious propaganda – "the opium of the masses"—was spread, so that was not a place they would want us to see, particularly, as the Finnish guide kept suggesting with her facial expressions and agitated hand movements, that it was a place of unique beauty. In fact I heard her use several times the words 'superb' and 'magnifique', which I understood. Next we were told that we would get to see Helsinki's most famous site, the Suomenlinna Sea-fortress. I clearly heard the Finnish guide use the word 'Russian' in her explanation, but Ion, without displaying the least amount of discomfort, told us that it had been built to protect the Finns against Swedish invasions. So much for history.

"When we arrived at the Suomenlinna fortress, the bus stopped right in front of it, and we stayed put while Ion and the Finnish guide were discussing things in French that must have been so confidential that they had twisted their bodies around so that we couldn't see their mouths, even though none of us, as far as I knew, could speak French. Finally, after about ten long minutes, when every one stopped looking at the fortress and started staring at the two people whispering at the front of the bus, Ion stood up and announced that since we were running ahead of schedule – our train wasn't due for another three hours – we would be allowed to get off the bus, as long as we stayed together as a group at all times and under no circumstances talked to anyone. Ion emphasized that if anyone broke the rules, we would be immediately ordered back on the bus and later suffer the consequences. At that point, two other men – who I hadn't seen before in the Olympic Village, and who up until that moment had sat quietly in the back of the bus – walked up to Ion, who whispered something to them, and then quickly went back to form our group's rear guard.

"Being the middle of a weekday, there were very few people visiting the fortress, mostly athletes from other countries, whom I recognized. Our group, even though we were about twenty, walked in such a tight formation that we must have looked like a large ant colony. Ion would occasionally tell us what we were looking at, after listening to the Finnish guide. We spent about an hour at the fortress, never lingering in one spot for too long and never falling out of our tight formation. When we got outside, within sight of our bus, I heard the Finnish guide whisper something to Ion, and pointing to two doors that displayed the initials W.C. Ion frowned for a moment, then announced that, since out ride to the train station was going to take us over an hour, we should make a bathroom stop, and he pointed to the two doors. As all the urinals were taken, I went into one of the toilet booths and closed the door behind me.

"Just as I flushed and got ready to walk out, I heard a knock on the panel board separating my toilet booth from the one next to me. I looked down and I saw the face of a man peering out at me from beneath the dividing panel. He was smiling and, in a hushed yet very pleasant voice, told me in Romanian to take the envelope that suddenly appeared next to his face, hide it in the lining of my coat, and not look at it until I got safely home in Bucharest. I didn't have much time to think about it, so I grabbed the envelope, pulled apart a little more of my coat lining, which was already loose, and shoved the envelope in it. I walked back on the bus without lifting my eyes off the pavement. I spent the long trip back to Bucharest, which took two full days, in a regular train cabin, with five other members of the Romanian Olympic staff. We tried to shift like stalks of wheat in the wind, to lean on each other for some much needed sleep. I didn't say one word until we got back to the Bucharest train station, where I quickly said good-bye to everyone and headed home.

"I had never been so nervous in my life; I am not a risk-taker by nature, and I knew that if the envelope got into the hands of the *Securitate* men, I would disappear like so many other people I once knew. I went into the kitchen and took a small steak knife and carefully wedged its tip into the tiny gap between the glued-on flap and the envelope itself. The envelope hadn't been sealed very thoroughly, as the flap snapped open with unexpected ease. Inside it there was a typewritten letter on plain bond paper; it wasn't addressed to anyone in particular, which made me realize that it was simply chance that I was the one who got it.

"The letter stated in very official terms that the reader of the letter had been selected by the Front for the Liberation of Romania, a Paris-based organization, to help in their struggle to fight against the tyranny of the sham government of the Romanian Popular Republic, which has no intention of helping the people of Romania, but merely keep it subjugated in ignorance and fear. And I could be a part of that noble struggle.

"The letter went on to say that they knew that I was not experienced at these matters and anything that I was asked to do would be very easy to accomplish and with a minimum of risk. In addition, for my efforts, I would be given 2,000 *lei* for every mission I carried out, but the money should not be considered as payment, but merely their way of helping me live a little better life until the yoke of Communism was yanked off the necks of the Romanian people.

"If I was interested in the challenge," the letter read, "I should go to Park Chishmigiu and wait on a certain park bench (a small diagram of the area was included) near the Swan Lake the following Tuesday at 6 pm, a time I knew very few people were around: it was too late for kids and too early for lovers. The letter ended with the admonition that, regardless of my decision, I should burn the letter immediately.

"I spent a lot of time trying to figure out what to do. In the end I decided to go; I had no family, other than my dying mother, no one to fill my head with thoughts of love, like you, and an otherwise monotonous life. Besides, 2,000 *lei* was a lot of money that could make my life in this hellish place a bit more livable. On Tuesday at six pm, I was sitting on the specified park bench, and as instructed, holding open a copy of Monday's *Scînteia*.

"By six thirty no one had shown up. The first ten minutes I waited, I realized the reason they had selected that particular bench: it was the closest to the lake and surrounded by a cluster of tall thin poplars. Beyond the trees there was a large playground, which was now deserted. Afterwards, I just sat there with my newspaper in hand, hoping for someone to show up.

"At six thirty-five, an old man with a severe limp wearing a beat-up felt hat walked passed me. There was nothing in his gait to suggest that he was the person I was waiting for: his stride didn't alter one bit as he walked past, and he never looked towards me. He then disappeared at the point where the path turned sharply behind the trees.

"Another fifteen minutes went by without anything happening. I gave myself a deadline of seven o'clock. I figured that if no one showed up by then, no one would. Around ten to seven, the old man reappeared, impassively shuffling along with the same limp I had noticed earlier, and still not once looking in my direction. But this time when he got to the bench, he sat down at the other end, and spent the next 5 minutes just catching his breath.

"At first I thought that he was my contact, but then I realized that he was just some old man who probably did this every evening, and this was the bench where he usually stopped to catch his breath. I looked at him for a long time, as he sat there his chin against his chest, breathing deeply. After a while my interest in him waned, and as I noticed that it was after seven o'clock, I got up and started to walk away. That's when I heard a voice far stronger than I could have imagined the frail old man capable of generating, "Sit down."

"I quickly sat down, my knees pressing against each other, staring into the quickening darkness, and remained motionless. It was another twenty minutes before I felt something touching my thigh. I looked down only to see a small package. I glanced at the old man, but he was gone. I grabbed the package, shoved it inside my coat lining, and walked home.

"Walking home, I thought everyone was watching me. First I thought I was walking too fast; then I thought I was walking too slow. I felt my sweat dripping down my back. When I got inside my apartment, I checked several times to make sure I locked the door behind me. I opened the package. There was a small box containing a tiny photo camera, several rolls of film, and instructions. There was also a letter. This letter, unlike the first one was addressed to me. It started with 'Dear Mr. Simion," and it thanked me for having the courage to be part of their just struggle against the tyranny of Communism. Then it went on to say what they wanted me to do. It acknowledged that as a member of the Romanian Olympic staff I traveled a great deal across the country to various venues where handball tournaments were held, and my job gave me a great deal of freedom of movement that otherwise would raise suspicion, if done by someone else.

"They knew that I often spent days and even weeks in four of the biggest cities in Romania: Pitești, Constanța, Iași, and Ploiești. Each one of them presented a different interest to them. The Russians were building a nuclear facility at Pitești and they needed me to report on the work in progress. Constanța, being Romania's only deep-sea port, was often host to Russian submarines and warships. They wanted me to count how many ships of each class I saw and report that back to them (They had sent along with the letter a chart that showed different types of vessels and their alphanumeric designation). In Iași, the Romanians had built an armaments factory, mostly machine guns, grenades, and rocket launchers, which were then shipped by truck across the border into the Soviet Union. They wanted me to sit up on a hill overlooking the factory from two to six pm on the day that I was there, and count the number of trucks that left the factory, and take down the codes that were imprinted on their side. In Ploiești, I was to count the number of still operating oil rigs and to observe any unusual goings on, such as departures of tank-car trains heading east. Whenever that happened, I was to count the number of tank-cars in each train. The letter ended with a warning. It brought up the photo camera and the great benefit to them of having pictures, but it also acknowledged the added risk to me.

"Since my duties with the Olympic handball team gave me a lot of flexibility in scheduling, and since I was known as a loner who liked going off by himself, I was ideally suited for the job. These people, whoever they were, did their homework.

"I have been doing this work now for over five years. At first, I was too scared to take pictures, but in the last couple of years I have become a real photographer. Every time I have some information or a roll of film, I go to the bench in Chişmigiu after dark, and place it in a tiny metal sleeve that has been inconspicuously mounted on the underside of the bench. Whenever I go, I find an envelope containing one hundred 20-*lei* notes. I'm very careful what I buy or how often I go to restaurants, again, so as not to attract attention.

"One of the things I forgot to tell you is that every time they leave 2,000 *lei* in the park, they also deposit $1,000 in a Swiss bank account. I have completed close to fifty missions in these five years, which means that $50,000 is waiting for me if I ever get out of Romania.

Manny had stopped, and gave a deep sigh of relief. He had been keeping that secret for five years. He couldn't tell anyone, not even his mother, who had passed away the previous year. But somehow he sensed he could trust me. That's when I kissed him.

XVII

Manny was kind and generous, and a wonderful lover. And he and Poldy got along surprisingly well. Manny was the only man in Poldy's life who understood what it felt like to be a boy without a father, and he took him to all kinds of sporting events. Working for the Olympic Committee, he could get the best tickets to any game. And Poldy wanted to go to all of them. At one point I was getting jealous; Manny was spending more time with Poldy than with me. He was the only man I went out with during the time Benno was in prison that Poldy didn't resent.

Poldy had gotten into the insufferable habit of knocking on my bedroom door in the middle of the night every time I had someone else staying over on the idiotic pretext that he had to use the bathroom, which, as I mentioned, was only accessible through my bedroom. I would shout furiously through the door that he should pee in the kitchen sink and shit out the window. He refused to understand that I had no choice; I was a woman without any job skills and I had to feed and clothe myself and him, and that took money, and no one was going to hand us money for nothing, not even my own brother. But things were different with Manny. Poldy didn't seem to mind him, and I know we tested his tolerance as things got pretty wild in bed at times, especially after a party at Lena's when we got home in high spirits.

My relationship with Manny lasted for a year and a half. I remember as if it was yesterday. I may have felt love for Daniel, but I never got to know him. With Manny it was different. For nineteen months I thought I was in heaven, but on March 17, 1959 he disappeared out of my life. I will never forget the day.

He was supposed to be out of the country for twelve days. He said the team was on a three-Balkan-countries tour: Albania, Greece, and Bulgaria. It was considered a low defection risk tour, as two of the countries, Albania and Bulgaria, were Communist, and Greece, even though a member of NATO, was pursuing a difficult balancing act of political neutrality under Constantine Karamanlis. Accepting defectors from Communist countries was widely seen as thumbing one's nose at the Soviet Union, something very few countries dared do in the 1950's. The team was scheduled to play some matches in Tirana; then they were supposed to take the five-hour bus ride to Athens. They had more matches in Athens, and from there they were to travel to Sophia for their final matches, before returning to Bucharest on the seventeenth.

Manny's schedule was always very exact. Before he left, he told me he'd return to his apartment by about eleven pm on the night of the seventeenth. So I decided to stay up and call him by eleven thirty. I figured that would give him enough time to relax, but not enough to fall asleep. As it turned out, I fell asleep and when I next woke up it was six am the next day. I knew I couldn't call him that early, so I took a bath and got dressed; I put on one of my nicest day dresses, a very simple blue chiffon dress with a V-neck that allowed plenty of room for a stunning gold necklace he had given me. By then it was probably two hours later, so I figured that by the time I got to his apartment it would be close to nine. It was a Sunday, so I knew he would have to be home.

I rang his bell, but no one answered. I waited there in front of his apartment for over an hour, thinking that he may have gone down to the market to buy a few things, as he hadn't been home in a week. I looked at the watch. I decided to leave. It was past 10:30, and I would have to find out later what happened. Of course a million worrisome thoughts crossed my mind. I always worried that one day he would get caught.

I walked down the stairs of his building, and as I passed the super's apartment, the super's wife, who I knew, rushed after me. She was a short, overweight woman well into her middle age, with graying strands of thinning hair held together with a piece of rope tied carelessly to one side. Her face was covered with parched skin that reminded me of a dried-out marsh.

"Mrs. Feingold, he's not back yet, but a number of Securitate people were up in his apartment all night," said the woman.

"What are you talking about?" I asked.

"I overheard them talk. They think Comrade Simion was an American spy."

I must've fainted because the next thing I remember I was stretched out on the super's couch, with his wife still yapping at me.

"Seems like he was able to fool everybody," said the woman.

The following few months were very difficult. The next day Securitate arrested me. I probably would never have seen the light of day again if not for Victor. I had never been so scared in my life. I knew I wasn't there because I had stolen a cheese drum. This was espionage; I had full knowledge of subversive acts against the security of the Soviet Union, and I didn't report them to the authorities.

I realized it wouldn't take these men long to get me to chuck everything I knew, and even things I didn't, out of me. They didn't just torture people; they used truth serums and other drugs to make people talk. When they took me into the interrogation room, I could hear men talking in Russian, not just Romanian. I was a dead woman, but I was too angry at Manny for abandoning me to realize my predicament. I kept swearing that if, by some miracle, I made it out alive, I would spend the rest of my life hunting him down. I couldn't bear the thought that I had fallen for a man who had deceived me and clearly never loved me.

Based on bits of information I was able to get out of Victor, my *Securitate* connection, Manny was last seen on the evening of March 12th walking out into the courtyard of the hotel they were staying at in Athens to smoke a cigarette. As soon as Victor told me that, I knew he had defected – Manny didn't smoke. During the time Manny was out in the courtyard, Ion Dragomir, the same *Securitate* man who accompanied the team in Helsinki, stood by the only exit door to the courtyard watching Manny. Suddenly, smoke, thick black billowing smoke, filled the courtyard, and before Ion Dragomir could figure out what was going on Manny was gone. Manny's handlers must've gotten wind of the fact that a list of MI5 agents working in Romania, which included Manny's name, had found its way in the hands of the GRU, the Russian intelligence agency. That information hadn't yet trickled down to the Romanian intelligence services, but his handlers didn't want to wait not knowing when he'd again be allowed to travel to a non-Communist country.

Victor, who I later learned was a colonel in SRI, the Romanian intelligence agency, had showed up just as a demented-looking security agent covered in tattoos jumped on top of me and started choking me.

Victor casually told them that I had actually been working for *Securitate* all along, and that he had arranged that I become Manny's mistress to keep them informed of Manny's activities, something Victor indicated I had been doing regularly over the last 18 months. Victor concluded, in a performance worthy of an Academy Award, that the traitor Simion turned out to be too clever even for one of their most experienced courtesans. I suddenly felt a lot more respect for Angelica, my brother's serving maid.

For years after I left Romania, I would ask everyone I ran into if they knew of a Manny Simion, but all I ever got was shrugged shoulders. It's been over fifty years, but if fate was to put him in front of me right now, I wouldn't hesitate for a moment to put a knife through his pitiless heart. But he's probably dead, which is why I'm hoping for an afterworld where I can run into him and take my long overdue revenge.

The shock and grief of losing Manny, and the realization that our relationship had been a sham, drove me for the first and only time in my life into a state of deep depression. I lost the will to live. I spent day after day in bed, wondering why I was hanging on to life. Friends came to visit, talked their heads off, and left. I was not good to be around. I was toxic. Slowly fewer and fewer friends came to check how I was doing. I was alone, free to spend whole days filled with misery and despair.

The money that was left over from the guinea pig venture was gone, so I told Poldy to gather all the trinkets that Manny had given me and bring them to the pawnshop on Edgar Quinet and take whatever he could get for them. This pawnshop, the only one in Bucharest, had become a vast repository of countless, magnificent objects of art that few museums could match. It was not uncommon to find works by painters of the Renaissance and the Dutch School or antique furniture or medieval armor or gold-threaded tapestries, and most of them at absurdly low prices. The Edgar Quinet pawnshop contained much of the wealth that was once in the homes of the former Romanian aristocracy, but had been traded for a few lei to buy bread or a new pair of shoes. Nothing ever got sold: the Communists, the only ones who had money, had no interest in art, and the rest had no money.

The sale of Manny's gifts brought enough money to buy food until I left Romania two years later, and, since Poldy had always done the food shopping, I wasn't a burden to anyone.

Then I developed a bald spot at the top of my head the size of a quarter. I didn't even notice it until Poldy brought it to my attention. I had been in bed for almost two weeks when I felt that I needed to freshen up. I was barely standing, leaning over the sink, unable to even wash my own face, when he told me that I was going bald. I told him to stop sponging my face and take me back to bed. His revelation certainly didn't help my state of mind. He asked few questions during this period and kept himself occupied with his homework.

Coincidentally, Anton was away visiting his parents. He probably would have been a great help had he been there. He was gone for the three weeks I spent in bed with my bald spot. Once the three weeks were over, I got out of bed, took a bath, put on a hat to cover my bald spot, and went on with my life.

XVIII

It's funny how some chance encounter, which at the time I dismissed as insignificant, later made such a difference. I remember one morning, when I was still with Manny, and Poldy was away at one of his sports camps, I decided to buy bread, so I got up at the crack of dawn and joined the bread line. This was the first and only time I did this. While on line, I met a man. His name was Odysseus, although everybody called him Ody. He was Greek. Romania had a very large Greek population, most of them living right in Bucharest. Ody was born in Romania; his parents had come from Greece during the time Romania was still a kingdom. At that time, Romania was a place where someone with a good business head could make a lot of money. But then they got trapped inside Romania when the Communists took over and closed the borders.

I was on line right behind Ody. He was tall and dark-skinned, with charcoal eyes, yet his hair was blond and cascaded in wild waves down to his shoulders. A long, droopy mustache that completely covered his mouth intersected his long, bony face. He looked much older than his 36 years. We had been on line for over three hours, and I could tell that he was dying to speak to me, but he was too shy. He just kept looking at me, and every time I thought a word was going to escape his mouth, he swallowed it back. He had this prominent Adam's apple, and I could see it bouncing up and down like a buoy. I kind of enjoyed his torment.

As we were moving closer to the front of the line, I could see the pile of breads getting smaller and smaller, and I began to worry that they'll run out of bread before my turn. As luck would have it, Ody got the last bread. I started to walk away when Ody ran in front of me and pushed his bread in my arms. He still didn't say anything. I took the bread, thanked him, and asked him for his phone number. That's when he first opened his mouth. He said that he didn't have a phone, so I told him to write down his address, which he did in a spectacle of clumsiness. After he walked away, I remembered that I didn't even pay him for the bread.

The day after I decided that I had mourned Manny long enough, I got myself *oysgepitzt* with cheeks full of rouge and blood-red lipstick, stuck on a ridiculous cocktail hat to cover my bald spot, and walked over to the address Ody had given me. He wasn't there when I rang the bell, so I waited on the stairs figuring that he couldn't be long. The stairway was dark and dank, and large chunks of paint were perilously hanging in mid air. I wondered what he did for a living if he lived there, and realized that he could never afford to treat me the way Manny did.

Then he appeared in the doorway. He was so shocked to see me that he almost fainted. I told him that I had been thinking about him and I wanted to see him. He seemed to become paralyzed with anxiety, so I told him that he should ask me up to his apartment. Still in shock, he nodded in agreement and began walking up the stairs. I followed him in the almost total darkness of his stairway for three flights. His eyes must have been accustomed to the dark. When he first opened the door, the apartment was just as dark as the stairway, until he turned on a lone bulb hanging by its own wire from the ceiling.

The apartment had one large room, which was bedroom, living room and dining room all rolled into one. There was a tiny kitchen on one side separated by a portiere. The bathroom was outside the apartment, and shared by the occupants of the other three apartments on the floor. The apartment was barely furnished: a single metal bed, a small chest of drawers, a small poker table placed in the middle of the room surrounded by three mismatched folding chairs. I quickly realized that this man could never help me, and I was determined to end the visit at the first opportunity, which I figured wouldn't be hard with a man who could hardly talk.

After about ten minutes of awkward silence, occasionally broken up by some throwaway questions that I felt obligated to ask, I stood up ready to leave. At that moment, Ody, unexpectedly, began his confession, at first displaying spastic incoherence, but later settling down, and recounting that he had been living so frugally because he saved every penny he made, as he was planning to escape across the border into Yugoslavia. When I reminded him that the border with Yugoslavia is marked by the very wide Danube River, he responded by telling me that he was an excellent swimmer and that he'd been swimming across Lake Floreasca every Sunday for the last 5 years. From Yugoslavia, he'd walk south until he reached Greece. He assured me that his plan was not as crazy as I might think, because his cousin had done it two years earlier, and Ody was now receiving post cards from him from all over the world. His cousin had gotten a job as a waiter on a Greek cruise ship and was making lots of money.

After hearing that revelation, I decided to stay. He also seemed to have loosened up, and the conversation became a lot more engaging. He told me that he had been able to save over 20,000 *lei*, which was a great deal of money in those days.

We remained friends until the day I left Romania. I can't say that I ever felt anything for him, but I know that of all the men I knew he probably loved me the most. I am certain that he was the one who would have given his life to save mine, and I wouldn't say that about anyone else. He wanted to be with me all the time, but I had other commitments, and he often got in the way. But his insistence was so relentless, that on occasion he got me to make some serious errors of judgment. He wanted to stay over all the time, but some nights were just not convenient.

One night I allowed him to stay over, though I had an uneasy feeling about it. My relationship with the Dentist had heated up again. It had been on and off for a number of years, but since he had no intention of leaving his wife I knew there was no future in it. I barely saw the Dentist during the time I was with Manny. But since Anton had needed all that dental work, I had to raise his level of interest in me, so I needed to spend more time with him. Mercifully, he was very busy and his wife was very jealous, so there were few opportunities for us to be together. In fact, the only way he could ever get away from his wife was by telling her that he was taking the dog for a walk. He only lived two blocks away. Then he would occupy me for ten rushed minutes and leave.

As Ody and I were returning from a restaurant back to my apartment, I thought I saw the Dentist hiding behind the building. Knowing I couldn't risk a confrontation, I told Ody to leave. But he began to beg me, and tears popped out of his eyes, so I allowed my emotions to muddle my judgment, something that I swore never to let happen. At around 1 o'clock in the morning, there was this incredible banging on the front door. As I didn't want the neighbors to call the militia, I ran over and cracked the door open.

The Dentist was standing there, his face contorted by fury, accusing me that I had a man in my bedroom, and calling me all kinds of nasty names. I told him that was not true, but he insisted on checking my bedroom. Thinking fast, I told him he would have to wait by the front door for a few seconds until I could put some decent clothes on for the sake of my fourteen-year old son who slept in the living room. He reluctantly agreed, and I closed the door. I rushed to Anton and begged him to let Ody stay in his room during the Dentist's inspection. He immediately agreed, and then we both dragged Ody's half-asleep, naked body through the living room into Anton's room. In the darkness of the living room, I glanced over, and saw Poldy's eyes blazing.

After the Dentist finished his inspection, he stormed out of the apartment mumbling to himself about how a man could have vanished like a fart in thin air. Ody emerged from Anton's room, fully dressed, acknowledging how tactfully Anton handled the situation by having walked out onto the balcony to spare Ody the embarrassment.

I recently heard Ody died in that same apartment, a lonely, grief-stricken old man, who, according to neighbors, frequently stood for hours at the foot of the building's darkened stairwell and howled out my name. For reasons unknown to me, Ody never put his escape plan into action: he never swam across the Danube and he never walked across Yugoslavia.

XIX

My mother had been getting worse ever since we left Ghimeş almost twenty years earlier. But the time she spent in Bucharest had been one continuous ordeal for her. The first ten years were a mixture of good and bad days, but the last five had been relentless bouts of pain. Six years earlier, she was diagnosed with rheumatoid arthritis, which gradually debilitated her to the point where she couldn't walk or hold anything in her hands. Two years later, a doctor recommended Cortisone, which at first seemed like a miracle drug. Suddenly, my mother was able to walk and do work around her apartment again. But Cortisone was not a cure; it just relieved the symptoms of the illness and it allowed her to function. In time the doses had to be increased for her to be able to continue functioning. Within a year's time, she had to triple the dosage. There was little known at the time about the drug, so the doctor was happy there was something on the market that would relieve my mother's pains, and help her function. Then, within a year, she was taking five times the original dose.

In June of 1958, my mother was diagnosed with lymphatic cancer, brought on by Cortisone overdose. The doctors gave her a year to live. In April of 1959, her condition had gotten so critical that the hospital released her and asked that she be taken care of by the family. The only treatment was morphine. In other words, just keep her comfortable. My father could no longer take care of her, so at one of our rare meetings at my parents' house, I casually suggested to Sammy that it would make a lot of sense to have my mother moved to his apartment as he had a full-time maid, an extra bedroom, and the needed financial resources.

Sammy violently rejected this preposterous idea, as he had members of the Communist Party constantly visiting him, and should they discover his mother's presence, which they undoubtedly would, as these men were taught to always snoop around, it would greatly jeopardize his career. When I asked how his bed-ridden mother's presence could jeopardize his precious career, he reminded me that she could only speak Yiddish, and, most alarmingly, when in pain, she would scream in Yiddish loud enough to be heard all the way in the dining room while he might be in the process of entertaining his Communist buddies. Therefore, he concluded that it would make far more sense to bring my mother to my house. I angrily replied that I had no time as I was always on the run struggling to eke out a meager existence. He dismissed my objections as evidence of my selfishness and lack of love for my mother.

For the next three and a half months, my mother and I slept in the same bed, although there wasn't much sleeping going on, because she would wake up several times a night in excruciating pain, and I would have to get up and administer the morphine. Her screams were so loud that I think no one in the apartment building slept during the last month of her life. I know Anton was quite unnerved, but he couldn't bring himself to complain, or maybe he was just too tired.

Whenever I needed to go out, I put Poldy in charge of

administering the morphine. He knew the routine. There wasn't much communication between the two: she couldn't speak Romanian and he couldn't speak Yiddish. They never got along either. My mother was extremely demanding and had no patience, and Poldy was fourteen. She kept screaming "*Oy, Meine Feesse!*" He had no idea what that meant, but he liked the sound, so he would mimic my mother's "*Oy, Meine Feese!*" His Yiddish chanting was accompanied by rhythmic hopping, satyr-like, throughout the apartment. She didn't see the humor in it. That's when she started yelling at him, "*Sha! Shveig! Farmach dos moyl!*" which only succeeded in expanding his Yiddish repertoire, so now in addition to "*Oy, Meine Feese!*" he would dance all over the apartment with boundless contentment, singing, "*Sha! Shveig! Farmach dos Moyl!*" She, however, took his attitude to mean that he was disrespectful and malicious, and demanded that I beat him whenever I got home. I would end up yelling and hitting him just to make her feel that I still respected her.

He then refused to sit with her, and I had to plead with him, and promised him that I wouldn't hit him again, no matter what my mother said. I also told him that he had to help out while I was out, because if he didn't, we wouldn't eat. So he reluctantly agreed, but then when I got home, my mother complained that he had tickled her toes, and again demanded that I beat him. So I did.

After a tortured life, she died in August of 1959, at the age of sixty-three. One morning, I woke up next to her and realized that she hadn't awakened me the whole night. I looked at her, and she looked peacefully asleep. I called Poldy for his opinion, and he also agreed that she was sleeping, and we both had no intention of doing anything to wake her up. After a while, I got suspicious and called Anton to look at her. Anton brought a mirror, put it up to her mouth and nose, and told me she was gone.

Now, I think about her all the time, and every time I do I start crying. I don't know why; she's been dead for over fifty years, and we didn't have a very close relationship. I seem to care for her more now than I did when she was alive. She was impossible in life, but she's become my guardian angel since then. I don't think Poldy has any fond memories of her; he tried to cheer her up and he got beaten for it. He never realized that my mother was in love with suffering, and any attempts at interfering with her love affair were grounds for harsh retribution. She probably contributed to his cynical view of life, for which I think he's grateful on some level. She made him realize at a very young age the connection between a good deed and reward: there is none. "*Oy, Meine Feese,… Meine leebe Mama.*"

CHAPTER 6
Waiting for Exit Visas
1959-1960

Greta has not had a good night's sleep and would rather have stayed in bed all day, maybe get up later and grab a yogurt, yet she has promised she'd keep going. She lifts herself on one elbow, runs her fingers through her tangled hair, then, quivering slightly, lifts the recorder off her night table.

I

In September of 1959, a month after my mother died, Benno was released from prison. I was not informed ahead of time. One day the doorbell rang, and there he was, expecting that the world had stood still for the five and a half years he was out of my life. He had been sentenced to ten years of hard labor for stealing cheese drums, even though, to my chagrin, he was released "for good behavior" after only five and a half years. I was not prepared for him. My life was going along in the way I had fashioned it to suit my needs and desires. He didn't understand that I was no longer the woman he left behind. He didn't understand that the years we were apart not only pushed me way beyond his reach, but that they made me realize I no longer owed him anything.

By humiliating myself in every conceivable way so that I could buy Benno salami and sugar and cigarettes, and then making those terrible trips to visit him in prison, I thought I had paid in full, plus interest, for what his family had done for my family. I no longer felt obligated to play the role I had played before he went away. He wanted to pick up things exactly where he had left off. He wanted me to resume being the dutiful little wife who put up with the idea that I was one of his possessions and was put on this

238

earth to see that his needs were always taken care of, regardless of the personal price I had to pay, while he remained oblivious to mine. He had not changed other than he had gotten a good deal grayer, and a lot more impatient.

As soon as he walked in, he wanted us to rush into the bedroom and, just like in the old days, pound me for ten seconds like a piece of dead meat. I flatly refused, and once I regained my self-control after the shock of suddenly seeing him, I told him that life between us was going to be very different from then on. I first tried to simply get him to leave and look for another place to live, if only for a short time until I got to sort things out. He refused, producing some official paper that showed that he had been reassigned to this apartment. It was the same kind of document that Anton produced five years earlier when he first moved in. I told him that, in that case, he would be sleeping in the living room on Poldy's sofa, and that he would have to do his own cooking, cleaning, and laundry. I was not going to be his maid. When Poldy came home from school – he was already in high school – I gave him a minute to say hello to his father. Then I told him to take all his stuff out of the living room and bring it into my bedroom, and that from then on he'd be sleeping together with me.

The next few months were very tense at home, as Benno was always there, not yet having found a job. I spent a lot of my time at Ody's place. Some nights I would come home really late, and just crawl into bed next to Poldy's sleeping body. Since we had had so little interaction over the past couple of years, I felt that this sleeping arrangement might be a good way to remind him of the loving relationship that we had shared when he was a child, so I would run my arm around his chest and squeeze myself against his back. He never acknowledged my presence, always facing the wall, yet I knew he was aware of me since every time I came to him, his body would stiffen up and I could hardly feel his breathing. I didn't give up though; I knew how to break down men, and he was just a little man.

Around December of 1959, while I thought Benno was getting used to the apartment situation, he began to act quite strangely. With still nothing to do, he would follow me wherever I went, thinking perhaps that I didn't notice him. If I went to Ody's apartment, I would notice him stopping about a half a block behind me, and then a few hours later, when I came back down, he'd still be there standing as if frozen by the winter chill. This went on for the next couple of months with no incident.

One evening around January – it was Ody's birthday – I went to his apartment with Benno tagging behind me as usual. I spent the night there. The following morning around ten thirty, while I was on my way to Lena's apartment – she was having one of her midday bashes, which she hadn't had in months – as I promised to help her set up, there was Benno, still standing in the exact same spot I had seen him twelve hours earlier.

I decided that I had enough of his spying, so I marched up to him. He looked worn and haggard, his gray stubble covered with ice. I told him that he was acting insane, and that if he didn't stop following me around I would notify the militia. Suddenly, his face contorted with rage, turned into the shape of a blowfish, with his lips projecting forward, and he spat right in my face. I slapped him so hard that I knocked him to the ground. Even though he was quite a bit taller than me, I was as strong as an ox. He jumped up, and clumsily lunged at me. I pushed him down again, while at the same time yelling that a madman was attacking me. Several men came to my rescue, and roughed him up some more. But I was gone by then. I was due at Lena's.

At the party, as coincidence would have it, a new face showed up, and a very attractive one to boot, so I didn't miss a moment to introduce myself to the new addition to Lena's group. He turned out to be a lawyer, which was most unusual, because at the time there were very few lawyers in Romania. The system had little need for them. The government owned everything, and when they decided someone was guilty, they just took him away for a length of time that never seemed related to the gravity of the crime he was accused of. If someone committed murder, he usually got five years, and there was a good chance he'd be back out in less than three. Of course, members of the Communist Party, like the man who savagely beat Anton, were above the law.

On the other hand, telling a joke that mocked the government resulted in sudden and permanent disappearance, as it did in Tudor's case years earlier. In some cases, the family of the vanished man would be informed years later of his death of unexplained causes. If the family would have the impudence to ask where the man was buried, they would be told that it was in an unknown grave, and that any further inquiries as to the man's passing suggested a troubling indifference to Communist ideology, which prided itself on focusing exclusively on life.

I made it a point to sit down next to the lawyer, whose name was Timor, although he said everybody called him Timmy, and told him about the hell that had become my life because of Benno. Timmy immediately advised me to get a divorce, and that he would be happy to take my case. Since this was such a clear case of brutality committed by an ex-con, I should have no trouble getting a quick, advantageous settlement. When I told him that I didn't have the money to proceed with the case, he gently touched my face and assured me that he wouldn't allow anyone to inflict hardship on a beautiful woman like me, not even her own husband. He also advised me not to go home again until the petition for divorce was accepted by the courts, which would also stipulate that if Benno interfered with me in any way, he would be immediately arrested. That would take about two weeks.

Timmy graciously volunteered to call the house to find out if Benno was there, and if he wasn't, accompany me that afternoon so that I could pick up some clothes and personal items that I would need for the next couple of weeks. As it turned out only Poldy was home. As I was packing, I heard Timmy terrorize Domnul Protopopescu, a kindly old man who lived next door and who, out of concern, rang my doorbell to inquire if everything was alright. Timmy, in a show of misplaced machismo, demanded to know his name and told him that he could easily have him picked up and put away for good, so he would never ask another question again. Domnul Protopopescu, frightened half to death, apologized profusely and ran back to his apartment. By then I was finished packing and went back to Timmy's place. I told Poldy that he should be happy since he would have the whole bed to himself.

Timmy lived in a beautiful apartment right on Boulevard Bratianu. I soon found out that he was a member of the Communist Party. Listening to him, I quickly realized that he had joined the Party out of shear expediency, and it had paid off. He was often used as a prosecutor in cases against people who were accused of having in some way sinned against the Government. He was fond of saying that he had a 100% conviction record, but then cynically added, although not without a sense of bizarre relish, that, given the way the scales of justice were set, a monkey could have been just as successful.

I liked Timmy and the time we were together, but his arrogance and that nasty streak of his, which was always just beneath the surface, always kept me on my guard. I never lost sight that ours was mostly a business arrangement.

Even though I had found a safe haven in Timmy's apartment, the outside world unrelentingly tried to invade it with the persistence of Attila's hordes. For once in my life, I didn't want to hear from anybody, yet the phone kept ringing all day with calls from close and distant friends burning with curiosity for details about my situation. It was a reminder that once I told Lena something, I, in effect, told the whole world. After the first week, I just stopped answering the phone, and agreed on a simple phone signal with Timmy in case he needed to talk to me from his office. After about two weeks of sanctuary, I realized I needed to rejoin the human race, if only on a limited basis. Some days I would drop by Lena's or call on Ody to assure him that my stay at Timmy's was strictly business, and that nothing had changed between us.

II

One day, as I was on my way out to see Lena, Timmy called from his office. He told me that he had just received a phone call from Benno who told him that Poldy was sick and that I should go over to check on him. Timmy thought it might be one of Benno's tricks to force a confrontation, but since he wasn't sure, he thought that we should go over and see how Poldy was doing. Timmy told Benno that I would go on the condition that he not be there. I hadn't heard from Poldy since I left the apartment two weeks earlier. Timmy met me outside the apartment building, and we went upstairs together. Poldy was in bed and clearly running a high fever. He seemed to have passed out, probably from hunger. Timmy thought it would be best if we took him to a hospital, although I knew that being my son, he was tough like me, and capable of fighting off anything that came his way.

Soon after we dropped Poldy off at the emergency room of the hospital, I received a phone call from one of the doctors. He introduced himself as Dr. Ganea and then he informed me that a rusty nail had punctured Poldy's foot causing a massive infection, which rose up the tibial artery, preventing the blood from reaching the lower part of his right leg for several days. Dr. Ganea expressed his regrets, but the only solution was to amputate the leg just below the knee.

In agony, I shouted at him "No amputation under any circumstances." The doctor, startled by my response told me that I was risking my son's life. I told him I didn't care what he thought, but he must come up with another suggestion. Dr. Ganea got quiet, but since I could hear his breathing, I began screaming at the phone like a crazy woman. I told him that he better bring my son back to me healthy and in one piece or else I'll personally come after him and stab him to death. He stammered something that sounded like he was going to call me back, and checked off.

Two minutes later he called back and said, while stuttering over every other word, that they would try a revolutionary procedure that involved draining the gangrene, though I should know that the procedure had never been performed at that hospital. And what's more, based on what they heard from other hospitals, there was still less than a 20% probability of success, and in that eventuality, they would have to amputate above the knee, which was worse, because without his own knee, he would always walk with a very unnatural gate. And even if successful, my son would end up with a limp. I told him I didn't care about a limp. I didn't want my son to be hobbling about on only one leg; I just could never bear it.

Three days later I heard from Dr. Ganea. He told me he had great news: my son's operation was successful and that thanks to his young age and great physical condition, he would recover, but as I had been told, he would retain a slight limp though serious enough to prevent him from ever doing any sports.

When they finally allowed me to see Poldy, he was asleep, and he looked quite a bit better. He had lost that deathly pallor and his breathing wasn't nearly as labored as it had been when I first saw him at the apartment, a sign that his fever was down. I never doubted he would make it.

While I was sitting there in Poldy's hospital room, Dr. Ganea came in. He told me that he thought I was the bravest mother he ever met and he shook my hand. That night I told Timmy to make sure that he brought up child neglect charges against Benno. After all, had Benno been less wrapped up in himself, he would have noticed Poldy's condition and notified me sooner. At the time, I was getting ready for the divorce trial, and I wanted to make sure that I denied Benno joint custody rights, besides I was stockpiling ammunition against Benno to neutralize all the nasty things I knew he would say about me. Timmy assured me he would be ready with the heavy artillery.

Two days before Poldy was supposed to be released from the hospital, I had the final court date on the divorce trial. Sammy, who I hadn't seen in months, showed up at Timmy's request. When he saw me, he looked away. I told Timmy that I was worried that

Sammy could mess things up, but he assured me that he'd do fine.

Benno's lawyer was so inept that I felt sorry for him. He desperately tried to paint me as a whore who neglected and emotionally abused her son, but every time he brought up my inadequacies as a mother, Timmy shot him down by reminding the court that he, a member of the Communist Party, was well acquainted with me and everything the other lawyer had said was merely a feeble attempt by Mr. Feingold, an ex-con and a former member of the bourgeois class, to get his claws into one of the finest examples of Communist youth. Timmy was brilliant.

Once he finished confounding the other lawyer to the point of incoherence, he called on Sammy, who as a member of the Communist Party himself, testified that he had known Benno when he was still in a position of oppressing the working masses, and it would be a grave mistake to let him have any custody rights. Sammy was paying Benno back for the stolen chicken story. This was the *coup de grace,* and I walked out of the courthouse a free woman, and fully vindicated. The court awarded me all the contents of the apartment and full custody of Poldy, something that I often felt was a mixed blessing, but at least I kept him away from Benno. Timmy, at my request, also asked the judge to officially change Poldy's last name to my maiden name – Sobel. I managed, in one fell swoop to eradicate the years of Feingold servitude.

After the divorce I went back home and had to deal with Poldy's convalescence and physical therapy to reduce his limp. At first, he displayed fits of such fury that his judgment seemed impaired. The first thing he did was throw out all his trophies, a task he carried out with surprising detachment. He never stooped down to the point of directly blaming me for his predicament, but his burning stare that followed me around the room made me think he was. I never filled the role of the martyr very well. Every time he seemed in a receptive mood I would sit at the foot of the bed and explain to him the circumstances that led to his limp, so that he would understand once and for all that it was not my fault. Besides, if it hadn't been for me, he'd have lost the whole leg.

III

Despite the divorce, things became even more strained. Benno was still living with us under the same arrangements that we had before. The Housing Authority often took months to find someone alternate accommodations, and I didn't have the right to throw Benno out on the street. One evening I took Poldy to see the movie *Ulysses* with Kirk Douglas, something I had never done before. When we got home, the living room light was out, so we just walked passed Benno, who seemed to be sleeping, as quietly as we could and went into the bedroom. Poldy crawled into bed right away, while I was still in the bathroom.

Suddenly, I heard Benno charging into the bedroom and yelling that he was not going to tolerate being disrespected by not having Poldy acknowledge him. I rushed into the bedroom only to see Benno leaning over Poldy's rigid body and shouting like a madman. I stood there transfixed, realizing that my life had become unbearable. Just as Benno started to pull away from Poldy's face, Poldy, limp and all, jumped out of bed and started pummeling Benno's ears with such unbridled rage that for a while Benno's head looked like a watermelon that was being tossed from one hand to the other. By then Poldy had grown almost as tall as Benno, but broader and more robust. I stepped in between them horrified by the prospect of Poldy killing his father. I wondered if some ancient curse was at play. When I finally pulled Benno away, I could see blood gushing out of his ears. I was afraid that he may have suffered brain damage, but I rejected the idea of calling the hospital. That's all I needed: being the mother of a son who mauled his father. Thankfully, Benno's bleeding soon stopped, and I warily walked him to his bed. No other words were exchanged that night. I was living in hell.

The next day Benno moved out of the apartment. By the time I woke up he was already gone. He had apparently packed the few clothes he had in the same small Government-issue canvas suitcase with which he returned from prison. Bucharest was like a very large *shtetl*: everyone knew everyone else's business, and there was no way to keep a secret. This obviously meant that my lifestyle was a common source of gossip, but I didn't care. I enjoyed shoving it in those self-righteous faces that didn't lift a finger to help me for the five and a half years Benno was in prison. If they were so concerned with my chastity, that would have been the time to make their righteous moves. They didn't care whether I lived or died, or whether a nine-year old boy went hungry every night. That's when I said 'fuck' their hypocritical morality. They had to deal with me and my unholy ways. I knew Poldy heard how people were badmouthing me, calling me a whore and a shrew, but he never uttered a word with even a hint of reproach in it. Despite his miserable character, he's always had more class than all the rest of them put together.

IV

About three weeks after he moved out, I found out that Benno had rented a furnished room on the other side of the city, and was working at a construction site as an unskilled laborer. He was over fifty, thin and frail, and had never held a job that required physical effort. He was probably counting on the years in prison as good training for laying brick or whatever work he was doing. I later heard that he had gotten himself a girlfriend, which in some inexplicable way irked me at the beginning, but, once I imagined what a dogface she must be, it helped me shed the last vestiges of guilt I felt towards him.

A few months later – it was spring, Benno called me out of the blue. He spoke very calmly. He wanted to take Poldy for a ride the following Sunday. I hesitated at first, but then his friendly tone helped me agree to it. The next Sunday, he showed up very punctually. He was driving a fairly new model *Dacia*, which apparently belonged to his girlfriend.

That's when I first met Benno's girlfriend. She was sitting in the passenger seat. As soon as she saw me, she jumped out of the car and rushed over to me to give me a hug. Her friendliness disarmed me. I was planning to be dismissive and sarcastic, but now I found myself smiling and thanking this absolutely stunning woman for taking my son for a ride. She could not have been more courteous to me, something I had stopped expecting from people other than my closest friends. She introduced herself – her name was Elvira – and then she pointed to her two children sitting in the back seat of the car. The girl was probably about seven or eight, and the boy about four. She assured me that there would be plenty of room in the back for Poldy, as they arranged to have her son sit in her daughter's lap. And off they went. I suddenly had this queasy feeling as I was watching the car drive away. I went back upstairs, put on one of my most alluring outfits and went to see Ody. When I returned about four hours later, they still hadn't gotten back. It wasn't until close to nine o'clock that I heard Poldy's uneven shuffle.

As soon as he walked in, he threw himself on the living room sofa, dismissing the thousand questions that I had planned to ask him by simply telling me that he was exhausted. Poldy reclaimed the sofa the day Benno left. He fell asleep immediately. I remember looking at his sleeping face and realizing that, although only 14, he was developing into a handsome young man. I suddenly felt very tired, but I wasn't able to fall asleep, and changing the sheets and the pillowcases didn't help. I had never had trouble sleeping; that was one of the few times it happened.

Over the course of the ensuing weeks, Benno and Elvira came every Sunday and picked up Poldy for one of their weekend rides in the country. I never got to find out what went on during those trips other than it often involved a stop at a restaurant by a lake. The only thing Poldy told me was that he heard Elvira tell Benno that she loved him, and that she thought that he was the nicest man she had ever met - kind, considerate, and attentive to her and her children. I knew Poldy was just trying to get a rise out of me. He was still a kid, and not smart enough to manipulate a seasoned puppeteer like me. I laughed in his face, and told him to save it for his friends, of which he had none.

V

One morning, as I was passing through the living room on the way to the kitchen, Poldy, who was already dressed and seemingly waiting for me, announced that he had been invited by Elvira to spend three weeks with her and her children at a house she had rented by the Black Sea shore. He informed me that he had decided to go. I understood that he wasn't asking for permission, and only that he needed to borrow one of my suitcases. I said of course, without flinching. I hadn't been there in years, not since before Benno was arrested when I went there with Lena and our boys and we stayed at Elena's place and we had such a great time.

Poldy then volunteered to inform me that Benno would only be there on weekends, as he had to work during the week; he had just been promoted to foreman. Poldy told me he would be leaving the next day. I went back into the bedroom, got dressed and went to see Ody. I didn't come back that day. When I finally returned to the apartment, Poldy, along with my suitcase, was gone.

The time Poldy was away turned out to be one of the busiest I ever had. A few days after he left, I found in my mailbox an envelope that bore all the official markings of a Government document. I couldn't believe my eyes when I read it. It contained a letter that announced that Greta Sobel and Apollo Sobel had been granted permission to expatriate, and that we had two months to settle all our affairs and make all the arrangements for leaving the country. The assigned destination was Paris, France.

The letter was not an invitation to leave Romania, but a command; once the petition was approved, the letter went on, we were ordered to leave the country in the most expeditious manner possible. The letter also indicated that from that day forward Greta Sobel and Apollo Sobel lost their Romanian citizenship and would subsequently be considered stateless. Two additional documents were attached entitled "Exit Visa" – one had my name typed on it, the other Poldy's. The instructions required that the form be signed and returned within 48 hours to the offices of the Ministry of Justice.

When I first read the letter I couldn't even remember what request for expatriation they were referring to. In my excitement I had forgotten that some four years earlier, when Benno was still in prison, Lena told me that Marcel had heard that the Government, in order to win favorable trade concessions with the West, had agreed to allow a few hundred Jews to leave the country. Marcel, being one of the country's economic watchdogs, had access to some very important people, which was how he found out about the exit visas, but, of course, he knew that an application for exit visa meant not only his immediate dismissal from his well-paying job, but the loss of any future employment opportunities. However, Marcel mysteriously managed to keep his job; I'd like to think it was because of his unique skills, but I doubt it. I suspect that in his capacity as financial watchdog he knew of many instances of corruption at the highest levels of the Communist Party, which presented his superiors with a dilemma: kill him or leave him at his job and never allow him to leave the country. They kept him there longer than anyone else, but ultimately, about six years after I left, they allowed him and his family to leave.

Marcel had also heard that requests for exit visas would be accepted for only one day, and he and Lena and Sergiu were going to get on line in front of the offices of Ministry of Justice by seven o'clock the night before, as they were expecting a huge crowd. I figured why not, and Poldy and I spent the night sleeping on the sidewalk in front of the Ministry of Justice. Marcel had been right. After we got on line, hundreds of people lined up behind us. Before long, the line went clear around the block so that people who got on line three or four hours after us were standing next to us yet a whole block behind us. Some of them tried to jump in our line, which led to a major brawl that brought the militia.

The militia, instead of trying to calm things down, started whacking people with their batons, which led to a bunch of them being carted off to the hospital for busted heads, broken bones, and God knows what else. After that, things calmed down, and those who were at the back of the line just accepted their fate. I had never slept on the street before – somehow the night, years ago, when we all slept in Chishmigiu Park did not seem to count – but lying there on an old beat-up blanket watching all that blackness punctured by pinholes of bursting light, I realized that all I had to do was fill my eyes with brightness until I would be forced to squint, as if staring at the sun, and the night chill would vanish.

The next morning by around ten o'clock a man in a uniform different than what the militiamen were wearing came out of the building and started counting people from the beginning of the line back. When he got to one hundred, which happened to be just four people behind us, he told everyone else to leave immediately or else they would be arrested. After everyone else left, we waited another three hours before the line slowly began moving into the building. Once we got to the desk of the official in charge, he asked for our ID cards; he copied down in longhand names and numbers and told us to go home. That was four years ago. I know Marcel had tried on several occasions to find out if there was any progress with the applications, but he always crashed against a wall of blank faces. After a while, we all came to believe that it had all been just another sadistic game the Government had cooked up for their enjoyment. So the matter was forgotten.

I learned many years later that these periodic waves of Jewish expatriations – some preceded ours, some followed – were actually due to negotiations between the Communist Government of Romania and the State of Israel. Israel was buying Jewish lives at extortionist's prices. I don't know if they ever established a price list, but I know that over the years, the State of Israel not only paid millions of dollars to the Romanian government, but also built factories all over Romania and shared its unique knowledge of agriculture with Romanian farm cooperatives in order to secure the freedom of Romanian Jews.

Authorization to allow Jews to leave the country presented the

Government with a huge public-relations headache. Communism did not work. Everyone, except for high-ranking members of the Party, led a miserable existence. Always hungry and fearful, people lived only with the hope of escaping to the West. Yet, the Government allowed Jews, only Jews, to emigrate to the West.

Initially, in order to justify this seeming inequity, the Government cooked up this lame explanation that Jews were allowed to leave in order to restore families broken up by the Holocaust. This argument fell apart when Gentiles realized that wasn't always so, like in my case – I didn't lose any family in the Holocaust. That's when the Government had to come up with something more creative, something that appealed to man's base instincts: hatred and greed. When I left, the disgusting pretext they finally settled on was that Jews were being thrown out, because they were nothing more than social parasites and enemies of the Romanian people. Furthermore, with the Jews gone, there would be more for those who were left behind; there would be more apartments and more food. It's amazing what people will believe when their minds are clouded with despair.

VI

The letter said that if we didn't return the documents signed by both Poldy and me within forty-eight hours, the authorization for exit visas would be revoked. That's when it hit me that Poldy was somewhere on the Black Sea shore. I knew this was my only chance to leave behind this hell on earth and start a new life. I immediately called Benno and explained the situation to him. But first, I had to call Stefania to get his phone number, which turned out as awkward as I expected; the old woman said coolly that she hoped that I find what I had been searching for at my next destination.

Benno told me that Elvira and the children were staying at a house in Mamaia, a couple of blocks from the beach, right in back of the Intercontinental Hotel, but they didn't have a phone.

I caught the next train to Constanța, which was supposed to get there by about 6 pm. While on the train, I slumped into convulsive laughter: I suddenly remembered the Black Sea cruise with Kitty and the crazy time I had selling those ridiculous sweaters.

From the train station, I figured I'd hitch a ride to Mamaia. I didn't plan beyond that. When I arrived at the Constanța train station, I couldn't find anyone going to Mamaia. Most people at that hour were driving back, since Mamaia was primarily a resort town, and I realized that I wouldn't find a ride until the next morning. So I spent the night on a park bench near Ovid's monument...Yes, Ovid, the Roman poet who died there in 18 AD after being banished from Rome by Emperor Augustus for reasons that remain a mystery to this day, but I suspect it was because Ovid happened to walk in while the sanctimonious emperor was having sex with his own daughter Julia.

The next morning, I walked into a public bathroom right outside the train station and fixed myself up the best I could – I was worried that if I looked too haggard no one would want to give me a ride – and walked over to the main road between Constanța and Mamaia. Within 10 minutes I was riding in a car with three East German girls. My German came in handy, as they were asking me about nightclubs in the area. I told them that I had not been there in many years, and the places I knew were probably no longer there. But I gave them the names of the places I remembered. They asked me, as that seemed their primary motivation, whether these places were full of men willing to show them a good time. I told them that all I could vouch for was that they were once full of men who showed me a good time. That bit of information must have satisfied them, because they went out of their way and drove me right up to Elvira's door.

Before I even had a chance to knock, Elvira came out onto the porch. I apologized for the intrusion, but breathlessly explained the source of the urgency. She congratulated me, and asked me if I wanted something to eat – I must have looked like I felt. I lied to her that I had just had some breakfast, besides I was anxious to get back. That's when Poldy came out of the house, and Elvira tactfully walked in.

On the porch, there was a small table with three wooden chairs around it, and I asked Poldy to sit down. I pulled the papers out of my purse, pushed them in front of him, and asked him to sign them. The papers clearly stipulated that children above the age of twelve must read them carefully and sign them only if they understood them and agreed with their parents' actions. In fact, there was a whole paragraph written in large bold letters that said that if a child above the age of twelve did not want to leave the country with his parents, he would be placed in the care of the Government and well rewarded for his courage. The note emphasized that by signing these papers the child would become stateless, without a home anywhere in the world. Poldy looked at the paper with the large bold letters, slowly read the paragraph, and then just sat there.

I was beginning to lose my patience. I had to get back to Bucharest by the next morning, and this kid chose this moment to antagonize me. I knew exactly what he was doing. He could read a whole book in a day, but now he was taking a half-hour to read a four-line paragraph that a monkey would have no trouble understanding. Finally, I shoved the pen between his fingers, and steered his limp hand across the page. I then folded the paper, and walked away. Not a word was said.

VII

As soon as I got all the paperwork in order, I let the word out that I was selling all my furniture, rugs, china, everything, since the only thing they would allow me to take out of the country was a 40-kilogram trunk filled only with clothes and personal items. Most of the stuff in the apartment were antiques; they came from Benno's first apartment, but I knew I'd be lucky to get anything for them.

A lot of people came by, but they weren't even looking for

bargains, they were looking for giveaways. Their argument was that I didn't need the money, since, on one hand, where I was going I'd find plenty of money, and, on the other, what would I do with *lei* anyway as they were worthless anywhere else. My answer was an icy, "I'm sorry you wasted your time. Good bye!"

I would have rather thrown these things in the trash bin than hand them over to those spineless toads. In the end, the Dentist bought a bunch of stuff, and so did Silviu Baragan, Anton's friend and the man Poldy always referred to as Pic's dad.

By the time Poldy returned from Mamaia, the apartment was already half empty. When he saw it, all he did was thank me that I hadn't yet sold the sofa on which he slept. By now we were less than a month from our departure date, but Poldy insisted on going to school until the day we left. I told him to suit himself, even though I knew he was just doing it to aggravate me. I then repeated that all his knowledge, and I agreed that his head possessed a lot of facts, did not amount to an ounce of smarts, which was why, even though I was an uneducated woman, I would always be able to outsmart him. He stuttered something incomprehensible, grabbed his books, and left. He told me later that evening that the school had made him sign some paper that said that he wouldn't join the French Foreign Legion in their colonialist war against Algerian independence. I screamed at him that he shouldn't have signed anything; what right do they have to make a 14-year old sign any such commitment, to which he got up and, exaggerating his limp, slowly hobbled into the kitchen, dragging the door closed behind him. It was curious to see how his continued stammer had forced him to develop a way of communicating without words.

With a week to go before departure, I found myself with bags full of *lei* that I didn't know what to do with. There was no one I wanted to give that money to, and I knew that lei would be worthless outside the country. I knew Ody could have used some money, now that he had spent all the money that he had saved before he met me, but I didn't feel in a generous mood. He spent that money out of his own free will, and it got him to be with me. I felt no obligation to replenish his coffers, particularly since I was leaving. Despite the fact that being with me saved him from getting himself killed trying to find his way to Greece, I was the one who brought him back from the dead, and that was worth every penny he ever spent on me. Besides, I knew he wouldn't have taken any money from me even if I had offered. He never lamented the loss of his money, just the loss of me.

It was Ody, however, who came up with the idea of what to do with the money I had made selling the contents of my apartment. I was no longer in the mood to be with him, and I told him so when he called me that morning, but he begged me to spend one last afternoon with him, so I agreed. He had never been so passionate as he was that last time. Afterwards, while we were having coffee, I told him about the money. He said that he knew somebody who was dealing in diamonds, another Greek whom he personally trusted, who would be willing to sell me some high quality stones. Smuggling diamonds out of the country was a serious criminal offense, and if I got caught they would first take away my travel documents and then my life. He said that it would be worth the risk. Diamonds are legal tender anywhere in the world, and wherever I ended up I was going to need some start-up capital. This was the best advice he or maybe anybody ever gave me.

The next day, carrying a rucksack full of *lei*, I met Ody and together we took the tram to the other end of Bucharest where his friend the diamond dealer lived. When I left the diamond dealer's house an hour later, I did not have a *leu* left, but instead I had eighteen shiny little diamonds. I'll never know if I got taken or not, but those diamonds gave me, a simple, uneducated woman, the faith that I will not just survive, but actually thrive, in the West.

Buying the diamonds was pretty nerve-racking, but nothing compared to getting them across the border. We were scheduled to leave the morning of October 18, 1960 at eight am from Gara de Nord, and the train would then travel for twenty-three hours through Communist territory, first through Romania, and then through Hungary. I would not be safe until we crossed the border into Austria. If any problem arose before the Austrian border, the *Securitate* men would bring me all the way back to their headquarters in Bucharest, and I would never be heard from again.

Two days before we left, I ate very little, mostly soft bread, which I knew to be binding. The night before our departure, I spent wrapping each diamond in little cellophane bags that the diamond dealer had given me. The following morning, right before we left the empty apartment for the last time, I went into the bathroom with a large glass of milk and swallowed each diamond with the help of a good swig. When I came out of the bathroom Poldy casually pointed to the large white moustache that graced my upper lip. I never really knew if he was on to me, but he did have his arrogant smile on that I often wanted to wipe off with a slap. I cleaned my face and we left, and this incident was never brought up again.

VIII

I hadn't seen Coty in many months, and as my departure approached, I desperately wanted to say good-bye to her. I knew she was mad at me, but I had no idea why. I tried calling her, once I even went to her apartment and rang the bell. Mircea opened the door, so I told him I wanted to see Coty. He hesitated, but asked me to wait. After waiting for what felt like an eternity, Mircea came back and told me that Coty was out.

"Mircea," I said, "I know she's in there. Why won't she see me?"

"Greta, please just accept it" Mircea said apologetically. "You know how stubborn she is and there's nothing anyone can do to change her mind."

"But why, Mircea? What have I done?"

"Don't ask me Greta. I don't know and she doesn't want to talk about it."

"But can't you ask her what it is that she's angry with me about?"

"I have Greta. She won't say."

I walked away in tears. Coty had been my closest friend, my first friend in Bucharest; she was my soul mate.

I went home and wracked my brain to think of a reason why Coty might be angry with me. I couldn't come up with anything. I knew she was insanely jealous and thought every woman had her sights on Mircea, but frankly I found nothing interesting about him.

Many years ago, right after they got married, she and Mircea came to live with me. They had been living in her mother's apartment, but after her parents left for Israel, they were kicked out and had no place to live. They were with us for several months; it was an awkward time. Coty hated Benno, especially since he constantly complained about their presence. Furthermore, Coty and Mircea were infuriating with their childish attempts to become invisible, and I didn't like Mircea.

My assessment of Mircea dated back to that time. Once I accidentally walked into the bathroom and found him naked. He was leaning over the sink with his crooked, pencil-thin dick in his hand whacking away. He was moaning and his scrawny, delicate arms, covered in sweat and long, streaky black fuzz, reminded me of a cockroach. I felt noxious and immediately closed the door. I don't even think he noticed me. So if Coty had read my thoughts, she would have known that I had not the slightest interest in Mircea.

I also knew that Coty, for all her intelligence and common sense, was a very superstitious woman. Years ago, her three-year old nephew Mihai came down with some rare form of brain cancer. The doctors, after multiple consultations and tests, concluded that the boy's chances for survival were almost nonexistent. There was a brain operation, very radical and experimental, that offered maybe a five to ten percent chance of recovery; on the other hand, all the doctors saw the do-nothing approach as a guaranteed death sentence. The boy's parents decided on the surgery approach, which was scheduled for a few days hence. During this time, Coty consulted a fortuneteller whom she visited regularly. The fortuneteller told her that, under no circumstances, should they do the surgery: if the boy is operated on, he will die; if he's left alone, he will survive. With that mandate, Coty went to the boy's parents to try to convince them not to proceed with the operation. She screamed, threatened and cajoled, and ultimately, the parents reasoned that since the chances for the boy's survival were flimsy either way, they might as well give in to the crazy woman who was besieging them. The parents informed the doctors that they decided against the operation. The doctors went on the offensive and accused the parents of infanticide, but the parents stood firm.

Two weeks later Mihai, who had been given up for dead, got out of bed and started playing. The doctors later examined him and found that the tumor had vanished and that he was in perfect health. No medical explanation was ever given.

Afterwards, every time I met Coty I made a point to ask her about Mihai, and every time she abruptly changed the subject. I knew from other sources that he was doing fine, but Coty sternly refused to talk about him. What's more, she refused to have anything to do with him or his parents – Mihai's father was her brother Jacob whom she had always been on excellent terms. These people, being so grateful to her, wanted her involved in the boy's life and sent her thank-you letters and presents, yet she sent them all back and ordered Mircea to tell them to stay away from her and to make sure that the boy never comes near her. Everybody knew that Coty was a bit wacky, but never to this extent.

I often thought about this incident, especially as a way of explaining Coty's rejection of me. I decided that the fortuneteller must've demanded something of Coty in exchange for the boy's life, something exceptionally dear to Coty, and I realized the biggest sacrifice for Coty would have been to deny herself of ever being in the boy's company or even ever having anything to do with him, and that's exactly what Coty did.

In the year leading to my departure from Romania, Coty shared with me that Mircea had been diagnosed with prostate cancer. She was beyond desperate. She came to me one afternoon and confessed that if Mircea died she would kill herself, that she could not live a day without him. I tried to give her all the comfort

I could, but what can one say under those circumstances.

Then I didn't hear from her for many months, which was very unusual. I was very busy with my crazy life and I sort of lost track of her. But when I tried to reconnect, she adamantly refused. I also heard from a mutual friend that Mircea's cancer was in remission. The only reasonable explanation I could come up with, and I've asked a lot of people for theirs, was that she sacrificed our friendship in order to save Mircea's life. The only comfort I get from this sad affair is that it tells me that our friendship was the most precious thing she had to surrender.

I left Romania without seeing Coty, without even saying 'goodbye' to her. Years later, Poldy once said that my friendship with Coty was my Camelot: perfect, short-lived, and so deeply buried in the past that it now seems more a dream than a reality.

IX

Three days before departure I still hadn't received the Government-issue trunk that I was supposed to pack with all of the belongings that I was entitled to take with me. The trunk had to measure no more than 75 cm in width, 60 cm in height, and 1.2 m in length. Our 40 kilograms of clothes and personal belongings had to fit inside. By then our side of the apartment was completely empty, except for the stuff I was going to take with me; all that was piled against the living room wall by the front door. Anton, in anticipation of the chaos preceding our departure, had left for places unknown, but not before saying goodbye to me in a detached, indifferent manner. I later noticed that he locked the door to his room, something he had never done before; I guess he thought he had things worth stealing, and I was the kind of woman who would do that, after all we had been through.

The anxiety over the arrival of the trunk was compounded by the fact that I had been advised by the emigration office that the trunk needed to be at Gara de Nord forty-eight hours before our departure, otherwise they couldn't guarantee that it would be inspected in time and, therefore, allowed to leave with us.

I knew very well that if the trunk didn't leave with us, it would never leave. Romanians are the biggest thieves in the world; thievery is in their blood. Poldy had read that an American writer by the name of John Gunther wrote a book about Romania as part of his *Inside Europe* series, and right at the beginning he starts off by defining kleptomania as an uncontrollable impulse to steal; then in the next sentence he extrapolates that 'Romania' – with emphasis on the mania – stands for kleptomania as applied to an entire nation: not a nice thing to say, but I often thought true.

I called the office that was supposed to supply us with the trunk, and I was told that they had run out of cardboard and they didn't know if they would be able to get it to me by the next day, or for that matter any time soon. I went out of my mind. None of my friends could help, so I decided to call Victor. I hadn't seen or spoken to him since he saved my life in the "Manny" espionage predicament, but I was out of options. I called the *Securitate* office and was told he was now working in their headquarters. I called him. He answered the phone. He immediately recognized my voice, and before I even had a chance to tell him why I was calling he said 'yes' provided I still looked as good. I assured him that I did.

Victor told me to stay home and that he would get back to me within an hour. I hung up and sat on the floor of my empty living room across from Poldy who was reading as usual. I realized that I had better fix myself up, as I looked a mess, unwashed, my hair still flattened down by a night of troubled sleep, and my face ashen with worries. I pulled out a sexy skin tight blue dress with short sleeves, fixed my hair, put on a thick layer of make-up to cover the cruelties of nature, and waited.

Half an hour later, Victor showed up with two of his men, dressed in militia uniforms, carrying a trunk. The men dropped the trunk by the front door and immediately left. Victor gave me a great big smile and a wink, and began walking towards me, when he noticed Poldy sitting on the floor. That was an awkward moment, but I quickly turned to Poldy and told him that he had to go right away to say goodbye to his grandmother, Benno's mother, as he wouldn't have a chance to do it at any other time before we left. He released another of his arrogant smiles, pushed himself up, and shuffled his way out the door, greatly exaggerating his limp. I could still hear his footsteps at the bottom of the stairs, while the impatient Victor had me already half undressed.

The next day I called the Dentist, knowing that he had a car, and told him that I needed to have him drive me to Gara de Nord. Taxis did not exist in Bucharest at that time. He said he couldn't do it; he had an office full of patients, and then he moaned about his wife not wanting him to see me. I told him that I loved him and that I wanted to say good-bye to him the way only I knew how. He suddenly started whispering and said he would be over by two at the latest.

I wasn't happy with the time frame; it was cutting things too close, but I didn't want to press him further for fear he would bolt altogether, and said I would be impatiently waiting for him. Poldy was in school so I didn't have to deal with that issue. At a quarter to two, I was already in the Dentist's car, with the trunk in the back seat, speeding towards Gara de Nord. By three o'clock I had deposited the trunk with the *jglob* in charge of the trunks scheduled to leave the country. I told him to give my trunk special priority, to which he nodded despondently. I turned to the Dentist and told him to give the *jglob* 100 lei, probably more money than he made in a whole week. This time, the *jglob* took his hat off, kissed my hand, and assured me that my trunk would be the first one he looked at. He called out 'thank yous' as the Dentist and I were walking away until his voice could no longer be heard above the din of the train station.

The Dentist drove me home, but he said he couldn't stay; he would be back later that evening. This revived the problem of having Poldy around when I didn't want him. I couldn't think of anyone to whom I hadn't already made him say goodbye to. I thought of Elvira, Benno's girlfriend, even though he had already called her to say goodbye. I called her up, and bluntly asked her if it would be a problem if Poldy spent the night at her house. She promptly agreed. No explanations needed.

When Poldy came home from school, I told him that Elvira called and she wondered if he would mind spending the night at her place and play with her kids, since they had been asking for him. He hobbled around the apartment, peeping around doors, and calling out "Where are you?" in a retarded, high-pitched voice, and then picked up his pajamas and left, but not before wishing me "Sweet dreams." No one was ever able to infuriate me as much as Poldy.

I hoped the Dentist would come early. I knew he couldn't stay long; after all he was just walking the dog. Thinking back on these incidents I can't help laughing out loud. He told me on several occasions his wife had gotten suspicious of these walks, and not because they took too long, but because, when he brought the dog back, the first thing the dog did was shit and piss all over the house. What he was doing was outrageous, but very practical: so as not to waste any time, as soon as he turned the corner of his house, the Dentist picked up the dog, and ran all the way over. He did the same on the way back, so the poor dog never got a chance to do its business. The wife kept badgering the Dentist with whining questions as to why the dog had accidents only when he took it for a walk, but never when she walked it. Apparently, after I left Romania, someone volunteered information to his wife explaining the reason why the dog restricted his accidents to only those evenings when the Dentist came home all sweated up. She divorced him, his practice collapsed, and the dog died.

X

That afternoon, I grabbed Poldy and we went to say 'goodbye' to my father. It had been two years since my mother died, and he was now living with the woman who had been his maid and housekeeper during the years when my mother had gotten too sick. She was short and dark and probably illiterate and a good twenty years younger than him, but she loved him. He was in his sixties and completely irresponsible, but charming and full of life.

My father was still running a soda stand, but in a different location, more central. His new place was much bigger than the one where Poldy worked as his apprentice. In addition to sodas, he was also selling hot dogs and ice cream. He even had fulltime help in the form of a very pretty, very cheery twenty-year old girl who referred to him as Poppy. I didn't have any details, but I was sure the girl did more than just prance around the store; my father spent too much time laughing.

When I got to his house, Marika –that was the housekeeper's name – had set up the table for a meal. I didn't eat anything, but Poldy did and even made her happy with a few compliments about her cooking. I knew she would always take good care of my father. As I was leaving I told him that I had meant to make time to see Sammy, but I had too much to do before our departure. My father shushed me with a smile and told me that he was sure that Sammy would understand, and besides they weren't even in the country; they were vacationing at their summer place in Varna.

I remembered how much Sammy and I loved each other when we were kids in Ghimeş, and how much I admired him back then. But with him a bigwig in the Communist Party and me the town slut, things had gotten very tense between us. I knew that by my departure, he would be free of a big source of embarrassment and possibly even a hurdle in his advancement within the Party. I was never to see my bother again, but somehow I didn't feel much regret about that.

I told my father that I would write to him often. He quickly allayed any possible future guilt by acknowledging that beginnings are tough and I should keep the focus on myself and my son. He also told me that I should probably avoid writing to Sammy as the Party frowned on members who received correspondence from the West.

As I got up to leave, my father told me that we had some old relatives living in Vienna who might remember me from the one time, some thirty years ago, when they visited us in Ghimeş. He didn't know their address or phone number, but their names were Isidor and Anna Sheinberg. When I told him that I didn't remember them, he smiled and reminded me that I was only a little girl at the time. I then hugged him and kissed him and we both cried. I knew then I would never see him alive again.

XI

At six o'clock the next morning, Elvira called to let me know that she wouldn't mind picking us up and driving us both to Gara de Nord. Fortunately, there was still a phone in the apartment, the one thing for which I can thank Anton. If it had been just me in the apartment, authorities would have removed it the day we received our exit visas. I threw whatever was still left in the apartment, including some leftovers, in a big bag that looked like it had been cut out of a fish net. It was frayed and dirty, but that was the only thing I had.

I then walked to the curb and waited for Elvira. All along, I could feel Poldy's mouth grinning wildly, as he marched unevenly behind me. Just as I got outside, I saw Elvira's car speeding down the street. In the shimmer of sunrise, the first thing I recognized was Elvira's teeth flashing a welcoming sign to me through the windshield. I never understood why this stunning, intelligent woman was so hung up on Benno. I knew Benno: he was moody and pompous, and a lousy lover. Did I miss seeing something that she saw?

Elvira was a terrific driver, and we made great time despite the rush hour traffic. We were on the train platform by 7:15. The *jglob* who took care of my trunk was there and, as soon as he saw me, came over to reassure me that the trunk was already on the train. I thanked him and walked away, although I knew he was expecting another tip. I then noticed that Elvira pulled out of her purse a 10-*lei* bill and gave it to him. I tried to intervene, but the words got stuck in my throat.

Elvira waved to me that she'd be right back and to wait for her. I stood there, looking down, observing the contours of my flat rubber-soled shoes against the pock-marked concrete platform, and felt my chest tightening around my heart: this would be the last time I would touch Romanian soil. I looked over to Poldy and I saw him pull a pebble out of a crack in the concrete and put it in his pocket. When Elvira reappeared she was carrying a large leather bag that I knew she had just bought from the station's sundry shop. She lifted the bag by its wide handles so that it hung suspended right in front of my eyes; the inscription on the side of the bag read "Bucurii din Bucureşti" – Cheers from Bucharest. As she handed it to me, she said the bag would help me remember only the happy moments. She was too refined a lady to tell me to my face that my mesh bag belonged in a trashcan. I thanked her and, without further inducements, dumped all its contents into my new leather bag, and threw it in the nearest garbage can.

My eyes stayed on the garbage can. For some inexplicable reason, I suddenly started sobbing like a child. Elvira gently shoved me towards the train door, and when we got there, she gave me a hug, turned away, and waved as she made her way through the crowd back into the terminal.

XII

Poldy and I were now sitting on the lower berth of our sleeping cabin, quietly waiting for the train to leave. I looked at Poldy, but his face looked impassive as usual. I decided to leave him alone, besides, after all the events of the last few weeks, I was about ready to collapse. As soon as the train started moving, a conductor walked in and asked us if we wanted anything. I asked him if it would be possible to set up the beds even though it was only a little after eight am. He said that it would be no problem provided we left the cabin while he set it up for night use. We walked out and wandered through the train, which by now was moving at a pretty good clip. When we got to the restaurant car, we sat down at one of the empty tables, and a waiter quickly brought us a couple of menus that had the words "Orient Express" embossed across their covers.

The prices were both in lei and dollars. I also noticed that they had Coca Cola on the menu. Poldy must have noticed that too and broke his vow of silence to ask me if I would buy him a bottle of Coca Cola. I said no, even though it wasn't any more expensive than the other soft drinks on the menu; I wasn't going to let him think that I was going to give in to him whenever it suited him.

He glanced at me with an icy stare, then reached into his pocket and pulled out a roll of bills. He slapped a 5-lei bill on the table and shouted to the waiter, "Coca Cola, Monsieur." I thought of asking him where he got the money, but I knew he wouldn't tell me. Besides I was pretty sure that he had gotten it from his father.

Coca Cola came in an odd-shaped little bottle, and looked like carbonated ink. The magnetism of that bottle of Coca Cola, the first one I ever saw, stemmed from the fact that whenever we heard any anti-American propaganda, which was just about continuously, it attributed the wickedness of American imperialism, at least in part, on the widespread drinking of this mind-altering elixir called Coca Cola. It was as if Coca Cola contained an ingredient that deprived those who drank it of the ability to recognize right from wrong, or to rise against those who deprived them of their freedom and self-respect.

It sounds ludicrous as I hear myself saying this now, but when someone hears something said often enough with enough conviction, that person ends up believing it.

I stepped on my pride and asked Poldy for a small taste of Coca Cola. He told me I should finish it; he thought it tasted too sweet and gooey. I don't think he ever took another sip of Coca Cola after that. In one of his many later tirades, he equated the absurdity of the entire Communist system in Romania with the Coca Cola story. He added that it cost him five lei, the price of that first bottle of Coca Cola, to find out that Communism was a sham.

XIII

When we got back to our cabin, the berths were set up. I took the lower berth. I changed quickly in the tiny bathroom that seemed to be wrapped in silver foil and exuding ammonia, and slid into bed. I didn't get out of bed, except for short intervals, either demanded by nature or by the border authorities, until we arrived in Vienna, almost twenty-seven hours later. I didn't sleep the whole time. I would sleep for a while, then sit up, take some water or food, then go back to sleep. Whenever I turned my eyes towards the upper bunk, I saw Poldy glued to the window, soaking in the passing scenery. I could see from his expression that he thought that Austria looked closer to paradise than anything he'd ever imagined.

I had been through many extremely stressful situations, and had always been able to handle myself with complete sang-*froid*. But, somehow, I found myself shaking every time they announced an approaching border. When we stopped at Curtici, the Romanian border town, I was so nervous that I told Poldy to tell the guard when he walks into our cabin that I was very sick. The guard, after giving me a quick glance, concluded that I was gravely ill and kept his distance fearing some contagious disease. He even told Poldy to notify the conductor as soon the inspection was over. Poldy said that he had already thought of doing that, but thanked the man anyway.

When we reached the border between Hungary and Austria,

I became even more anxious. I had had a dream that the Hungarians, who I knew to be a lot cleverer than the Romanians, would be carrying x-ray machines that would immediately show that my stomach was full of diamonds. I was so frightened that my jaws had locked and I couldn't even utter one word. I wanted to give Poldy some additional instructions on how to deal with the border guard when he came into our cabin, but couldn't. I just lay there with my eyes wide open. When the border guard walked in, Poldy gave the man a big smile, handed him our papers, and then proceeded to use a couple of Hungarian profanities that I had taught him, like *gherem bozny,* that made the man double over with laughter. I think if it hadn't been for all that laughing the man would have left sooner and spared me the added anxiety. But we were now in Austria, and I finally allowed myself to breathe.

The last day of the trip I actually spent time looking out the window. It was September of 1960 and Austria was like a garden in full bloom. It is to this day that I cannot find the words to explain the change I saw with my mind's eyes once I crossed the Iron Curtain. It was as if I had taken a magical step, behind me the dreariest, most frightful place in the world, in front of me just sunshine, birds singing, and perpetual bliss. In reality, there were many more years of struggle in front of me, and in many ways these years entailed a far more backbreaking struggle than I went through in Romania, but the years of fear were over.

Once we crossed the Romanian-Hungarian border, all the lei I still had with me, while they weren't many, became worthless. As I still couldn't get out of bed, I gave Poldy a 20-lei bill to buy me a sandwich from the restaurant car. I had seen on the menu exactly what I wanted – it was a sandwich of chicken slices and sour pickles on mayonnaise, and it cost 12 lei. He came back a minute later to tell me that they wouldn't sell him anything for lei anymore, and the menu, though still titled "Orient Express", had changed to show that the only acceptable currencies now were dollars and forints. We were in effect penniless, as our lei had become worthless. I felt angry as I could have bought extra food at the restaurant before the border crossing and avoided the renewed worry that we're going to have to go hungry at least until we reached Paris.

I looked into the leather bag Elvira had bought me. There was a quarter loaf of stale black bread and half-a-jar of prune marmalade hidden under a dirty pair of underwear. I told Poldy to take the bread into the bathroom and soak it in water. That made it at least soft enough to be able to slice it with a knife that he had begged one of the waiters to let him borrow. Once he sliced the bread thin enough, and spread the marmalade over it, we were able to bite into it, although I warned him to be careful not to leave a tooth in there. Throughout our passage through Hungary, we subsisted on stale bread and marmalade.

Within an hour of crossing into Austria, the train stopped and a German voice over the loudspeaker announced that we were in Vienna and we would be there for four hours. I was lying at the time in my couchette, in a state of detached stupor, thinking that it had nothing to do with me. Suddenly, I felt a rush, probably caused by hunger pains, and jumped up.

The train had been sitting in Wien Westbahnhof for about fifteen minutes when I remembered my father's parting suggestion to look up my old Viennese relatives. I couldn't remember their names, but I knew Poldy would: "Isidor and Anna Sheinberg." I pulled myself out of bed, got dressed, and walked off the train. I asked the conductor where I could find a phone book. He understood me perfectly. I may not possess any intellectual gifts, which accounted for the difficult time I had in school, but I could learn a language just hearing it for a while. I spoke Yiddish at home in Ghimeş; I learned Hungarian and country Romanian in school; I learned high class Romanian in Bucharest; and I learned German – *Hochdeutsch* – from the Feingolds. I went on a three-day cruise of the Soviet Union, and I came back understanding Russian.

The phone book listed one Isidor Sheinberg. I asked one of the train station attendants where Maria Rilke Strasse was and he said that it was only a short 10-minute walk from the station. I grabbed Poldy and off we went. Right, left, left, right. 12 Maria Rilke Strasse. I looked at the names above the mailboxes, and sure enough, there was a label that said Isidor and Anna Sheinberg. It was right in the middle of a beautiful autumn day, a Saturday; the chances of finding someone home were close to zero. I rang. A long silence followed. I was about to walk away, when I finally heard a high-pitched woman's voice coming across the intercom. It was German, the Feingolds' German. Suddenly my wits left me and I couldn't say one word. The voice kept repeating, ever more irritated: "*Wer ist Wer? Wer ist Wer? Bitte, Wer ist Wer?*" Finally, out of desperation, I said: "*Ich bin die Tochter von Isaac und Ana Sobel.*"

There was silence on the other end. I waited for what seemed like an eternity; then a man's voice came on the intercom and asked, "*Woher Kommen Sie?*" So I answered, "*Ich Komme aus Romania.*" "*Moment, bitte,*" was the response. I could then hear the two voices burble softly to each other; I couldn't make out what they were saying. Finally after what seemed another eternity, the front door buzzed, though I didn't know what it meant. Poldy pushed the door open, and we walked upstairs to the second floor.

When we got there, the apartment door was cracked open and slivers of two faces were peering through. I just stood there holding Poldy's hand. This time it seemed even longer than the previous times, but ultimately the door opened and we were let in. "*Bist du klein Greta?*" asked one of the voices. "*Ja.*" Two tiny old people shuffling along in an apartment so dark and dank that it felt that we were somewhere beneath the surface of the earth. The tiny man, who I could recognize by his deeper voice, asked me in German to sit down, pointing to an old, frayed armchair. Poldy took a position behind me. The two old people sat on the other side of the room almost out of sight, on two, what seemed like, children-size rocking chairs. "*Das ist Meine Sohn,*" I volunteered. "*Oh, Ja, Sehr Schön!*"

Once the two old people settled down, they began asking me

questions about Ghimeş and my parents. They wanted details: what was my father's name, what he did, where we lived in relation to the *shul*, whether I had any siblings. I answered all their questions. After the interrogation was over, I pulled out a picture of my parents that I always carried with me. The man got up and grabbed it from me; then the two of them walked together over to a desk lamp that had been previously turned on, and carefully examined the picture. Then they both disappeared. A minute later they reappeared holding a picture of their own. They returned my picture and handed me theirs. It was a picture showing four people. I recognized two of them as my parents in their younger years. I presumed that the other two, much shorter people were the two in front of me. I pointed to my parents and said, "*Meine elteren.*" They suddenly seemed to relax. They came up to us and wanted to give us each a hug. We both had to stoop to be able to put our arms around them. Then the all-important question was asked: "*Bis du hungrik?*" I thought they'd never ask. "*Danke schön.*"

We were moved over to a table covered with a large doily. The doily was removed and a white tablecloth was placed in its stead. Then all the food they had in the house, I'm sure, was placed on that table. They encouraged us to eat as much as we could, although no such inducement was needed. While Poldy and I were eating, they were circling around us like boxing referees, pushing dishes closer to us, pointing to foods we had not yet noticed in the prevailing darkness of the room. They had turned one small lamp on to the side of the table, but it didn't occur to them to push open the heavy shutters and let in the sunshine. As their arms were passing in front of my eyes, pushing food back and forth, I saw a string of tattooed numbers right above their wrists.

By the time Poldy and I finished eating, they had stopped hovering. They had both resumed their seats on their little rocking chairs, and stared at us from the distance. They could never have imagined the amount of food that we were able to consume. I'm sure we ate at that one sitting more food than those two little people would have eaten in a whole month. When we finished, they went around the table craning their necks over the empty dishes, shaking their heads. "*Sie essen sehr gut*," remarked the little man focusing his attention on Poldy. "*Mein sohn hat kein Deutsch*," I quickly intervened. They both nodded pensively, probably wondering how I could have allowed that.

I thanked them as convincingly as I could make it, but told them that we had to get back to the train station. They didn't seem anxious to hold us any longer, and Poldy and I stepped out into the hallway, saying goodbye as we went. Just as we were about to begin our descent down the steps, the old woman called out, "*Vart!*" We stopped. The man came out to us with what seemed like a small piece of dark paper. It was a bill of some sort. Then, in a bellowing voice that I would never have thought possible from such a diminutive body, he said, "*Na! Dos is …gelt…..*" "*A dank! A shainen dank*," I responded in Yiddish this time, and quickly put the banknote in my purse. Thinking probably that I was not sufficiently impressed, they volunteered that the banknote represented a great deal of money. I thanked them again, bowed, and kissed their hands. That's when they finally felt pleased with my reaction to their generosity.

On the way back to the train station, I was so excited that I forgot about the tensions between us, and I grabbed Poldy and, before he had a chance to pull away, I gave him a big kiss on his pale cheek. Surprisingly, he didn't pull away, and allowed me to enjoy the moment. We were rich, but I didn't dare take out the banknote in the middle of the street with people walking all around us. In my excitement I rushed him along, forgetting his limitations, but he forced himself to keep up with me. I think he understood what a big moment this was for me. I knew that I would not have to worry about finding a place to live, food, nice clothes. We were set. And even if the money were not enough to retire on, it would still keep us going until we got settled in, found a decent job, and most importantly, made some rich friends.

When we got back to the train, I was so eager to look at the banknote that I left Poldy on the platform. His limp still made it difficult for him to make that big step up onto the car. I was already in our cabin, ready to open my purse, when I glanced out the window and saw him looking back at me. His eyes did not look angry, just amused at my excitement. I don't think he understood how important it was for me, a woman without a profession, not to be constantly worried about the future. I think if he understood that, he would not have been so judgmental and intolerant of some of the things I had done. I ran back to the platform and helped him onto the train. When I finally closed the door to our cabin I carefully pulled out the banknote from my purse, and unfolded it. It said: "The United States of America, In God We Trust, 20 Twenty Dollars 20."

"It's a Twenty Dollar bill," I said quizzically to Poldy. "That doesn't sound like so much money. Some of the sandwiches on the train cost six dollars." "Four Coca Colas," responded Poldy, in a sarcastic tone. "It's enough to turn us into hard-core capitalists." I threw a pillow at him. I didn't know whether to laugh or cry.

We were speeding towards our final destination: Paris. Reality was beginning to set in. The basic question of where we would go after we arrived at the Paris train station was beyond my powers of conjuring even the most implausible of futures. It was clear to me that the twenty dollars I got from the old couple in Vienna wasn't going to cover more than maybe one night in a shabby hotel room. But which hotel? Do I just walk the streets around the train station until I find a hotel sign, and then walk in and inquire about a room. What language do the French speak other than French? I didn't think Yiddish or Romanian was going to help me much. And then what about the next day? I will need a job, but what do I know how to do? How do I run into a wealthy Jew who is ready to do a mitzvah for a woman who's no longer in her first flush of youth, and who has a gimpy, bad-tempered son in tow to boot. Do I stand on a street corner and call out to everyone who looks Semitic, "*Red'n Yiddish?*"

All we had was a visa that allowed us to remain in France for ninety days. We were expected to move on after that; where nobody told me. We would probably have to go to Israel, a prospect that didn't really enthrall me, but at least I imagined that in Israel they're set up to welcome immigrants – they set them up, start them out with an allowance, find them a job. I grudgingly acknowledged that Israel would probably be good for Poldy. They can find him something to do in a kibbutz, and he'd have a life, but for me all that sounded like my life was over. I would end up milking cows or picking oranges. That was not the reason I left Romania.

If I thought before I left Romania that I would end up in Israel, I would never have left. Suddenly Communism didn't look so bad. Lena was still there, and Ody, and all my other friends and admirers. In the last few years, I didn't have to worry about where my next meal was going to come from. In fact, my life was pretty good. I had nice clothes, a great social life, and I knew the language and the ways of the people. I had never realized until much later in life that people from different countries are not separated just by language, but far more importantly, by the way they silently communicate.

That is why to this day I can only feel comfortable in the company of other Romanians. And despite his denials to the contrary, Poldy, who has no accent and has spent most of his life in America, is still more at ease in a European setting. Both he and I are part of a transitory, sacrificed generation, and my only satisfaction is that his children are at home.

As I was drifting into sleep, I looked out the cabin window just as we were passing a small Austrian town. It was named Rothschild; that was Coty's family name, and my thoughts wandered once again to Coty and I began crying. At that moment I felt, and I probably still feel that way, that the biggest heartache of my life had not been caused by the miseries of Communism, but by how Coty, the only woman I ever loved, discarded me, the way she discarded Benjamin years earlier.

As I look back at our twenty-one-year friendship, I chuckled at the profound differences in our lives' courses. Unlike mine, Coty's life had been entirely consumed by her devotion to the man in her life. I didn't think it was love or at least not love alone; it was an obsession or, maybe more accurately, an addiction. She was addicted to Benjamin, but then she substituted him with the more intoxicating Mircea to whom she's remained emotionally and psychologically enslaved. She could have been a great concert pianist, but she squandered her gifts nursing a man-child. But she didn't want to be a pianist or a mother or anything other than what she was.

Coty's bohemian indifference to society kept her perpetually happy and enchanting, and that's why I loved her. Yet, after over two decades of intertwined lives, in which our closeness seemed to have gradually forged a new soul that we both shared, she no longer wanted to know me, she didn't want to see me or even hear about me, and her remaining friends, whom I appealed to, were not allowed to mention my name in her presence. I have spent countless nights of self-flagellation trying to imagine what was preventing her from reaching out to me – discarding the fantastic idea of the Faustian bargain with the fortune teller – and the only thing I was able to come up with is that she, a woman who believed in the occult, saw in her horoscope or weekly coffee-grounds readings that she would be better off without me. I vigorously disagreed…and still do.

CHAPTER 7
Paris
1960-1962

*G*reta *has not made vinete since the last time Poldy visited her. It was the only kind of food she knew she could still entice him with. Today, for the first time ever, she was going to treat herself alone to the one dish that she still prepared better that anyone else.*

Earlier in the week, she had bought two fat male eggplants – fewer seeds – and left them by the windowsill to ripen. Now they were ready. The days of grilling the eggplants on a burner and then scalding her fingers peeling their blackened skin were long gone. She added a few ripe cherry tomatoes and chopped onions and the lime-colored treat was all hers to savor. Greta put on lipstick; she was now ready for the recorder and the last chapter of her European saga.

I

We arrived at *Gare du Nord* in Paris on October 20, 1960 at 9 am. We sat frozen in the cabin, our home for the last two days, until a grouchy French conductor snapped at us, "*Oh, madame! Vite, vite. Vouz devez decender tout de suite. Le voyage est finit, compronez?*" I understood that we needed to get off the train. The place was deserted. The only thing that caught my eye was our trunk sitting all by itself at the far end of the platform. I quickly jumped off the train and walked towards it, but then I suddenly remembered Poldy and turned my head. He was standing at the top of the stairs, staring down at me with that cheeky smirk of his. I had forgotten that stairs, especially down stairs, were his nemeses. I raised my arm, which he grabbed with both hands, slowly making his way down the two challenging steps. As soon as he reached the ground, he quickly unclutched my arm, hesitated for a moment, but thanked me.

As if we had rehearsed it, Poldy and I sat at the same time on the trunk and waited motionlessly for a good omen. I noticed for the first time that the train cars of our "Orient Express" were labeled with Roman numerals. There were small wooden plaques with 'III' etched on them at either end of the car that had been our home for the last two days. A few cars had plaques with 'II''s on their side, and one car had pretty brass plates with 'I''s. Having left behind Communism's delusions of solidarity that came from the leveling power of egalitarian privation, we had entered a world of gradations separated by the size of one's purse.

Before I left Bucharest, Lena told me that she wrote to her brother Fred who had been living in Paris for ten years telling him that I was coming and that I needed someone to help me at the beginning. Coming from Romania, a backward Communist country, the West seemed very daunting. In Romania, everything was decided for you: where to live, what to say, or mostly what not to say, what to watch – movies, mostly Russian, were the only form of entertainment - or listen to, which was largely Communist propaganda, and what to read, which were books and newspapers that presented a paranoid vision of the West. The books of Charles Dickens were very popular, because of their bleak view of a capitalistic society. But of course, no one seemed to notice that Dickens saw a very different world than the one we have now.

Communism was particularly skilled in telling people where to go, which was never beyond the watchful eyes of their handlers. In retrospect, the Coca Cola incident that happened on the train seems humorous fifty years later, but at the time, I was actually nervous that that drink was going to turn Poldy into a zombie-like creature, not unlike those crazed Americans, whose caricatures appeared daily in the pages of *Scînteia*, who couldn't wait to drop nuclear bombs on anyone who didn't agree with their ways.

Fred had written back to Lena, saying that he would be more than happy to take me under his wing, the sort of role, he went on, he had been preparing himself for when his baby sister would one day settle in Paris. He promised her that he would be waiting for me on my arrival at Gare du Nord, especially after Lena told him that I was still as hot looking as when he last saw me.

As I was sitting there on that trunk, my back pressed against Poldy, I realized that I may have changed the venue, but I was still in survival mode, and the West, regardless of how advanced and sophisticated it was, when it came to a poor, uneducated woman, it was operating on the same old-fashioned barter system: my body for a piece of bread.

I stood up and told Poldy that if someone showed up to tell him to wait; I would return immediately. I found the sign "Femmes" and walked in. I went over to the mirror; I looked frightening. I took off my blouse and, with a piece of toilet paper, swabbed my underarms. I took another wad of moist paper and rubbed it between my legs. Then I put my blouse back, brushed my hair and put on some much needed lipstick and rouge. When I got back to the platform, Poldy was still sitting there alone. I asked him if anyone had shown up, to which he looked at me sideways and grimaced like a cat. No one could make me feel as stupid as he did.

"Someone could have shown up and left maybe to make dinner arrangements or book a hotel," I explained.

"Oh yes, I forgot, the President of France stopped by and invited us to his palace," said Poldy. I slapped him. He touched his cheek, but quickly reclaimed his infuriating grin, and uttered an arrogant, "Thank you." At that moment, I knew that Poldy would never have a heart.

I pushed him over and sat next to him. After a while, I felt hungry, and started eating some of the leftovers that I had pocketed during our Viennese feast. But I suddenly remembered the diamonds in my belly and stopped eating, knowing I wasn't ready for them.

After three hours of waiting, I realized that no one was coming to my rescue, nor would there be any more short cuts in my life. I told Poldy to wait by the trunk, and I got up to do what I knew I'd end up doing all along: walk around and find us a place to stay. I wasn't thinking how I would pay for it.

Fortunately, once outside *Gare du Nord*, I was right in the middle of the city and there were hundreds of hotel signs. I needed to quickly develop a knack for picking out places that were cheap yet clean. I finally saw a hotel door whose glass window was dressed with a shear white curtain on which roses, carnations, and buttercups had been pinned. Buttercups had always been my favorite flowers and I took that as a sign. I walked in. The smell of freshly baked pastries filled my nostrils.

A fat, friendly-looking woman sat demurely behind the counter. Through hand and body motions, I conveyed the message that I needed a room. She asked me if I was alone. I stretched my palm out to about the height of my shoulder, although by then Poldy was taller than me. She nodded and unfurled the knot that had appeared between her brows the moment she first looked me over. I managed to understand that she wanted to know whether I intended to rent the room by the night or by the week. I stood there speechless, as my ability to communicate in French was so limited that it didn't allow me to finesse the situation. Thinking I didn't understand the question, she repeated it with a droll combination of words and gestures. I had never allowed myself to be so vulnerable before, but I felt that I had no choice. I showed her the twenty-dollar bill. She asked me if that was all I had, to which I belched out a most convincing '*oui*.' She then decreed that she would let me have the room for 20 dollars a week, much less, she quickly added, than she charged other customers, but she understood my predicament. Fortunately, her declamations were accompanied by a highly accomplished array of hand and head movements that allowed me augment my limited understanding of what she was saying. I was, nonetheless, amazed at how much I understood.

I had heard French spoken at the Feingolds'. That was whenever they didn't speak German, which became less and less as the war was progressing and news of the Nazis' treatment of Jews was getting through. In fact, by the end of the war in 1945, they had stopped speaking German altogether, and had switched to French.

This bizarre twist of fate was helping me now. I was sure I was risking the woman's wrath, but I had to tell her that we had no food. When I saw her brows furl again, I quickly assured her that I had *'beaucoup amis'* in Paris and I planned to reach out to them the very next day. She then swiftly lifted the twenty-dollar bill from my hands and stuffed it in her dress pocket, adding dismissively that *Petit Dejeuner* was included.

I felt victorious. I had at least a week to figure out what I needed to do. I had no idea what *Petit Dejeuner* really consisted of, but having heard about the French love affair with food, I assumed that it would be a repast large enough to fill us for the day. I then got Madame Cortiz, as that was her name, with whom I later became very close, to lend me a dolly and off I went back to the train station.

When I got there, I didn't bother asking Poldy if anyone had shown up. Unfortunately, I knew the answer. Poldy looked like he hadn't budged an inch.

After getting the trunk onto the dolly, I, pulling and sweating, began the arduous task of transporting all my worldly possessions to our new home: Hotel d'Europe, 58 Rue de Vienne. Poldy, walking in his unsteady, wavering manner, kept pace at my side.

As soon as Madame Cortiz saw me in the doorway with my trunk in tow, she told me that someone will bring it up later, and then proudly led the way up a dark, rickety staircase. Every time we reached a floor, I thought this was it, but Madame Cortiz, huffing and puffing, kept climbing on. We finally ran out of stairs when we reached the sixth floor landing. I wanted to bring to Madame Cortiz's attention that my son had a limp, and walking up and down these stairs would be tough on him, but I felt that I could not ask another favor of this woman. Poldy would have to get used to it, besides we weren't planning on staying at Hotel d'Europe very long.

When the door swung open, I saw a room much larger than I expected. Madame Cortiz acknowledged that it was a long way up, but it was the biggest room in the hotel, and it even included a little kitchenette where I could cook my meals and not have to spend money I didn't have on restaurants. She pushed the window shutters aside and I could see that we had a grand view of the street below and, since we were so high up, I even had an exciting view of the tall shaft of the Eiffel Tower, which, having never seen it before, took my breath away.

I asked Madame Cortiz if we were close, pointing to the Eiffel Tower, as it looked like it was just behind the squat building across the street. She laughed and said no, then added with a forced smile that the only place in Paris from which one does not see the Eiffel Tower is the spot right under the wretched eyesore. It wasn't until much later that I realized the comment was a reflection of Parisians' love-hate relationship with the stark Erecto set, and that she wasn't the first to have said it.

While I was thrilled with the size of the room, and adoring the view, Madame Cortiz noticed Poldy's infirmity, and immediately apologized and suggested that we move to a lower floor. She told me she had a room on the second floor; it wasn't nearly as big and it didn't have a view of the Eiffel Tower, but it would be a lot easier on my son. I nervously looked at Poldy, but his expressionless face assured me that he hadn't understood one word. I told her that he was a sturdy boy and the view from the room was worth the extra few steps. She nodded slowly, while staring into my eyes.

As she was leaving, Madame Cortiz mentioned that the bathroom was outside in the hallway, and that it was being shared with only one other room, which was currently occupied by a young woman from Portugal. She added, placing her hands on her hips, that the young woman never had any visitors. The upbeat tone of Madame Cortiz's pronouncement was clearly meant to reflect more on the respectability of her establishment than on the young woman's social circumstances. I had already noticed that even this early in the morning young, gaudily-dressed prostitutes stood in perfect indifference in front of most of the other hotels on the street, but not Hotel d'Europe's, and Madame Cortiz's bit of gossip was accompanied by an array of self-congratulatory gestures, least of which was a persistent beatific smile. I turned towards the steel tower framed by my window, and when my eyes returned to the room, Madame Cortiz was gone.

The room was furnished with a double bed on one side of the room next to the door, and a single bed all the way at the other end of the room right under the window. A small clear glass vase with freshly cut lavenders sat on a small rectangular wooden table. The flowers released a dizzying scent that made me wonder whether this rather drab room was not an enchanted garden that had been waiting for me to break its spell. I think the two years I lived in that room were, in many ways, the closest I had ever been to Paradise.

Rocking back and forth on the single bed, Poldy pronounced, in his inimitable perplexing fashion, that he liked the room despite the long climb. "The accommodations are tolerable, but the altitude is a real bonus."

Along the walls, there were two tall chests with drawers and one armoire, which more than sufficed our storage needs. In the middle of the room, there was a small wobbly wooden table and four rusty metal chairs whose seats were covered with crisscrossing strips of fabric that, as testimony to their extensive use, severely sagged, though not all to the same depth. In fact, two of the chairs, which were all we needed, were still in fair shape. I made a mental note to never use the other two. As I was completing my cursory inspection of our new quarters, I noticed that Poldy had since stretched out on his bed and, as he was staring out the window at the dramatic vision of steel, he was rhythmically kicking the wall with his gimpy leg. I walked over and closed the window shutters.

II

Deciding it was time, I went outside to the communal bathroom, but not before gently knocking on the door of the room occupied by the young Portuguese woman prepared to say that as her new neighbor I wanted to meet her and say hello. Fortunately, she wasn't home, so I locked the bathroom door by slipping the corroded latch into the eyehole. I looked for the toilet, but there wasn't any; all I could find that suggested the same function was a hole in the floor with two corrugated oval platforms on either side of it. When I stepped onto the platforms, their location and size seemed to confirm my suspicion that they were islands reserved for one's feet. I stood there leaning against the grimy wall behind me, mulling over ideas for safely carrying out my task.

When I came out of the bathroom and walked back into the room, I found Poldy in the same position I had left him, although he had stopped kicking the wall. I grabbed the leather bag Elvira had given me, and, as I was about to dump its contents on my bed, I noticed a small tag inside it that assured the reader that it was made of the finest Romanian leather. I, unaccountably, decided to examine the bag: it was made of two large slices of coarse, stiff leather sewn together in a crude manner to which two wide handles of braided leather were added. The large brown sign "*Bucurii din Bucureşti*" stamped on its side was lopsided and already beginning to peel. The bag hadn't been carrying any joyous mementos from Bucharest, but I grinned, as I knew that it soon would.

I emptied its contents on the bed: a compact, a lipstick, a torn white handkerchief with a tiny red apple embroidered in one of the corners, an old leather purse, and thousands of crumbs. I grabbed the handkerchief and smiled bitterly; it was the same handkerchief that almost put a hole in Daniel's coat twenty years ago. Before I left Bucharest, I had heard that Daniel was living in Paris and that he was married and a very successful surgeon. I made a mental note to look him up.

I double checked the bag to make sure that it was completely empty, and then made my way back to the bathroom. Once safely behind the locked door, I took off my panties, and then slipped one leg at a time through each of the bag handles. I pushed the handles up to my crotch, and then placed my feet on the corrugated islands across the hole in the floor, while making sure that my ass was totally immersed into the bag. Geared up so, I began the strenuous process of gut squeezing.

It took over an hour until I felt that my digestive system had accomplished its task. I then slid the handles off my legs, and warily set the bag on the floor. That's when I noticed a bidet partly concealed by surrounding darkness. I was ecstatic. As I was washing myself I chuckled: there is a bidet but no toilet in this grimy French bathroom, which seemed to perfectly typify the French view of life: sex is far more important than comfortable regularity.

There were no heart-stopping crises. After sifting through a leather bag full of my own excrement, I held in my gross, disgusting hands my fortune shining through eighteen little cellophane bags, to which I am indebted for most of my future acts of pure *chutzpah*. Over the years, I sold most of them. What I got in return, though, was far more than money; it was the confidence that came from knowing that my back would always be protected. I scrubbed the cellophane bags and carefully placed them in my dress pocket. Then I began the nauseating task of washing the bag. I initially thought of discarding it, but I knew I could never get it passed Madame Cortiz in its current state. I spent the next half hour in front of the slop sink, cleaning the bag with a tooth brush I had found behind the bathroom waste basket, and scrubbed and washed and scrubbed and washed some more until I felt that further efforts would be useless. I later doused the bag in cologne and set it upside down on the window sill to dry. When I was done, the bag looked like it had done duty at a rock quarry for the last ten years.

By the time I got back to the room, Poldy was asleep and

the sun was sitting above his head on our windowsill. I took the eighteen cellophane bags, placed them inside the cup of one of my bras, covered it with the other cup, and tied the whole thing with its straps. I looked around for a good place to hide before deciding that placing the bra inside several pairs of stockings in the deepest recesses of my lingerie drawer would be just as safe as anywhere else. That's when I felt that if I took another step I'd end up falling on my face, so finally I allowed myself to just collapse on the bed.

III

I did not wake up until the following morning. I immediately realized that I had overslept, so I jumped out of bed, and my first reaction was to wonder where I was. The only recognizable thing was Poldy's slouching figure sitting on one of the chairs. He informed me that it was eight forty-five am and that breakfast was only going to be served for another fifteen minutes. I yelled at him for not waking me up earlier, to which he simply responded that I was up *now*. He then hobbled out of the room. I jumped out of bed, washed my face quickly, ran a comb through my hair, grubbed my purse, and down the stairs I ran out of fear that breakfast would be over or that they might run out of food, a feeling that had originated in Romania and later stayed with me throughout the rest of my life.

As soon as I was downstairs, Madame Cortiz wished me good morning, and cheerfully assured me that there was plenty of food left. There were several small square tables scattered throughout the room. People speaking in different tongues occupied every table. I could distinguish Portuguese, Arabic, and some Slavic language, probably Slovak or Serbian. Poldy was sitting at a table with three people who were speaking Arabic. He had gotten himself a cup of coffee and a small plate on which he had placed a croissant, a brioche, and a piece of baguette smothered in butter. When I looked at the thin long table, which served as the supply

post for all the food, it finally occurred to me that Madame
Cortiz's *Petit Dejeuner* consisted only of coffee, very strong I later
realized, and a large basket of baked goods. I looked around for
an empty chair. As there weren't any, I decided to stand close to
the basket and, whenever I thought no one was looking, throw
a few pieces of bread in my purse. I purposely placed my coffee
next to the basket so reaching over as often as I was would not
appear suspicious.

After breakfast, as Poldy and I were heading back to our
room, Madame Cortiz came up to me and handed me a couple
of croissants and a few slices of bread, and, conspiratorially asked
me to hide them in my purse. My knees went soft; if I opened
my purse, Madame Cortiz would see that I had already pillaged
her bread basket. While my mind raced to find a way out of an
embarrassing situation, Poldy pulled out a napkin from his pocket,
and wrapped up the contents of Madame Cortiz's open palm, and
without saying anything, began the long arduous trek back to the
room. I gave Madame Cortiz several rounds of "Merci beaucoup,
Madame", and awkwardly stumbled after him.

After I emptied the contents of my purse and combined them
with what Poldy was carrying, I lined them up like soldiers on
the bare shelf above the sink. There were twelve assorted pieces –
brioches, croissants, muffins, slices of bread. I was never to forget
again my first line of defense.

I went back downstairs and asked Madame Cortiz if she had
a moment she could spare me. She told me to wait for her by the
front desk while she cleaned the breakfast area. I sat down on one
of the old armchairs opposite the front desk, which gave me a good
vantage point for watching her. Madame Cortiz must have been
in her late forties, yet her hair was already almost entirely gray; she
was wearing a green plaid dress with short sleeves and a high neck
line, over which she tied an apron of tiny blue and white flowers.
The dress was fresh and the presence of the apron gave the entire
outfit an agreeable look of unlabored fashion. Her appearance
was much enhanced by her inescapable dexterity. Although she

was clearly a good twenty kilograms heavier than she needed to be, her arms moved so swiftly through the air that all that extra flesh hanging from the upper part of her arm seemed to barely keep up with the rest of the limb. There was an inherent grace in her movements, which was made that much more surprising by the presence of all that extra weight.

At that moment I was convinced, not knowing whether she was married or not, that Madame Cortiz had a very active sex life. I was never to learn whether my assumptions were correct, particularly since I was to see her every day for the next two years, and not once did I see a man in her company, but I sensed that when this woman went to bed, however infrequently that was, as she seemed to always be there on the ground floor of the hotel, there would be a man waiting for her, longing to have her hefty thighs wrapped around him.

Madame Cortiz touched my shoulder to snap me out of my impish thoughts. She asked me how she could help. I explained the situation the best I could, and concluded by asking her if she knew of any organization that helped people like me, Jewish refugees from Eastern Europe. She took a long look at me as if trying to reconcile some incongruity, and then caught herself and allowed her eyes to meet mine. She apologized for not knowing of any herself, but suggested that I speak with the French Jewish couple that owned the hotel across the street, as they might be able to help.

I ran across the street and entered a hotel lobby not nearly as cheerful as the one Madame Cortiz presided over. I asked for Monsieur or Madame Chinaque. The man behind the counter, while all along avoiding my eyes, answered in a quivering voice that he was Monsieur Chinaque. He was a short, but well built man with thick black hair, streaked with an occasional white strand, sheared very close to his scalp, and incredibly hairy arms. I asked him if he spoke Yiddish, thinking that would make it at lot easier to communicate. He gave me a flat 'no.' "*Mais, qu'est que vous suggèrez, madame? Nous sommes en France ici. Je suis Français, ma femme est Française,"* he responded in a highly irritated voice.

I apologized quickly, and went back to struggling in French to explain the purpose of my visit. On several occasions, he asked me to repeat what I had said, as my broken French, mixed with German and God-knows what other language, obviously escaped his powers of comprehension. At one point I even resorted to picking up a pencil and drawing a picture of what I thought Europe must look like, and placed Bucharest on one side and Paris on the other, and then drew a line between them. I then drew a stick figure that I wanted to pass for me and placed a Star of David on top of the straight line that was supposed to represent my body. Finally he understood what I was looking for, and recommended that I go to 124, Rue Saint-Lazare, where I would find the offices of COJASOR. As he was writing down the name, as I had never heard of it, I could see a string of numbers tattooed across his wrist. He dismissively told me that those people might be able to help me. I thanked him profusely, and was about to kiss his hand when he nervously pulled it away. I walked out of the hotel, but not before hearing him call "Shalom" after me.

IV

Armed with a map of Paris that bore an ink line drawn by Monsieur Chinaque, I headed for 124, Rue Saint-Lazare – right on Rue de Londres, right on Rue de Clichy, right on Rue Saint-Lazare. It was, as he had said, a ten- or fifteen-minute walk. The offices of COJASOR were located on the top floor of a five-story walk-up building, behind a large glass door that was kept locked. The woman behind the desk facing the glass door looked at me and after some brief hesitation buzzed me in. She looked barely out of her teens, with huge green eyes that seemed to follow my every move.

In another round of embarrassing blend of broken French and hand movements, I began explaining my predicament, when she interrupted me, offered me a seat in an adjoining room, gave me a stack of papers, and asked me to fill them out. As writing had always been one of my nemeses, I went back to her and, in a barely audible voice, made the embarrassing confession that I couldn't. That's when she asked me if I spoke Yiddish. My eyes lit up; I said "*Yo.*" Just minutes later, another woman, middle-aged and quite attractive, dressed in a matching skirt and jacket over a white silk blouse, came out and began a rapid bombardment of brief questions, which I countered just as rapidly.

"*Red'n Yiddish?*"

"*Avodah!*"

"*Vi ruft men eich?*"

"*Greta Sobel.*"

"*Vi gait es eich?*"

"*Ahf maineh sonim gezogt!*"

She smiled and quickly left the room.

When she returned, she put her hand on my shoulder and told me that, for the next three months, my son and I would each get 100 new francs per month, and we can have our meals at their cafeteria. In the meantime, we should make arrangements to emigrate to Israel, and we should start that process immediately by visiting the Israeli consulate. She warned me that after three months they would no longer be able to support us, but that would be okay since by then we should be on our way to Israel. I asked her about all those papers that I had to fill out. She answered that they were mainly intended to establish the legitimacy of the applicants; my Yiddish fulfilled the same purpose. This was one of many times when Yiddish, a language that for many years I was embarrassed to speak or even admit that I knew, came to my rescue.

Beginning the next day around one o'clock, Poldy and I walked over to the COJASOR cafeteria to have our lunch. The cafeteria was on the third floor of 124 Rue Saint-Lazare, a large open room bisected by long metal tables. At one end of the room, there was a short counter where people – tired, cheerless people – holding trays with both hands would slowly shuffle past two healthy-looking female servers who quietly transferred the contents of several stainless troughs onto thick, white ceramic plates. After completing their meals, the same people would return their plates to the servers and exchange them for 3-tier aluminum mess kits containing soup, a main dish, and a dessert, usually a piece of pie or cake, to be had for dinner. The only condition for being served the next day was the return of the mess kits. I followed this protocol for two days with Poldy; afterwards, I sat alone at a table, while Poldy convinced the servers, sometimes through riotous pantomime, that he should be given two portions of everything.

The next few weeks in Paris were pretty quiet. We spent the days sightseeing: we walked up and down the Champs Elysées, we visited the Louvre, the Sacré-Coeur, Les Invalides, L'Arc de Triomphe, and of course the Eiffel Tower; we also ploughed the Seine on a *bateau mouche*, and we took the Metro everywhere. I knew I had promised the woman from COJASOR that I would contact the Israeli consulate, but the idea of traveling again, especially to a place that conjured images of hard manual labor and collective living, was to me, at least for now, intolerable.

The weather was perfect, even though we were told that it normally rained during that time of the year. It also seemed that Poldy and I had tacitly agreed on a temporary truce. It was nice listening to what he had to say as we walked through the Louvre; it was like having a private tour guide. I would stand there and look at a painting or a sculpture, as he would rattle off what made each of them a work of art. I never denied that he possessed vast knowledge, though I would never let him know it, besides all that knowledge would never take the place of a soul.

V

When I first arrived in Paris, I sent postcards to Bucharest to my father, Ody, Lena, and a bunch of other friends to let them know that we were safe and getting on just fine. I also sent a postcard to Elvira – she had been so wonderful to me in the end – and reminded Poldy to send a postcard to his father.

Benno, probably at Elvira's prompting, sent word to his cousin, a well-known Parisian physician, whom I didn't even know existed, that we were in Paris and in need of help. After we had been living at Hotel d'Europe for about four weeks, Madame Cortiz stopped me one evening as we were returning from our daily sightseeing expeditions and told me that a Dr. Maurer had called and wanted us to call him back. The next morning, Madame Cortiz helped me dial the number, as it was the first time I made a phone call in Paris. A woman answered the phone, who, as soon as she realized that I was struggling in French, switched into Romanian. She told me she was Dr. Maurer's wife, Dr. Maurer being Benno's first cousin, and they had been living in Paris since before the war, which, she explained, was why I had never heard of them. She invited us to their house for dinner the following night. When I mentioned the address to Madame Cortiz - 8, Rue Lincoln, 8th Arrondissement – she assured me that these were very wealthy people.

The following evening we took the metro to the Franklin D. Roosevelt station and walked the short block over to a three-story townhouse. Streams of light radiating through the high vaulted windows, each with its own intricate wrought iron latticework, accentuated the building's ornate Empire façade. We climbed the four marble-clad steps beneath a square-pillared portico to a glistening black, highly lacquered door. The door resembled a large domino tile standing on its short side, with a blank lower half and a round translucent leaded glass window pane representing the giant dot on the upper half whose glow led our way up the steps.

Once inside, a young uniformed maid showed us into a large sitting room reminiscent of the Feingolds' green wallpaper-covered parlor room of old. There were three people sitting side by side on an ornate divan, who, upon seeing us, leaped up as if electric current had suddenly coursed through their sitting cushions. The first hand I shook was Claudine Maurer's, Dr. Maurer's wife, next was Dr. Maurer's, and last was Madame Eveline Lasker's, Claudine Maurer's sister, and a recent divorcee. We were then pointed to two chairs located right under a large, multi-colored chandelier. I had a flashback to the time I was interrogated at the *Securitate* offices.

Dr. Maurer reigned over the conversation like an orchestra conductor, pointing to his wife and his sister-in-law whenever he deemed it was their turn to talk, but he pointed mostly to himself and, whenever that happened, the previous speaker had to cease talking immediately. The recitations were in French; Poldy and I hadn't said a word yet. Later in our visit, Dr. Maurer urged me with the help of a broad servile smile to call him Octavian, which he then followed with a series of questions about our life back in Romania, our journey from Bucharest to France, and finally our sojourn in Paris, which he also proceeded to answer: "Life was rough in Romania, especially at the end, wasn't it? Tiring train ride, I can only imagine? Paris hasn't quite shown its light to you (You understand my allusion, dear friends – Paris is the City of Light), has it?"…and so on.

Madame Maurer interrupted her husband's interest in our plight by remarking what a beautiful bag I had. She was admiring none other than my dependable "Bucurii din Bucureşti" bag. Since it looked like an archeological find, its appeal was understandable.

I decided that I better say something in my broken French. I first complimented Madame Maurer on her good taste, and told her that the bag had been an impulse purchase just before I left Bucharest. As she was continuing her compliments on Romanian artisanship, the uniformed maid I had seen earlier appeared to announce that dinner was served. All three of them sprung up again and began marching towards the dining room. I immediately followed. Poldy needed a bit more time to catch up with us, as the venue change had been unexpected and rapid. The dining room was a vast chamber dominated by a table that I have only seen the likes of in movies of Medieval stories. There were twenty-four distantly-spaced chairs around its long dark expanse. The five of us occupied a small corner of the table, with Dr. Maurer at the head, the two ladies at his right, and Poldy and I at his left, with me sitting next to Dr. Maurer.

During dinner, Dr. Maurer – or should I say Octavian – held court, telling stories that, from the expression on the faces of his two female companions, had been told more times than life had prepared them for. He pointed to a small red white and blue ribbon attached to his lapel, and informed us that he had been awarded the highest honor bestowed upon a French civilian, the title of 'Chevalier de la Republique' for his role in the *Maquis* during the war. He went on to describe the many lives of French Resistance fighters he had saved with his medical skills, and that he even knew Jean Moulin personally. The entire lofty soliloquy was spoken with great theatricality, which explained the multiple grease spots on Octavian's tie. At one point, probably in response to our dumb expressions, Octavian confessed that he could only speak to us in French as he had forgotten the Romanian of his youth, besides it was good experience for us to hear pure French spoken, as only through French, the language of Voltaire, Rousseau and Victor Hugo, can we ever hope to rise above our current lowly status.

I could say that the dinner consisted of turtle soup and *paté de foie gras* and pheasant on the glass with truffles and profiteroles stuffed with liquid gold, but I frankly don't remember any of it other than Poldy and I stopped for pizza on the way home.

After dinner, which was consumed with the utmost expediency, Octavian rose from the table and disappeared, with his wife and sister-in-law close behind, possibly to allow us to admire our surroundings without any distractions. Poldy and I were still sitting at the table still covered with china, crystal, and silverware, when darker thoughts entered my mind. I immediately retracted my hands off the table and ordered Poldy to do the same. The doors of the dining room were closed, but I could still clearly overhear Doctor Maurer, in perfectly enunciated Romanian, angrily scold Madame Maurer about her desire to prolong the evening.

They later reappeared bearing gifts. Octavian gave my fifteen-year old son a solid black silk tie already adorned with grease stains. The presentation of the tie was accompanied by a lengthy elucidation on its merits, as he apparently had worn it at many state banquets. Poldy responded by thanking Doctor Maurer with multiple "*Mercis!*" accompanied by an equal number of deep bows. I was beginning to feel that these people, no matter how blinded they might have been by their own self-importance, would nonetheless begin to sense that Poldy was just mocking them and deny me whatever advantage I might have had otherwise. But they couldn't stop commenting how impressed they were of Poldy's fine manners.

That's when I turned to Poldy. He had wrapped Doctor Maurer's tie around his head like a bandana, which made him look ridiculous, especially since he betrayed no awareness of his appearance, keeping an air of absolute gravity. I burst into convulsive laughter. I couldn't stop; I felt humiliated. I started coughing into my cupped hands trying to pass my fit of laughter for a coughing spasm. All three of them seemed greatly concerned. Claudine rushed to get me a glass of water. Doctor Maurer ran out of the room to return with his medical bag. Eveline restricted herself to "Oh, my God! Oh, my God! Oh, my God!" While everyone else was having a minor meltdown, Poldy sat erect in his chair stroking his tie.

The reason my hosts never suspected Poldy of foul play was because his outrageous conduct seemed to support their expectations. He and I were after all uncivilized boors, products of a system – Communism – not far above cannibalism on the evolutionary scale, not expected to have ever seen a tie, and even if we had, we certainly wouldn't have known what to do with it.

I stood up, my cough under control, and announced that I was fine, but that we needed to go home. They seemed to be in full agreement with me. I thanked them again and began to retreat towards the front door. Madame Maurer ran after me and handed me a skirt, which she breathlessly explained was manufactured by Tricosa, a factory that she and her sister owned, the largest textile factory in France. She mumbled an apology, and her eyes betrayed a sense of regret and shame. That's when I reached inside my "Bucurii din București" bag, took out my compact and maybe one or two other items that I had in it, quickly stuffed them into my pocket, and handed her the bag, acknowledging our gratitude for their generosity, and my desire to repay for it with something I knew she would like to have. Despite her vehement refusals, I shoved the bag in her hands and walked out into the evening air. As the three of them stood there framed by their palatial doorway, glued to their deep-pile Oriental rug, Poldy and I made our getaway, firing, over our shoulders, numerous rounds of "Merçi beaucoup."

Once on the street and confident that we were sufficiently out of range, we looked at each other started laughing and thumping our feet, but that lasted for only for a moment. Poldy remembered his state of siege with me and quickly stiffened up. We continued in silence the rest of the way to the Metro station. I sometimes wonder if Poldy would have continued laughing if he had known the whole history of the "Bucurii din București" bag.

To my surprise, two days later Madame Cortiz informed me as we were getting back from lunch at COJASOR, that Madame Claudine Maurer had called, and she wanted me to call her as soon as possible. I thought for a moment whether I should bother, but a kernel of curiosity drove me to it. I called the number she left – it was her office number. She immediately said in Romanian that she must see me and asked me if I could meet her the next day alone around two o'clock at the Café de La Paix. I hesitated at first, but then I agreed.

As I entered the café, I saw her sitting at one of the many small round tables evenly covering the floor, looking anxious. I impassively sat down across from her and, bearing a broad grin, turned to face her. She grabbed my hands and began apologizing for the rude reception I had received the previous day, but she was a prisoner in a house run by a self-centered fool, and she was tired of their constant quarrelling. Despite all her wealth and station in life, I felt sorry for her, and I told her so. We talked for a long time; she seemed genuinely concerned with my situation, and promised to offer some real help, and she did. Afterwards, during the months I was still in Paris, we talked on the phone almost every week, and, in later years, we would meet every time I was in Paris, all without Dr. Maurer's knowledge. We remained friends until the day she died four years ago.

VI

Claudine's help came in the form of a name: Teresa Pinsky, a wealthy Romanian expatriate who had lived in Paris for many years, and was at the center of a very extensive Jewish-Romanian social milieu. The very next day I called Teresa, and she immediately invited me to her apartment. She lived at 23 Rue de Provence, which, though only a ten-minute walk from my shabby hotel, was worlds away in its feel of social advantage and elegance. I climbed the one-story flight to her duplex apartment. As I walked in, she hugged me as if we knew each other for years. She was tall, taller than me by two or three inches, a full head of jet-black hair cropped very short, a bit too boyish for my taste, but coiffed to perfection, and although some of her features didn't appear to coexist harmoniously with others, such as her rather prominent nose, with its two gaping nostrils, and her round little-girl face, it all seemed to come together in the end as the vision of a clever, stylish woman who has had life licked. Many of her friends thought she looked like a little less elfin Audrey Hepburn, but I didn't see that. These same friends seemed to think that I looked like a more glorious version of Ingrid

Bergman, something I never quite saw, though I understood they were just trying to be gracious.

The apartment, on the other hand, was magnificent. The lower floor consisted of a cavernous party room, the site of Teresa's glorious bashes. It was furnished with eclectic period pieces – sofas, love seats, small tables and chairs – that created an atmosphere of relaxed elegance. Surrounding the room on three sides was a wrap-around balcony where I often watched those unique Parisian sunsets. Upstairs must have been the bedrooms, though I never saw them. I once heard one of Teresa's ex-lovers rave about the round bed and the mirrored ceiling.

Teresa was in her early forties, divorced, and fully committed to not wasting another moment devoted to anyone other than herself. She was the mother of two daughters, one sixteen and the other fourteen, and like me, did not have the greatest relationship with them, particularly the sixteen-year old. The fourteen-year old was studious and quite homely, with a round swarthy face and bulbous eyes, but, unlike Poldy and her older daughter, respectful of her mother's self-gratifying life style as a now-or-never proposition.

In no time Teresa filled the void I felt by leaving Lena back in Bucharest. She had parties all the time, where I acted as the co-hostess. Before every party, the daughters would be shipped to Teresa's father's house to spend the night.

I don't know where Teresa found the men, but they were always there, ready to dance, to flirt, or to steal a kiss. I began feeling like a woman again. I wasn't prepared to jump into bed with anyone at the time, besides none of them appealed to me enough for that.

VII

At one of Teresa's frequent parties, a man walked up and bowed to me. As I was staring at him, without any idea who he was, Teresa jumped in and informed me that the man's name was Fred, Lena's bother. Fred, whose shiny bald head was blinding me, uttered in exaggerated tones of grave despair that had he known how beautiful I was he would have turned heaven and earth to meet me at the train station, but unfortunately he had to do something of great consequence, something I did not bother to remember.

He rose from his absurd stooping and leaned against me, confessing that his wife would be out of town that whole week and we could have Paris as our playground. He reeked of perspiration mixed with the smell of some cheap aftershave. I smiled encouragingly at this conceited idiot's babblings. He promised that he was going to pick me up next day in his brand new Peugeot and drive me to Forges-les-Eaux in Normandy, a casino town, where we would spend the day gambling and shopping. In the evening, we would dine in a three Michelin-star restaurant in Rouen, which would be conveniently located next to a three Michelin-star hotel. I continued to smile blankly. Fred took that to mean that he needed to sweeten the deal, and he remembered that the last time he visited Forges-les-Eaux, he had seen a beautiful necklace in a jewelry store window, which he knew before he even met me that had my name on it.

The man was beginning to foam at the mouth, so I put a stop to the charade. I told him to pick me up at my hotel, Hotel d'Europe, the next morning around eleven o'clock. I had never seen a happier buffoon in my life. He practically ran out of Teresa's apartment; I think he was afraid I would change my mind.

Before I left, I took Teresa aside and told her how Fred had promised his sister that he would help me when I first arrived in Paris without money or connections, how I waited for him for hours at *Gare du Nord*, and how he never showed, nor even took the time afterwards to look me up and see how I was doing. Teresa got so furious, she swore never to let him in if he ever tried to show his face again.

Early the next morning, while Poldy and I were having breakfast, I told Madame Cortiz that if a gentleman came looking for me to tell him that I had moved out of the hotel. If he insisted, she was to tell him that another gentleman had picked me up earlier in a Rolls Royce. Poldy and I finished breakfast and left for a relaxing sightseeing venture at the Louvre. When I got back that evening, Madame Cortiz later told me that promptly at eleven o'clock, a very tense gentleman showed up. When she gave him the message, he got so irate that he tried to muscle his way into the hotel hoping to find me hiding somewhere, but the stout Madame Cortiz pushed him out the door so hard that he landed flat on his back on the sidewalk. For the next hour, she kept seeing him lurking outside, but then he was gone, and, thankfully, I never heard from him again.

VIII

A week or so later, Teresa took me aside during one of her parties and apologized for never asking me about my money problems. I didn't have anything to hide. I told her I was flat broke. She scolded me for not having told her sooner. The very next day I was working as a salesgirl in her father's lingerie boutique, "La Belle Epoque", which, of all places, was right on Rue Saint-Lazare, a block away from COJASOR. The old man, a widower, was very nice to me and paid me 1,200 francs a month, which was more than double the combined stipend Poldy and I were getting from COJASOR.

After I had been working for about a month, the old man asked me into his office. He spoke to me in Romanian. He politely asked me to sit down while averting my eyes. He told me that he'd been a widower for a long time and that he was very lonely. At first, his confession made me feel awkward, but the modest, unaffected manner in which he presented himself touched me in the end. He had been watching me every day and had become obsessed with me: he wanted to touch me, to hold me, but nothing else – he was too old, besides he respected me too much. He told me that if I were willing to occasionally stay the night at his house to help him disperse the crushing loneliness he would double my salary.

I sat there speechless, weighing my options. Life had taught me enough hard lessons on the price of impulsivity. The old man took my silence as a prelude to my turning him down, so he reemphasized that he has not been with a woman for many years, and I would not have to do anything other than just sleep next to him. I shrugged my shoulders and agreed.

It turned out to be an excellent decision. Once a week and sometimes once every two weeks he would come to me as I was standing by the counter, and most politely asked me in tremulous whispers if I would mind stopping over that night. Teresa never knew about this – that was his request – and although I didn't grant many such requests in my life, this one I did. He was a sweet old man, and all he wanted was someone warm to lie next to. He never touched me, which, at least at the beginning, felt weird. I understood that he was impotent, but I couldn't understand why he wouldn't want to at least touch my breasts or put his hands between my legs. I felt I was too young to have reached the age of respectability.

I would sometimes wake up in the middle of the night and hear him sob like a child. He never told me why, and I didn't think it was my place to ask. Only now do I understand: he was mourning the death of his youth.

IX

I decided that the best way to deal with Poldy was to tell him that some nights I wouldn't be home, and just leave it at that. I knew he wouldn't ask why; in fact I heard him mutter thank you for letting him know. He had begun attending a local public all-boys elementary school called Ecole des Petits Ecuries, which I owed to Teresa. She knew the principal, a repulsive old man with a white beard who reminded me of Karl Marx, who occasionally attended Teresa's parties and made everyone's life miserable walking around and correcting people's pronunciations. He was like the French language Gestapo, and he had a particular dislike for the way I pronounced his language, as he kept referring to French. I later found out that the ass-hole was born in Romania.

Poldy wasn't very happy at Ecole des Petits Ecuries because they stuck him in second grade; that's the grade they determined his French was at, so he had to spend the whole day with seven-year olds. Several times he asked me not to make him go, but he needed to do something, and if his French improved, I assured him, they would place him in a higher grade. Three months later he was still in second grade, though, according to Teresa, whose French was better than most Parisians', he was speaking fluent French, and should have been moved up. She complained to the principal who grudgingly moved him into fifth grade, which was the highest grade they had. He was now with eleven-year olds – not much of an improvement in his eyes.

As the Algerian War was raging, every time a French soldier died, the class had to stand and observe a moment of silence. Yet, because Poldy was not French, he was not allowed to stand. Naturally, the other kids began to avoid him, a situation the teachers did nothing to prevent and which Poldy capitalized on by acting bizarrely. One day, as he was sitting in class, his face suddenly became covered in blood though the school infirmary couldn't find where it had come from. Another day, he reeked from feces. He was again taken to the infirmary, but again they couldn't find the source. The last incident was when he went around distributing Mao's Red Book. They told me they found over a hundred copies on him. After that, they told him he would not be allowed in school again, and they sent me a note describing all the things that he had done and that he wasn't welcome there anymore. After I read the note, I was very calm. I told him he was on his own, and that he needed to find a job. He asked me what I thought he was suited for. I told him to find a job that required annoying people. He said he would contact the Russians and ask them if they needed another volunteer like the dog Laika that was sent up in the Sputnik rocket. I told him that was a very good idea.

X

By fall of 1961, we had been in Paris for almost a year. Our visa had expired and COJASOR had long-ago stopped helping us. The HIAS, on the other hand, was pressing us to go to Israel. I wanted to stay in Paris. I was having a wonderful time, money was not an issue, and men loved me. Poldy, as usual, didn't share my feelings. He hated Paris and wanted us to leave; he didn't care where, just not Paris.

One day when I came home from work to take a shower and change, there was a fat envelope sitting on my bed. Poldy had written me a twenty-page letter. I looked it over, but since I had no time, I told him I would read it later, and threw it in my night table. I had to run. It was one of the nights I was spending at Teresa's father's place. He was first going to take me to dinner, my first time at Maxim's. I was terribly excited. I put on my best outfit, which incidentally, the old man had bought for me. He had great taste: it was a blue chiffon flair dress strewn with tiny flower bud appliqués.

Several days later, while I was looking for my earrings, I found Poldy's letter. I took it out of my night table, and looked at the bulging envelope for a long time. On the front of the envelope, it read, "To My Mother and Co-Owner of My Destiny." As I read that address, I knew exactly what the twenty-page letter was about; I wasn't going to waste my time reading the feeble manipulations of a boy. I threw the letter in the trashcan. The next day when I came home, I found every page of the letter thumb-tacked to the wall of our hotel room. They looked like Martin Luther's theses on the walls of the Wittenberg church. They were still tacked to the wall when we left that room for the last time a year later.

I decided to try to extend our French sojourn visas. The marriage option, although there were quite a few men who would have married me, did not appeal to me. There wasn't anyone special, just men I would flirt with to boost my ego, but that was it. Even though I had promised myself that I would never appeal to the old man for help, I decided that these were extraordinary measures and asked his advice. His answer was not what I expected: he told me to leave France as soon as I could – it wasn't a healthy place for my son and me to build a future - too much xenophobia, too much anti-Semitism. He suggested I consider America. I was crushed by his answer, and I told him so. I thought he wanted me around. He said that I could never imagine how much, but he was old and he would soon die, and my son and I deserved a normal life. I was so angry with him that the next day, when he asked me if I could spend the night with him, I told him 'no.' He lowered his eyes, and said, "Perhaps another night." He never asked again.

That first year in Paris was rather uneventful, but it meant more to me than most of the other years in my crowded life. It was a year of many firsts. It was the first time I wasn't afraid to admit that I was Jewish. It was the first time when I felt I could say what was on my mind without being afraid that *Securitate* would arrest me the next day. It was the first time I pushed back when someone leaned on me in a crowded Metro. It was the first time I woke up from a nightmare, looked around, and smiled. It was the first time I tasted freedom.

XI

Many of Teresa's guests were Romanian expatriates, and the major topic of discussion among them was other Romanian expatriates. I usually kept away from these people because I felt their conversation always had an elitist edge to it, such as:

"Did you know that Iancu Spirea lives in Paris?"

"Not Iancu Spirea who graduated with us from Cantemir High School?"

"Yes, the very same. He's a gynecologist with a wonderful practice in the 6th Arrondissement. We should get together with him."

Or:

"Guess who I ran into last week at Bon Marché at the Coty counter? She was getting the "boudoir" treatment. You'll never guess. Stefania Alecsandri."

"Who?"

"You remember Stafania Alecsandri? We all graduated together from St. Ecaterina's Convent. Did you know that she became Lucia Sturdza-Bulandra's understudy in *La Folle de Chaillot*? We saw her together at Madame Bulandra's theater. Ah! Now you remember."

These conversations usually made me feel very itchy and mean. I wanted to interrupt some pretentious, overbearing, pinch-cheeked witch and ask, "Excuse me, but did I not see you in one of the *Securitate* cells getting gang-banged by twelve unwashed *jglobs*?"

One night, as I was sitting alone on one of Teresa's sofas, I overheard two men having the following discussion:

"I assisted Dr. Berhardt this morning. He had his hands full with a coronary bypass on an eight-year old."

"So how is Daniel these days?"

"Eh, you know him. Never a happy man, though I don't know why. I know his wife loves him and that beautiful daughter of his, Greta, is a delight."

"Does he still drink?"

"I'm afraid so."

My ears perked up. They had to be talking about Daniel Bernhardt, the medical student I met when I first arrived in Bucharest, my first love, Daniel who treated me to *mititei* and who told me if I didn't stay with him I would be miserable for the rest of my life. That was eighteen years ago and a world away.

I had a burning desire to contact him, but what would I say to him? Do I tell him that I'm a refugee and living in a seedy hotel with my disagreeable fifteen-year old son? Maybe, but I had to see him and I asked Madame Cortiz to find his address.

One evening, I took the metro and went to his house. He lived in a brownstone-type villa in a very elegant neighborhood on the Left Bank. I was about to ring the bell, when I looked at myself and realized that I was wearing a cheap dress, no different than the one he first saw me in, while he had become a renowned surgeon. I shut my heart off to him back then because, as a poor medical student, the prospects of his ever amounting to anything seemed paltry, and love, after spending a life of poverty, was too abstract a topic when compared to marriage into wealth and comfort. I wondered what might have been had I said yes to him that night in the pub after seeing *Now, Voyager* with Bette Davis and Paul Henreid. I'm sure I would have been able to make him happier than he seemed to be now, but would I? I would have escaped the marriage to Benno and I would have missed the miserable years that followed, but now life was good to me, and besides I was never one to look back and wonder "what if?"

I stood there for a while outside Daniel's townhouse when the front lights went on. I threw myself against the adjoining building and waited breathlessly. A tall, corpulent man wearing a trench coat and a fedora emerged. His long face was rutted with evidence of deep heartache and he was limping slightly. Walking next to him, holding his arm with both hands was a young girl, maybe sixteen or seventeen, her face beaming contentment. She was blond and beautiful and full of life, and I heard him call her

Greta. I felt I knew everything about her.

A few weeks later, I had another occasion to eavesdrop on a conversation by a group of expatriates. This time they were talking about an attorney by the name of Jacob Rothschild. I remembered that was Coty's brother's name and he was an attorney.

I interrupted the expatriates' conversation.

"Excuse me, does Jacob Rothschild have a sister named Coty, a pianist?"

"Oh yes," answered one of the men. "The poor woman is still in Romania. She's married to a gypsy fiddler, and gave up everything for him. Imagine someone like her, coming from such a distinguished family, and with so much talent. She could be giving concerts here at Olympia, yet she she's still there in that miserable place, and they won't let her leave because of him, because he's not Jewish. I tell you it's criminal."

"Do you happen to know Jacob Rothschild's phone number?" I asked.

"No, but I'm sure it's in the book."

The following week, I called Jacob Rothschild. He knew immediately who I was. Coty had often talked about me. I told him I wanted to write to her. He didn't think it was a good idea. I asked him why. He said he didn't know, but I didn't believe him. He, however, gave me Coty's address. I thanked him and said 'goodbye.'

As soon as I got home that evening, I wrote to Coty. I wrote her a long letter, the longest letter I ever wrote. I told her how much I loved her. I told her that I didn't do anything, certainly nothing that deserved her shutting me out. I begged her to forgive me. I told her that I knew people in Paris who could help her and Mircea get out of Romania. I told her that I would pay anything to bring her to Paris. I told her how much I needed her. And I told her I was crying while I was writing the letter. Like a teenager, I put on lipstick and sealed the letter with a kiss. She never wrote back. She left a hole in my heart.

XII

On an early October day of 1961, I woke up and told Poldy that he didn't have to go to school that day. I told him to put on his dress pants, one of his white shirts, and Dr. Maurer's tie. He nodded. When we were ready to leave, I noticed that he didn't have the tie on. Flaunting one of his grotesque grins, he informed me that he had used it as a down payment for the services of a prostitute. I was ready to slap him again, but I was in too much of a hurry. I knew the tie was gone, that he probably just tossed it in the Seine. We left for the American Embassy.

After explaining to the man in uniform at the gate the purpose of our visit, he let us in. Once inside, we waited for about a half hour until a slender slightly hunched-over Nordic-looking man with thick glasses came over and asked us to follow him. We sat down around a small rectangular table inside a room that exceeded the dimensions of the table by mere inches. The process of reaching an empty chair beyond one already occupied required an awkward dance-round-the chair routine.

The man, who never introduced himself, speaking in broken French, informed us that, although the immigration quota for Romania was filled through the year 1970, we would be able to come to America under the "Refugees from Communism" quota. He explained with an uninterrupted stream of pathetic hand gestures, seemingly for our benefit, that individuals of stateless status who have escaped from the abuses and privations of the Communist regimes of Eastern Europe were treated under a special statute. There would be a brief waiting period devoted to physical exams, background checks, etc., but within the next four to six months we would be afforded the great fortune of entering America – the land of unlimited opportunities, provided of course that once there we conducted ourselves worthy of such privilege, at least until we became American citizens.

The news had a miraculous effect on Poldy. It was as if a cloud had lifted off his continually stormy face. On the way back to our hotel, I couldn't even think of America as our home, and told him that he was wasting his breath trying to convince me how wonderful things would be for us there. In fact, a couple of days later, I noticed that he had added another ten or twelve sheets on our room's walls. I knew they were about how much better our life would be in America: we would live in a real house; I, with my vast working experience in "La Belle Epoque", would be able to get a well-paying job as a saleswoman in a fancy shop in New York City; and, most surprisingly coming from him, I would find a good man to marry and live a life grounded in constancy and true love. I only scanned the contents of his letter, but it was enough to want to choke him.

I was thirty-seven, and everything he wrote sounded like I should come to terms with the vile notion that my good years were behind me and I should settle down and become some schlemiel's maid and bed warmer. I wanted to kill him and probably would have if he had been there. I wanted to tear off every one of those sheets he had pinned to the wall, but I didn't want to give him the satisfaction of knowing that I had read them.

That evening, I changed into one of my "sexy" outfits: push-up bra, low cut dress, blood-red lipstick, lots of jewelry, and a pair out of my collection of "throw me down and fuck me" shoes, and went to Teresa's place. Poldy, wearing a sarcastic grin, waved me goodbye. He thought my days were numbered? Well, I thought, we'll see.

As usual, even though it was a weeknight, by ten o'clock Teresa's vast apartment was full of people that kept her two maids constantly shuttling large trays filled with all kinds of intoxicating fluids and divinely epicurean hors d'oeuvres. The place was unusually hectic. I decided to put all negative thoughts out of my mind and whirl the time away. That night I glowed. It must have been past three o'clock when I noticed that the crowd was beginning to thin out, and as usual, once that began, within a half hour the place was empty. The two maids were busy cleaning up, taking glasses and dishes away, wiping off and brushing up. I was sitting on one of several overstuffed sofas lining the party room, while Teresa was saying good bye to the last guests. Suddenly, a man with dark brown eyes set deeply in his skull and concave cheeks that made him look sullen even when he laughed, materialized out of thin air. He was dressed in a black double-breasted business suit, which made his presence that much more unexpected given everyone else's *leger* dress style.

He couldn't have been one of Teresa's guests because his appearance looked untarnished by the reveling that had gone on over the previous five hours. The man walked over with slow measured paces, and sat down right next to me, before I even had a chance to respond to his request for permission. He put his arm along the sofa behind my back and leaned over so that his face was within inches of mine. His name was Michel, he softly informed me, and he knew my name, and further claimed to know a lot about me.

I sat motionless, transfixed by his intense, impudent stare. I suddenly felt his fingers groping at the roots of my hair, and slowly pushing my head forward until our eyelashes met. There was a slight odor of sweat exuding from inside his buttoned-up jacket. He unbuttoned his jacket with his free hand, releasing a rush of powerful masculine odors, and I fell limp into his arms. When I finally gathered the strength to push him away, I noticed Teresa looking down on us with the kind of amused smile one reserves for infants who have just splashed baby food over their faces in order to attract attention. "Michel will take you home," Teresa announced.

"Where do you live?" he asked me as he was driving away.

"I live in a one-room flat with my son."

"I see." Having said that, he expertly maneuvered his small car along narrow crooked streets until he arrived in front of a double door, on which the name "Hotel de Paris" had been painted with little regard for symmetry. He cut the engine and briskly walked inside. A minute later he reemerged, smoothly eased me out of my seat, and guided me up the stairs. He never turned the light on, yet enough light entered the room through the unshuttered window to enable us to see each other's body as if a movie projector had us contoured on a silver screen. He gently sat me on the bed, kneeled in front of me as he unhurriedly, skillfully undressed me. He then had me watch him take off his clothes.

By then, my eyes had adjusted to the semi-obscurity of our surroundings, and I could observe the elegance of his movements, the hard sinews of his body, the audacity of his engorged penis. He slipped his arms under my thighs and back, and lifted me like he would a child, and moved me deeper into the bed; then he climbed next to me. I closed my eyes and waited motionlessly, expectantly, to be instructed. He dedicated his entire body to exploring mine. I felt him everywhere, from the tips of my earlobes to the contours of my legs. I felt enveloped in rigid velvet. I never thought my body could undergo such upheaval; I was consumed with passion; I could see my chest rising and sinking; gulps of air entering and exiting, as if powered by the thrusts of a magnificent engine; orgasm plunged upon orgasm.

And then, unexpectedly, I felt myself being filled the way a small leather glove must feel when a large hand forces its way into it. I gasped once, and opened my eyes. His body was flush atop me, except for his upper torso, which was propped up on his arms. The first thing I saw were the drops of sweat dripping from his body onto mine. I then looked up into his wide-open eyes flashing with satisfaction and pugnacity. He knew I was under his spell. A merciless grin betrayed his parted lips that quivered every time he thrust into me. I was never going to leave this man, this man I knew nothing about; I was going to remain in Paris and "*Tant pis*" to Poldy.

When I woke up the next day, the surroundings looked strange and unplaceable; even the man who was sitting fully dressed in a black suit in front of me seemed only remotely familiar.

"Good morning, Greta. Here's coffee and a croissant," Michel said cheerfully, as he held the saucer near my chin, so the coffee aroma emanating from the cup would enter my nostrils. I grabbed the cup and saucer. "I already had a cup, and since I am a working man I have to leave, but I'll call you later. I'll get your number from Teresa."

Having said that, he got up, walked to the door, and flicked his raised fingers by the side of his face. "Some night, eh?"

After the door closed my first reaction was that I've been had like a two-bit whore. That feeling was reinforced when I spotted a twenty-franc note lying on the night table. But once I calmed myself down, something I've always been able to do, by talking to myself, "I've been through more shit than anyone else. No one's going to get the better of me. This fucker is going to keep on coming to me until I'm done with him. And when I'm done with him, he's going to beg for me, but I'll be going to America."

I got dressed and left the hotel. On the way out, I noticed that next to the twenty-franc note was a tiny scrap of paper that informed me that the money was left in case I didn't have any "*argent comptant*" for a taxi. As soon as I got back to my hotel, I showered, changed, and even though I was over two hours late, I went to the shop. The old man didn't say anything when he saw me; he just glanced at me for a second, and then turned and hid in his office for the rest of the day. I asked the cashier, an old woman who had been with the shop for over thirty years, if she minded writing a short note from me to the old man. I explained to her that my French writing is even poorer than my speaking, and she agreed. The note simply read, "I've applied for American visa. It should arrive in less than five months. Greta." I spent the rest of the day thinking about how I would go about regaining my self-esteem. I knew the first step was to meet with Teresa and find out as much as I could about this Michel.

XIII

When I arrived at Teresa's later that evening, she wasn't home. The younger of the two daughters was there, and she told me that her mother had gone out of town and wouldn't be back for several days. I was about to leave, when on a hunch I asked if she knew someone by the name of Michel, and then proceeded to describe him. She thought for a while, then said that he sounded like her mother's accountant. I asked her what she knew about him, to which she said, "Nothing." Yet I persisted.

"You don't know if he's married or has children or where he lives?"

"Oh that. Yes, he's married and has two children, a boy and a girl," she answered casually.

"Do you know where he lives or his phone number?" I continued my interrogation.

"No, but I'm sure it must be on one of his invoices. I always see them lying on my mother's night table. Do you want it?" she asked me.

"Yes!" The girl ran off into her mother's bedroom and reappeared immediately holding a piece of paper.

"If you want I'll write it down for you, okay?"
I nodded.

"Michel Ungar. Contable Diplômé. 123 Boulevard des Capucines, IIe."

"Thank you, Danielle," I said, as I folded the paper and pushed it in my coat pocket.

I remember not knowing what to do with myself. I wasn't used to spending evenings in my depressing hotel room, especially when I knew Poldy would be there, but as I had no other place to go, I headed towards Rue de Vienne on foot. I knew the streets pretty well by then, and, as it was a mild evening, I entrusted myself to my feet knowing that the walk would do me good. All along the way the shops were lit up, and buzzing with shoppers. I occasionally stopped in front of a shop window to see what they had on sale. I was all right financially, so if I wanted to buy something, something reasonable, I could certainly do it, but I had never been an impulse buyer. To this day, even when I know everything is just what I want: price, style, fit, and the right mood, I still hover around that jacket or pair of shoes sometimes for hours, trying to convince myself that I deserve it. But not that night. Unexpectedly, my eyes fell on a gorgeous burgundy taffeta housedress that took center stage in the window of a brightly lit boutique. I walked into the boutique, uttered the obligatory, "Bon jour, Madame," and pointed to the housedress. I watched silently as the saleswoman undressed the mannequin and placed the housedress inside a giant box. I paid, bid the woman, "Bon soir, Madame," and walked back out on the street.

As I was getting closer to my hotel, I realized that I was on Rue Saint-Lazare standing right in front of "La Belle Époque". I looked inside. The light was still on, and, as the office door was open, I could see the old man sitting at his desk with his head leaning against the back of his chair. He didn't move, and his mouth was slightly opened. I thought something might have happened to him. He had confessed during one of our earlier meetings that he was eighty-seven years old, and that he had a bad heart. But he stirred, so I walked on.

When I got up to my room, no one was there. It was still early. Poldy must have gone to a movie, I thought. He had always been a big movie buff: Jean Marais, Gerard Philippe, Eddie Constantine, and there were several movie theaters in our neighborhood. I took off my clothes, turned off the lights, and went to bed; I was exhausted. I quickly fell asleep.

I was awaken by the sounds of laughter. The light had been turned on and, standing by my bed was Poldy, and next to him was Michel, with his arm around Poldy's neck, pointing to me and making snoring sounds. I touched my face, no make-up; my hair, a mess; the nightgown, a tattered piece of cotton dating back to Romania. My voice deserted me.

"What...what...what's going on?" I stammered.

Michel, this time dressed in a casual green turtle neck sweater and khaki pants, balanced by a long blue scarf that he had loosely wrapped around his neck several times, casually told me that they went to the movies to see *Le Masque de Fer* with Jean Marais, and then they went to a Moroccan restaurant and had lamb couscous.

"I had a glass of wine," Poldy chimed in.

By then I had regained my composure, and, with the biggest grin I could find, I dismissively asked, "How do you two gentlemen know each other?"

"Well Michel, I mean Monsieur Ungar is the accountant for "La Belle Époque", and since they're doing inventory, he stopped by to tell you that you don't have to go to work tomorrow. Then I asked him to wait, and when you didn't show up, we went to the movies."

"And whose idea was that," I asked looking at Michel.

"Oh, yes. That was mine," admitted Michel.

I told both of them to turn around and remain that way until I told them otherwise. I grabbed my new burgundy taffeta housedress and my new pocketbook, a leather bag I picked up after my unexpected parting with the "*Bucurii din București*" bag, this one bearing the far less enticing name of "Printemps", and left the room.

While I was in the bathroom, I tried to sort things out. Obviously, Michel wanted to be with me every bit as much as I wanted to be with him. That was clear. But why go through my pig-headed son? I resented when men thought they could win me over by befriending my son. I could have spared Michel the discomfort of an evening with Poldy, if he had only asked me. Time spent with Poldy would not count towards his obligations to me. I had no intention of bringing those two together, and yet they were like best buddies. I decided to play along to see where it led. I fixed myself up as best I could, which I decided was pretty good, took off the nightgown and put on the housedress. I had no underwear underneath, which aroused me, as the stiff material rubbed against my thighs. I made a mental note to keep my legs crossed at all times, particularly if Poldy was sitting opposite from me.

When I reentered the room, the two boys were locked in a game of arm wrestle. Remembering Michel's firm arms, as they were gliding over my body less than twenty hours ago, and Poldy's scrawny constitution, the seemingly even stance was another yellow flag along my course of finding out what Michel was after. I allowed the boys to play out their game, as I made coffee, and I put a cup next to Michel, expecting some sort of a reaction, but none came. I sat and watched as the boys continued to entertain themselves without the least sign of acknowledgment of my presence. I was enjoying this game, which was obviously being played for my benefit by both players, although, without knowing their specific motives, I knew they were most certainly widely different.

Almost an hour had gone by and I was beginning to lose my patience, so I walked over to the table and announced that it was a quarter to eleven, and all boys must go to bed to get their rest because tomorrow they might be called upon to perform some strenuous task. Poldy insisted that he wasn't tired, but Michel, as soon as I finished my admonition, got up and headed for the door. I told Poldy I was going to walk M. Ungar down the steps.

The stairs were dark as usual, as the only light was generated by Madame Cortiz's desk lamp, which on the upper floors, where we were, became a faint beam that largely dissipated itself on its long journey up the center of the spiral. As soon as I closed the door, Michel pinned me against the wall and began groping under my housedress. The realization that I had nothing on drove him into such frenzy that he lifted me onto his ravenous penis, and began slamming my back against the wall right outside my room. As Michel was furiously assaulting my flesh, I could hear Poldy's syncopated walk approaching the door. I just had enough breath left in me to yell to him not to open it. I then heard him slowly walk away.

When we finally got to the bottom of the stairs, Michel told me not to worry since the boy liked him. I then understood at least part of the game he was playing with Poldy. I found out the rest when Teresa came home from her tryst.

Her lover, Teresa proudly informed me, was a count whose family could trace its roots back to the Crusades. He took her by private plane to his villa on the Island of Corsica, where he tied her up and then plunged his entire fist inside her vagina. She assured me that he had small delicate hands and the experience was quite exhilarating, although she wouldn't have minded a straight fuck on occasion. But then the count was well over seventy and only infrequently, and after great effort on Teresa's part, capable of producing an erection. I wondered why a woman of her means would trouble with someone so old even if he were a count. She responded by unveiling a diamond bracelet, which he had bought her at Cartier that cost 175,000 American dollars. I smiled satisfied, wondering what a fist inside of me would feel like.

I told her that I needed to know everything she knew about Michel; yes, Michel Ungar. I already knew that he was married with two children, and that he was a wonderful lover. Teresa, in years past, seemed to also have sampled his gifts.

Michel has had a wretched relationship with his wife; they hadn't had sex in years for reasons Teresa wasn't sure of, although it might have had something to do with his constant philandering. Nonetheless, his wife had refused to give him a divorce, yet she spent with abandon every penny he made, and for his part, he put up with it for the sake of the children, whom he adored, especially the young one, Sylvie. That's why he was constantly in debt, and rarely in a position to treat a woman to even a prix-fix menu restaurant, which, from what I gathered, was the primary reason Teresa broke up with him. He had been Teresa's accountant forever, and before that he was her father's at "La Belle Époque." I wanted to ask Teresa why a woman like her who has all the money she'll ever need would give up a lover like Michel, but I realized she had given me the answer earlier. I suddenly understood that first night, when he took me to a hotel, must have caused a major hole in his finances.

XIV

The next couple of weeks were very hectic. A letter addressed to me was delivered to Madame Cortiz. When Poldy passed by the front desk that evening on the way to see a movie, she gave it to him. I, however, did not see that letter for close to two weeks.

The day after my visit with Teresa, she called me at the shop, something she had never done before. As the old man walked up from the back of the store where the only phone was located to tell me that his daughter wanted to talk to me, I saw the tortured expression on his face, so I reminded him that Teresa and I had been friends all along and the call must be related to some party Teresa was probably planning. He handed me the phone and left me alone in the room.

Teresa sounded very excited; she had just received a call from her count, who wanted her to spend the following ten days with him on his yacht, which was docked in Nice. It was October, Teresa reminded me, the best time of the year to sail the Mediterranean – warm days, cool evenings, endless clear skies.

I understood her excitement, but as I didn't quite share her enthusiasm, I asked why she had to call me at the shop, especially since I was going to stop by that afternoon. She mocked my patronizing attitude, and then for the *coup de grace*, she informed me that the count had agreed to have her bring along another couple. Teresa convinced him that it would make a cruise on his 25-meter yacht with a crew of six more cheerful if another couple came along. The count told Teresa to bring along whomever she wanted, and she had already called Michel and he agreed, and that I needed to leave the shop right away and start packing, because the count was coming around in his Hispano Suiza by six, and we were going to leave right away.

As I came out of the old man's office, I saw him standing there with his eyes closed. I stood in front of him, waiting for him to open his eyes. I wanted to say something, something to dispel his agony, but in the end I didn't know what, so I just left. I rushed home, threw a bunch of frilly things in my suitcase, and ran over to Teresa's.

The count had planned to drive that night only as far as Fontainebleau, where he booked two suites at *Le Maréchal Vaincu*, from where we would start early the next day on our way down to Nice. It would take us about two days at the count's driving speed, according to Teresa, to get down to La Côte D'Azur. I asked Teresa how Michel would have explained to his wife a disappearance of almost two weeks. She said she had taken care of that. She knew Louise personally, and had called and told her that Monsieur Pinsky, Teresa's father, was interested in opening a lingerie shop on the Riviera, and they needed Michel along to assess the financial risks and benefits, for which he would be handsomely compensated. It wasn't difficult to convince Louise, particularly after the bit about the handsome compensation. That's all Michel meant to her.

I left without seeing Poldy. I scribbled a few words on the back of an envelope I found around the room saying that I'd be back in about two weeks, and that in the meantime he should just behave himself. I wanted to leave him some money, but all I had was a 500-franc banknote, and I certainly wasn't going to leave him that much money. On the way out, I found some small coins in my coat pocket, and ran back and dropped them on the table. He came home that evening with the letter from the American Embassy. Of course, I only found that out much later.

XV

At six o'clock that evening, as I turned the corner onto Rue de Provence, I saw in front of Teresa's building a canary-colored automobile the length of a city block that seemed to have steered itself from another era. As I approached, the rear door opened. I peeked inside. The count, or at least the man I assumed to be the count, was driving; Teresa, who was sitting next to him; and Michel, sitting at the very edge of the enormous backseat and flashing a triumphant smile, had his arms raised towards me. As soon as I glided my butt onto the vanilla-colored leather banquette, we bid adieu to Paris, and off we went as if into a dream. I devoted the first few minutes surveying my environment: glistening wood panels, miniature crystal light fixtures, and gold-plated trim.

The trip was the climax of hedonism, and Michel could not have been more attentive. He wanted me and had me every night, not in dark hallways or sleazy hotel rooms, but in places fit for a queen.

An hour after we left, we arrived at our first destination: *Le Maréchal Vaincu*. The hotel, which had only four rooms, though each room was in fact a full, ultra-elegant apartment, did not announce its whereabouts. As we approached it down the long gravel driveway, it looked like an elegant private home. The building had once been Louis XIV's gardener's home, part of the *Palais Fontainebleau* complex. It had recently been purchased by a cousin of the count and converted into a very exclusive, outrageously expensive hotel.

As the count brought the car to a stop in front of the hotel entrance, liveried attendants opened its side doors. The count and Michel jumped out quickly and, as if they both attended the same rehearsal, they turned and extended their arms to their ladies. The air was cool and filled with a fusion of aromas, though the sweet scent of linden and the pungency of pine seemed to dominate. We walked into the hotel lobby, which was like no hotel lobby I had ever seen; it reminded me, maybe not in size but certainly in its appearance – the lush gold paint, the elegant sconces, the rococo-style frescoes - of the library room across the way in the Fontainebleau Castle that I had seen with Poldy when we first came to Paris.

A waiter wearing a powdered wig showed us to a pair of matching Louis XV sofas facing each other in front of a low table. The count ordered champagne and caviar. I started to giggle but Michel pinched me.

As we were sipping champagne, the count held court,

explaining to us the details of our voyage. Michel and I, our bodies pushed closely together, leaned forward and stared at the count, trying hard to convey to him that it didn't matter to us where or when or how. Michel was vigorously kneading the flesh of my buttocks. All I wanted was to go to our room.

My third glass of champagne gave me the courage to ask.

"Count, do I have to call you Count the entire trip?"

Michel hid his amusement in a handkerchief, but Teresa stiffened up. The count stammered for a second, then smiled. He had an angular, stern face traversed by deep wrinkles, that made him seem to be somewhere in his late sixties, but his tiny frame – barely five feet tall – topped by a large head covered with yellow fuzz made me feel like I should make baby faces at him and tickle his chin. His miniature hands were in perpetual motion creating elaborate shapes that framed his large colorless eyes. His entire demeanor conveyed a childlike gentleness.

"No my dear," answered the count with a lilt in his voice. "You and Michel may call me Louis. I won't tell you my entire name; we just don't have enough time. This is just a brief adventure *à la nous.*" And he burst into a bout of high-sounding squeaks that I was sure were supposed to pass for laughter. Teresa, greatly relieved, joined him. I drained my champagne glass and put on on a fat, contented grin. Fifteen minutes later Michel and I, in a room fit for Marie Antoinette, were making love.

The next morning, before I even had a chance to tax Michel's prowess as a way of sustaining my delicious state of mind, there was a knock on the door. It was Louis.

"Vite, vite. On doit nous dépêcher."

"Why, are we being attacked by the hordes of Tamberlaine?" I asked, my voice rippled with sarcasm.

"No, we must get on the road as soon as possible," shrieked Louis breathlessly through the closed door. "We must reach Lyon by no later than six o'clock. We have dinner reservations at a new restaurant run by a young man who I believe someday will be France's greatest chef. His name is Paul Bocuse. The reservations are for nine o'clock, but by the time we rest a bit, bathe, and get dressed, it will be time."

Michel thanked him for all that information and assured Louis that we will be right down.

Besides, we weren't going to miss our incredible breakfast, which we knew was waiting for us in the gazebo. I jumped into the bathtub and turned on the shower, when suddenly the curtains were pulled aside and Michel appeared holding a barstool. Would I mind if we shared the shower? He placed the stool in the middle of the tub, sat on it, and, while I was scrubbing shampoo into my hair with my eyes closed, cupped his hands around my buttocks and lifted me onto his eager lap. I clasped my feet tightly around his back, and then the only thing I felt was the pulsating jet of water oscillating slowly up and down my back; while the rest of me was liquefying into a soft mold around my lover's body.

When we got down to breakfast, Louis had a reproachful stare, but Teresa's wink quickly reassured me that we had nothing to worry about. Louis, who seemed to think that we were on a military expedition, turned out to be sweet and very considerate once he realized Michel and I had no intention of challenging his role as our leader and host – yes, he was paying for everything, and I can't even begin to imagine what that whole trip must have cost.

It was a gorgeous day, with a flawlessly blue sky flecked with tiny bubbles of white foam. With a casual flick of a switch, Louis ordered the car's roof to recede into a space between our back seats and the vast trunk. We were now speeding along a perfectly straight road lined with young poplars. Sitting there, in the back seat of that magnificent automobile that somehow defied the laws of motion, with my eyes closed, devoid of any past or future, unwilling to give in to any other reality than what was just there in front of me, stretching my neck out to meet the onrushing breeze that was engulfing my face and arms, I knew the meaning of bliss, guiltless, egocentric bliss.

I was startled out of my trance by a tickling sensation that radiated from my clitoris and quivered my whole body. Michel had reasserted his presence by sliding his hand between the buttons of my dress and inside my panties. I looked up in horror, thinking that Louis or Teresa could detect the indecent deed taking place just a few feet behind them, but I noticed that their line of sight, limited by the high backrest, prevented them from seeing anything below our chests. With a sigh of relief, I gave Michel a 'naughty boy' smile and allowed him easier access to his target. I closed my eyes and slid slowly across the smooth leather until my back was lying on the seat, and then lifted my legs onto Michel's lap. I narrowed my eyes to the point that everything around me appeared as if covered by a thick piece of gauze. I made no attempt to stop my heroic lover from sliding my willing body further onto his lap and then, concealed beneath a blanket that he requested under the pretext that he felt chilled, entered me, carefully, gently from the back. I gasped; I felt a combination of exhilaration and pain.

Paul Bocuse's restaurant, housed in an oval-shaped birthday cake-like structure topped with stacks of square-shaped layers of white chocolate, justified Louis's obsession with punctuality. The service reminded me of the magical castle in the *Beauty and the Beast*, as dishes appeared and disappeared without our ever noticing any waiters, and it always happened just as we were all ready to move on to the next course. I was convinced that we were under the spell of a sorceress who was watching us and ordering her fairies to cater to all of our wishes. The food was indescribable, not only because it was so unbelievably delicious, but also because the count had placed all the food orders ahead of time and I had no idea what I was eating, nor did I dare ask.

We stayed that night in a beautiful *auberge* just outside of Lyon. We were all exhausted, and for the first time Michel showed signs of humanity as he fell asleep before I had a chance to get to bed. I remembered the promise I had made to myself the morning of the first night we were together, when I thought he had just used me as he would a whore, and realized that this man was obsessed with my body, that I had infected him in a way for which he was not likely to soon find a cure. I kissed him gently on the slightly parted lips, and quickly fell asleep.

The next morning, Louis subjected us to the same *reveille* routine, but this time we were prepared, wished him good morning through the closed door, and promised him that we would be down very soon.

The drive from Lyon to Nice took us through some of the most beautiful scenery I had ever seen. We passed through the foothills of the Alps, and once we entered Provence, we found ourselves along a narrow road high atop a mountain ridge, from where I could see an undulating ribbon of cobalt far below on one side and the awe-inspiring grandeur of granite gray on the other. Off into the distant haze in front of us, I glimpsed the specter of the fabled Côte d'Azur.

As the sun was still hovering along the horizon, we pulled into Negresco's parking lot. The plan was to spend the night there, and early the next morning we were to board the count's yacht and start our cruise around the Mediterranean. I didn't know if we were going to call on any ports or just float around, but either way, I knew I would have a wonderful time.

The next morning by ten o'clock we were already at sea, with just a faint outline of the coast behind us. It was another glorious day, and Teresa and I were already lying on the fore deck in our bikinis soaking up the sun. The men had gone on an in-depth tour of the yacht, at Michel's request, and Louis was delighted to show his nautical expertise as he chose to personally run the tour. They finally completed their tour just as the steward announced that lunch was being served in the aft dining room, under a large umbrella set up for the occasion.

The next few days were all perfect. There were several ports of call; we stopped at Cannes, and Teresa and I did some nude sunbathing, which, since I had never done it before, was very liberating; we also stopped at Monaco, where we spent a long night at the casino. Apparently Louis was well known there, so he just opened us each a line of credit of 10,000 francs, and told us the money was ours to keep, including all our winnings. Given that proposition, I chose to spend the chips playing the slot machines. Doing that, I wasn't winning, but at least I wasn't losing much either. I was not a gambler; if I hadn't felt embarrassed I would have just pocketed the 10,000 francs and left the casino. Teresa did not have this problem; she sat herself at the 50-franc blackjack table. By the end of the evening she lost the whole 10,000 francs. Michel, who I hadn't seen all evening, suddenly showed up behind me, grabbed my breasts shamelessly, and told me that he won 10,000 francs. However, when he heard that Teresa had lost everything, offered to return his original 10,000 francs to Louis. Louis generously dismissed his offer, which was very good news for Michel. I also thought that with this money he might be able to be a bit more generous with me when we got back to Paris.

The moment we walked into the casino, Louis headed for the roulette table. He was there for four hours, but when he left they rang a bell and then placed a black cloth across the table, which led to a hush in the room: "*Il a cassé la banque, il a cassé la banque!*" was what I heard everyone say. And in the process he had won 250,000 francs. Whatever discomfort I might have previously felt about his spending all that money on us flew out the window. I went to see the table draped in black; it was quite a somber scene. There was going to be no more playing at that table that night. The table was dead. I then got to see what 250,000 francs looked like. I had never seen the count so happy. He told us that we're all invited back in three months, because one of us brought him luck, and since he didn't know which one, he would just have to bring us all. We all accepted.

I cannot remember another time in my life when I felt so completely happy. Yet I knew that soon reality was going to get a hold of me and start trashing me about as before, and maybe even harder and more viciously to pay up for this unauthorized departure from my prescribed fate. But on some masochistic level, I conspired to immerse myself in this brief fairy tale with a mystic's zest knowing full well that by doing so I would be making my return to reality that much more painful. I remember the line from *Casablanca* when Humphrey Bogart tells Ingrid Bergman that they'd always have Paris. I always thought that to be one of the saddest lines ever told.

While the act of living in the moment allows us to block out the surrounding indignities, the act of recollection is always a slave to our strongest emotions, and those are always fueled by our insecurities. Paris came crushing down on me. That night I didn't sleep. Typically, after one of our intense love making sessions, I would be asleep within a few minutes, but not that night. I kept thinking about everything that was waiting for me back in Paris, and Poldy's image loomed large and foreboding.

XVI

We returned to Paris one day short of two weeks from the day we left. It was the afternoon of a midweek day and the squalor of the hotel room had never struck me so hard. Things I had never noticed before – the torn couch, the tattered carpet, the rusty chairs, the large sheets of paint that were barely holding on to the wall, the musty odor that pierced my nostrils when I opened the door – now seemed unbearable. How could I have lived in this foul place for so long? And more painfully, what prospects did I have of living better anywhere else? The fairy tale was over, and Prince Charming was a poor accountant who was married to boot.

Poldy showed up a little while after my return. I didn't even notice when he walked in; suddenly he was standing there in front of me. I felt vulnerable in his presence, and I knew I couldn't ever allow him to see that. He was holding a letter in his hand, and seemed to be waiting for me to acknowledge his presence before he handed it to me. I noticed that the envelope had been opened, and to quickly reestablish the balance of power in our tenuous relationship, I grilled him on his authority to open a letter that was addressed to me. He sneered and stepped back, giving me a chance to read it.

It was from the American Embassy, and it requested that we come on the noted date for a physical exam. It went on to say that if we failed to show up on that date, our application for visas would be purged from their file, as it would reflect our lack of interest in coming to America. I looked at the date. It was yesterday's.

I was suddenly in a state of panic and, even though, I swore never to do it, especially not in front of Poldy, I began to sob uncontrollably. All I could think of saying was, "What will I do? What will I do?" Poldy just stood there impassively, observing my reaction with pursed lips and raised eyebrows.

I dragged myself over to the bed, and, out of exhaustion brought on by feelings of hopelessness and depression, fell into a deep death-like sleep. I didn't get up until the next morning.

When I sat up at the edge of the bed, I felt leaden and achy, and my mouth tasted foul. I tried to stand up, but fell back onto the mattress. I pushed myself up again. I looked around, as if searching for a reason to put myself together and go on with my life. Poldy wasn't there, which somehow made my agony even worse.

On the floor, right next to the bed, I noticed the envelope from the American Embassy. I didn't remember leaving it there; I figured Poldy put it there so I would see it when I got up and renew the process of self-bashing.

I again grabbed the envelope and looked inside. There was the letter that I had already seen. I opened it. I again looked for that all-important date of the mandatory exam. It had now been crossed out with a black marker. Next to it, there was a round rubber stamp showing an eagle with its wings spread, clutching a branch in one talon and a few stalks of grain in the other. In the middle of the eagle's chest, there was a small rectangular window in which a new date was printed. I looked at the wall calendar – it was the next day.

I tossed the paper as far as I could, turned, and then shoved my face inside the pillow. I started wailing louder than I could ever imagine, finding some comfort that the pillow would largely muffle those sounds. "Son of a bitch! Son of a bitch!"

By the time Poldy came home I had decided to act very casual about the whole matter. "So you changed the date for the physical," I said very nonchalantly when he finally showed up. It was after ten o'clock, and I wouldn't give him the satisfaction of asking him where he'd been.

XVII

As I had been aware of from the beginning, once darkness descended upon our neighborhood, so did dozens of young prostitutes who lined the sidewalks of just about every street around Gare du Nord. Our little street, Rue de Vienne, was no exception. While it might have been distracting at the beginning, after a while, I stopped noticing. I fleetingly thought in the first weeks after we moved in how all this open-air flesh trade might affect Poldy. I later decided that it might not be a bad idea if he actually picked up one of those girls who were probably not much older than him and allowed himself to experience sex, and stopped twisting it in his head into something foul and wicked. On a couple of occasions when I saw him sitting around the room, moping or daydreaming, I suggested that he go see a movie or 'anything else he wanted to do'. Hoping that he'd get the hint, I would give him 25 or 30 francs, far more than the 5-franc price of a movie, and enough not just to engage one of those girls, but even have a few francs left over for a '*pourboire*' to show that he knew how to treat a girl. He would take the money, go out, and return two or three hours later.

When I asked him if he had had a good time, he simply placed his palms flat against his pants, and then quickly raised them while making gunshot sounds. It was a pitiable attempt at imitating a gunslinger, but I didn't understand why he was being so smug; Poldy never did anything without a reason, albeit distorted and cynical. He didn't bring back any change either, but I didn't get the sense that he had spent the money on a prostitute. I imagined that if he had, he would have seemed less tense, less prickly. He would never tell me what he did with the money, but I knew I was smarter than him, and one day he would slip up. In the meantime, his passion for movies seemed to have grown to a steady three-evenings-a-week regimen: Tuesdays, Thursdays, and Saturdays. The schedule appealed to me immensely; Michel and I could finally look forward to being together from seven to nine pm on at least those three days without the distressing presence of Poldy.

When I tried to reduce Poldy's movie-going allowance to five or at least ten francs, he immediately grumbled: I either continued to give him at least twenty-five francs each time or he'd stop going to the movies altogether. I knew not to call his bluff as the evenings with Michel were just too delicious, so I continued to allow myself to be blackmailed by that little hustler.

XVIII

One night while Teresa was having one of her all-out bashes, her older daughter Monique did not want to go out. Teresa knew that she couldn't have her daughter there; every time Monique attended one of her mother's parties, she smuggled men back to her room and seduced them, often successfully. That big little tramp had decided she would outdo her mother's sexual escapades not just in sheer number, but also in the deviant nature of their content. She clearly had a self-destructive streak. She was a spectacularly beautiful girl, who at seventeen could have had any man fall desperately in love with her, but she had a penchant for multiple partners, and to satisfy her cravings she would end up looking to pick up men in some of the sleaziest bars in Paris, largely frequented by "*blousons noir.*" These thugs, mostly angry Muslim Algerians opposed to the War, would not only end up ravaging her insides, but pound her into a bloody mess. Nevertheless, after a few days in the hospital, she was ready to run back, despite Teresa's desperate efforts to protect her daughter: private guards, police escorts, drugging her to sleep.

When I found out that Monique was not planning to go out man-hunting the evening of her mother's party, I told her that she could sleep in my bed at the hotel. Naturally, the nights of sleeping at her grandfather's house were long gone. She knew Poldy would be there, and I think, when she heard my offer, she felt titillated by the prospect of teasing him. I knew exactly what she would be up to, so I warned her about his bizarre personality, and told her how miserable he had made my life with his sanctimonious silences. She told me she knew exactly what to do, and off she went filled with an ardent sense of purpose.

I didn't see Monique for a quite a while after that, but when I ran into Poldy the next evening, his opaque façade revealed nothing of what had gone on the night before. Hoping to break the ice, I asked him if Monique had been there the night before, to which he nodded affirmatively. I pushed on by asking if he had been a good host, to which he looked at me askance, walked out of the room, holding his tooth brush and soap, as if he had to get ready for bed that very instant.

It was three weeks later when I finally found out what actually occurred that night between Monique and Poldy. I received the disgusting details directly from Monique. As I walked into her mother's apartment, she rushed up to me and told me that she had something urgent to talk to me about. She told me that when she first arrived, Poldy seemed glad to see her and behaved quite charmingly, offering her a cup of coffee and some *petits fours* that had been left over from Teresa's last party. Monique said she told him she appreciated the similarities in their situation, both children of divorced women who were racing against time to enjoy their fleeting youth, and as reminders of their fears that once their youth was gone they would be tossed into society's trash can along with all the other middle-aged women. In the meantime, the children could either let themselves feel victimized by the circumstances or take a more enlightened attitude and accept and even thrive at doing their own thing, whatever that might be. Monique knew Poldy was a big reader, so she told him that instead of allowing himself to be unhappy, he could find satisfaction in the enchanting world of books. Poldy did not interrupt her once.

She went on to admit that she had found fulfillment in the company of men, and he should not be judgmental about that. She didn't hurt anyone; in fact she brought pleasure to herself and the men she was with. She said that although at seventeen she might be considered too young by middle-class standards, she was actually quite ripe according to the customs of earlier ages. Women in the Middle Ages got married at thirteen and fourteen, and besides, it is not a matter of age, but of being emotionally ready for it, and she knew she was, because she never regretted any of it. Poldy continued to listen carefully, which led Monique to think that he was receptive to her comments. When she finally stopped, Poldy thanked her for her insights, and suggested that they immediately go to bed. Monique took that as a positive sign, and asked to use the bathroom first. When she returned, Poldy was sitting on his bed next to my overnight bag holding his toothbrush in one hand and what looked like a paintbrush in the other. She told him that if he was a good boy special delights were waiting for him after he brushed his teeth and did whatever else he had to do in the bathroom to get ready for bed.

While Poldy was out of the room, she stripped naked, got into my bed, and covered herself to the chin with a sheer bed sheet, whose transparency made it superfluous.

When Poldy came back, he was wearing concentration camp-style striped pajamas, which he must have bought while I was away. On the pajama top, he had painted a large Star of David that was still wet and dripping gobs of red paint. He stopped at the foot of the bed, and, staring right at her, with a big grin on his face, wished her sweet dreams. He then proceeded to shuffle across the room, exaggerating his limp, while what seemed like lumps of bloody matter splattered around him. At that moment, Monique freaked and ran out.

She was found unconscious the next day, after having been savaged by a particularly vicious group of "blousons noir." She stayed in the hospital for two weeks that a time, and when she finally came out she was also diagnosed with a virulent strain of Hepatitis. I always knew Poldy could bring out the worst in people. What I couldn't understand was how he was able to clean the room so well; I looked everywhere, but there was no sign of the red paint. I thought that maybe Monique had made it all up, but subsequent circumstances convinced me that she had told the truth.

After that incident, I decided that Poldy was always going to be a pain in the ass no matter what I tried to do, so I might as well do what I wanted without worrying about his approval.

As for Monique, a few years later, life took a bizarre turn. One day, she showed up at her mother's door in the arms of an Italian duke. The duke, young and handsome, fell in love with her and soon asked for her hand in marriage. If her deviant sexual escapades were done to top her mother's, she clearly succeeded, but who would have suspected that she was also going to outrank her mother. Monique married the duke, clearly a couple of notches above her mother's count, and she ended up living in a castle somewhere in Tuscany. To endure the bucolic life of a ducal estate, her husband allowed her frequent trips to Paris in their Lear jet. Three years into the marriage – she had already given birth to a baby girl - her plane crashed on the return trip from Paris. I was already in America when it happened, but Teresa told me that the duke cried like an infant during the funeral. She was twenty-one years old.

XIX

The medical exam Poldy and I took at the American Embassy was absolutely uneventful. As we walked through the gate, a very young soldier – he looked Poldy's age – asked us some questions I didn't understand, but as soon as I handed him the letter, he pulled a piece a paper out of his sleeve and handed it to me; it was a floor plan already marked with our directions. He pointed to the directions and saluted me. I was very impressed; I had heard of American efficiency, but now I knew why these people ruled the world. As soon as we walked through the door marked with a red cross, we were greeted by a middle-aged woman with her hair rolled up in a huge bun and glasses pushed all the way to the tip of her long ski-slope nose. She was sitting at a desk facing an enormous green typewriter. She motioned to us to sit down on a long wooden bench; there was no one else there.

After we had been sitting there for a few minutes, she said to us in perfect, unaccented French that we wouldn't have to wait long. Just then a young man in a white coat came in, smiled, and asked Poldy to follow him. While I was sitting there, I looked up at the woman who was busy typing and I noticed a mole the size of a Topolino attached to her chin.

A few minutes later, a woman also wearing a white coat came for me. She was big and black and spoke with a strange accent. She pronounced "oi" like in the word coiffure as 'oy," so I became mad-moy-zell, with which she started every one of her instructions. I had seen black people before, but she was the first one I talked to. She displayed a surface kindness that I was sure would disappear if I strayed from her instructions. She stood there talking to me while I got undressed, but it didn't bother me; I had been through worse in Romania. She repeated information that I already knew: "Sick people are not allowed in America." She then handed me a cup, pointed to a toilet behind a paper screen, and told me to pee in it. This instruction was followed by several deep-knee bends. She then grabbed my arm and stuck a long, fat needle in it; I hadn't noticed that the needle was attached to a glass tube, which quickly filled with what I assumed to be my blood. It was red, deep red; I had never seen it before. She called me by my name and she told me her name was Beulah and she said she liked Jews and that Sammy Davis Jr. was Jewish. I didn't know who Sammy Davis Jr. was. She then took me to another room and gave me a chest x-ray. Finally she grinned at me and told me to get dressed.

When I got back to the Topolino woman's room, the sole wooden bench was occupied by a young family of Hassids: two teenagers and three babies, so I waited for Poldy standing in the opposite corner of the room. Then Beulah came in and I waved to her; she looked at me, but her expression suggested that she had no idea who I was.

The reason I still remember so vividly a medical exam that took place fifty years ago, an exam that was no different that fifty other such exams I've had since then, is because there was so much riding on it. If they found something wrong with me, they wouldn't have let us go to America, and although I wasn't so sure I wanted to go, I still wanted to know that I was good enough to be an American.

A week after our physicals, I received a letter saying that our American entry visas were approved. There was no mention how we did on the exams.

The following weeks were filled with chores related to our looming departure. We had to show up one day to be fingerprinted; another time we went to be debriefed about our life in Romania. We were told that this was a mere formality to enable us to qualify as political refugees. The last time we went to the American Embassy, we were handed the entry documents, including our plane tickets, and luggage tags. We were told at that time that when we arrived in New York we would be met by someone from an organization called NYANA, who was going to find us a place to live and give us money to get us started on our new life. That's when we were given our departure date:

February 27, 1962. My heart sank when I heard that. I spent the next two days at Teresa's crying my eyes out, but being the survivor that I'd always been, I got myself together and resignedly awaited for the fated day.

During that whole time I felt too tense to make any time for Michel, who nonetheless came by the shop several times, tactfully explaining to the old man that the reason for his visit was related to his accounting obligations. The old man had a small corner of the counter cleared where Michel sat dwarfed by mounds of paper. All the while I felt his eyes following me around the shop desperately trying to meet mine.

When I finally accepted the fact that I was going to America, I decided that I might as well make the best of the little time that I had left in Paris. By then it was already the end of December.

XX

One evening, while I was alone at Teresa's, Danielle came over and asked me what I thought of my portrait in the newspaper. I thought the introverted little girl had finally lost her mind. She ran back to her room and returned with a copy of *Paris Soir*. On the first page of the art section, she pointed to a picture, a woman's portrait. The woman's face seemed to be melting, as lumps of flesh had drooped so low that some of them had already fallen on her bare breasts. It was a disturbing vision of death. As I was staring at it, Danielle pointed to the name under the picture: Greta Sobel. The adjoining article talked about a master art class that was being run at the Louvre for gifted youngsters. The name of the artist was given as Benno Feingold, Jr. I don't know what I hated more: the picture or the repulsive name Poldy had adopted in his demented game to get the better of me. I instantly understood what was happening with the movie money and why he was home so rarely and where the red paint that drove Monique crazy came from.

I didn't go home that night. I knew that if I had, I would

have killed him. The next day, Danielle took me to the gallery where the painting was on display. I finally saw the original; the woman's face looked like an animal's bloody carcass. The gallery owner, an effeminate little man with pink polish on his nails, wanted to know if I was interested in the painting; it was selling for 1,000 francs. I told him he must be out of his mind. He said that he couldn't think of a better investment: a modern-day Van Gogh, he said. I told him that he got the insanity association correct, but that was it. I was convinced the whole episode had been staged for my particular displeasure. When I, eventually, ran into Poldy, I didn't say anything, and neither did he, but he knew that I knew. The only concession I made was that when we left France a few weeks later, I allowed him to buy a trunk for his canvasses and art supplies. Danielle shipped it to him long after we'd left, when he was already living in a college dorm.

There is a post-script: Teresa, during one of our weekly long-distance phone calls that continued for many years after I settled in New York, informed me that months after Monique died, she was invited to visit her granddaughter in Tuscany. As she entered the castle, she saw Poldy's offensive painting of me hanging in a most prominent spot. The duke, pointing to the painting, related with typical Italian excess Monique's great love for it. As I was listening to Teresa, I wondered whether I had given birth to the latest embodiment of Mephistopheles and Monique's death came as a result of some Faustian bargain she had made with him to secure the title of duchess and outdo her mother.

XXI

Next time Michel stopped by the shop I whispered to him that he could come over. Our communications were difficult at best: I couldn't call him at home or at his office, nor could he leave messages for me at the shop. And the messages Michel left with Madame Cortiz were rarely delivered, though not deliberately. Madame Cortiz was so busy all the time that she just kept forgetting.

The following evening Michel came by, but not before he told Teresa about it, who cleverly intuited that we wanted to be alone, so she invited Poldy to spend the night at her house. He eagerly accepted, which immediately made me suspicious.

When Poldy arrived, Danielle was there. Teresa told me the next day that despite her initial apprehension, she thought Poldy had behaved respectfully, and that he and Danielle played chess and then spent half the night talking in Danielle's room. Teresa didn't know what they actually talked about, but she assumed it was just inconsequential banter, the kind one would expect from two young teenagers. Teresa assured me that he could stay over as often as I needed to have him out of the way. I let Teresa know how happy I was that things turned out so well, but secretly I didn't believe for a second that Poldy would engage in inconsequential banter. He never did anything without some ulterior motive.

Michel and I spent the following night together in my hotel room. He was loving and considerate as usual, but I felt something was missing. I blamed it on the long time we had not been together, and my inability to clear my head of all the fears about leaving Paris and traveling to America. Next morning I told him I wanted to be with him as often as possible until the day I left. He asked me about Poldy. I told him that Teresa seemed comfortable having him over as often as I wanted, especially now that she knew I was leaving in two weeks. He said he couldn't come for a couple of days as he was leaving Paris to visit his son, who was attending the Naval Academy in Toulon.

XXII

Several days later, Teresa stormed into the shop, asked her father if she could have a private word with me, and whisked me out of the store. I had never seen her so upset. She pinned me against the side of the building and began screaming hysterically that since Poldy had been sleeping over her life had become hell. Danielle had become impossible, critical of everything Teresa did, and insisting that she spend time with her father, Teresa's former husband. Teresa, at first, didn't have a clue why this pliable, respectful girl had suddenly turned into an out of control, angry shrew, but the fact that Danielle kept referring to herself as a modern Electra raised Teresa's suspicions, and she decided to go to a library and look up Electra. Once she read the myth, she immediately realized that Poldy must have been behind Danielle's dramatic personality change, and went into a panic thinking about the ideas that he may have planted in Danielle's tiny brain.

Teresa went home and interrogated Danielle, who at first adamantly refused to incriminate Poldy, but Teresa was no fool, and she threatened Danielle that unless she confessed to the whole story, she would send Danielle to live with her grandfather, something that was tantamount to being banished to Siberia. The poor girl quickly admitted that Poldy had gotten out of her the circumstances behind Teresa's divorce.

Teresa had told the girls that their father had never loved anyone but himself and that he was to blame for the loss of their younger brother who apparently died in a swimming accident when they had all been on a holiday in Brittany. The accident not only broke up the marriage, but also stripped the father of the will to live, which accounted for his subsequent financial collapse. But at Poldy's urging, Danielle found out that her father was living somewhere in Paris in modest surroundings after Teresa cast him out. Up until then, Danielle did not know much about him because Teresa was against the girls having any contact with him.

Upon hearing this story, Poldy reproached Danielle for not preventing Teresa from destroying her father, and told her that she had a responsibility to avenge him. He suggested that she follow Electra's example, relating only the parts of the myth that supported his ravings. He, in a show of infinite wisdom, dismissed the thought of having this simple girl kill her own mother as being too cowardly and debasing, although he lamented the expedience of such an act. He did counsel her on how to make her mother's life miserable, the way he had made mine. Needless to say, Teresa was on the verge of a nervous breakdown, and informed me that under no circumstances would she ever allow Poldy to see Danielle again. She apologized for her frantic behavior, and assured me that this incident would not affect our friendship.

At that point I was so furious with Poldy that I frankly didn't care whether he'd have to spend the whole night walking the streets when Michel stayed the night. Yet I thought that it might be a bit less drastic if I asked my neighbor, the Portuguese girl who lived in the room next to mine, if she would mind having Poldy sleep on the floor of her room the nights Michel was over. Astrid was a sweet, shy girl in her early twenties, so small and slender that she looked barely adolescent. I didn't know what brought her to Paris, and I never saw her in anybody's company. Whenever I ran into her she was either coming from work as a cashier in a Portuguese ceramic distributorship or on the way to our communal bathroom. She was extremely courteous, always bowing whenever she saw me, something that I found a bit disconcerting at the beginning.

That evening when I ran into her by the bathroom, I explained to her the whole situation. She was not a child, so I figured she would understand. I always lived by the principle that the difference between an honest person and a liar is that an honest person tells the truth when he knows it would be as effective as a lie, while a liar lies because he unaccountably fears the truth. She agreed immediately. Frankly, I was somewhat taken aback by the level of enthusiasm with which she agreed.

The night Michel came back from visiting his son at Toulon, he came straight to me. Poldy was reading and barely acknowledged Michel's arrival. I walked over to him and matter-of-factly told him that he was going to spend the night in Astrid's room. After he confirmed that I was talking about our next door neighbor, he immediately stood up and, in soldier fashion, marched to the sink to pick up his toothbrush and then did a quarter turn and walked to the chest of drawers where he kept his pajamas, selecting the same pair of pajamas that he wore for the Monique incident, and, making another quarter turn, headed for the door, but not before hissing a 'lovely night to you both' salutation.

The following several nights played themselves out quite similarly. In fact, as soon as Michel walked in the door, Poldy got up, gathered his toothbrush and pajamas, and walked out the door. The routine suited me just fine. I was curious though to find out what happened in Astrid's room, and Poldy was certainly not one to volunteer information, so I knew I had to wait until I could ask Astrid without having her think I was prying.

About a week later I got my chance. I met her as she was walking out of the bathroom. I asked her whether Poldy had been an imposition. At first she blushed and seemed unwilling to speak, but I assured her I knew that Poldy had problems and that if he had become a nuisance I'd understand.

She took me into the bathroom and closed the door behind us, an act of boldness that I didn't think she was capable of. I was prepared for the worst: that he had insulted her, questioned her motives for living a libertine life in the City of Sin, admonished her for abandoning whomever she may have left behind in Portugal. Astrid's story was quite unexpected. She told me that the first night when Poldy walked into her room, he apologized for the intrusion, begged her not to notice him, and wedged himself into a bare corner of the tiny room and went to sleep.

The second night, after he crawled into his corner, she broke the silence by asking him whether he was comfortable, to which he responded that he was, and, furthermore, she shouldn't worry about him.

She continued talking, telling him about her lonely life and what brought her to Paris: she had gotten herself pregnant in a place that considered that a worse sin than murder. She came from a small village in the north of Portugal where Camoens drew his family roots. Poldy's acquaintance with the obscure poet apparently inflamed the young woman, who continued discussing *The Lusiads* with Poldy until the next morning.

The third night he slept over, Poldy went straight to his corner and, despite Astrid's exhortations to renew their discussion of the previous night, he remained silent. Finally, she got out of bed and walked over to him. He was lying there with his knees under his chin, sunk so deeply into that corner behind Astrid's dresser that she had trouble finding him at first. She thought he had disappeared, left the room without her noticing it. She pulled him out, and when she touched his face, it was soaking wet. Pity moved her to take him into her bed. He didn't resist, he just lay there like a corpse. She unbuttoned his pajamas, and slowly moved her hands across his body. She kissed him and told him that she wanted him to be with her. She then took his penis in her hand and gently held it as she climbed on top of him. She continued to stroke his penis, to kiss him fervently, to wrap herself around him. Yet he remained impassive, his penis showing not the slightest sign of life. The following night he dug himself back into his corner, and didn't utter a word.

After Astrid caught her breath, she begged me not to ask her to have him over another night; the boy obviously had some serious sexual problems, and it was frankly too painful for her to have him around. I told her I totally understood, and I thanked her for trying to help him.

XXIII

My last appearance at Teresa's was only two days before my final adieu to Paris and I was as depressed as I ever remembered myself to be. I was furious with everyone: with Poldy for manipulating me into this unwanted departure; with Michel for letting me go; with Teresa for having such a charmed life; and with God for always teasing me with the "good life" and then snatching it away.

While I was sitting there on Teresa's couch hoping for some celestial sign that would tell me that things would stay just the way they've been, a woman I had seen before at Teresa's but never talked to approached me.

" I heard you were leaving for America," she said.

"Oh yes, the day after tomorrow," I said. "I'm not looking forward to it."

"May I introduce you to Mister Mendelovitch. He's an American, just in from New York. I'm sure you'll want to ask him a lot of questions."

"Not really," I answered, hoping the woman and her American would go away.

A tall, drab man with a hideous haircut and a grin that revealed an unhappy dental situation sat next to me. He stuck his hand out and I reluctantly shook it. It was big and slimy and I pulled mine back in disgust.

None of my body signs that would have discouraged even the most intrepid pursuer seemed to dissuade him. He seemed determined to talk to me even though his French was awful. I think the reason I sat and listened to him was because his struggle to communicate with me was so incredibly pathetic.

"America is the greatest country on earth. If you need money all you do is go to the welfare office and they give you money. If you need furniture, you can pick up last year's model sometimes still in its original wrapper that someone has left on the sidewalk on his way to buy this year's model. I'm a millionaire and I've only been in America ten years. Ten years ago I was an immigrant just like you and look at me now."

I looked at him in his ill-fitting suit, but there was a brashness and an exuberance about the man that I liked. He was clearly uneducated; I saw it in his rough hands and awkward posture and obvious social uneasiness. And yet this man became rich in America. If he could do it, so could I, and I would return to Paris a rich American in lavish minks and chauffeured-driven limousines and everyone would want my company. And I would stay at The Crillon and Poldy would be back in America torturing someone else and I could spend magical nights with Michel. I thanked Mister Mendelovitch and left Teresa's looking forward to the next episode of my life.

XXIV

The following night was our last night in Paris, and I would have been damned if I didn't spend it with Michel. Michel, also recognizing the special significance of the event, had stopped at a barber on the way over so that when his face touched mine, it would feel as smooth as everything else that he touched me with. He whispered that in my ear, which got me to orgasm before I even took my clothes off, and Poldy was sitting right in front of us, facing the window, staring at the soaring metal shaft of the Eiffel Tower.

I ordered Poldy to get ready for bed. He proceeded in his usual automaton fashion to perform his nightly preamble to sleep. The whole time, Michel and I were sitting on top of my bed blazing in erotic hell, wishing this lame boy would move faster. Finally he slid onto his sofa, and turned his back to us. I turned the light off, and the two of us, as if on cue, started tearing ourselves out of our clothes. We hungrily lunged at each other and devoured ourselves in sexual ecstasy. At one point the large bowl-shaped ceramic lamp that had been sitting on the little night table next to my bed came crashing down. It felt like the room was in the middle of an earthquake, but thank God we didn't stop. I knew at that moment that I, just like Ingrid Bergman in *Casablanca*, would always have Paris.

XXV

The next day, with Poldy in tow, I was on my way to America, and a life as insipid as it was different from what I had known. I was thirty-eight, so in a way I understood that this was not only a physical journey, but a metaphysical one as well. I had had a good run; now it was time to settle down, and what better place than America.

Michel was caring and considerate to the very end. Our flight to America was leaving from Brussels, so he drove us in his tiny Peugeot from Paris to Brussels the night before our departure, but he couldn't stay. He had to drive back immediately, but not before he made sure that I was settled in my hotel room. I was certain his impatience to return to Paris meant that he had already found another woman, but I didn't care. We both knew it was over. It would be years before we saw each other again, and when we did we were strangers, just as I had expected.

Since I had a whole day to spend in Brussels, I figured I'd go see the sights. I asked the concierge what was worth seeing given that we only had a few hours. The young woman looked at me with a face contorted by irony and said, "This is Brussels madmoiselle, not Paris. You're in the most boring city in Europe." I persisted. "I can't believe there is nothing to see in this big old city."

She stared at the ceiling and then, after a few moments of silence, she cryptically said, "Manneken-Pis and you're in luck; you're just two blocks away from this greatest of Brussels monuments, and off we went to see it.

When we got to the Place de la Vielle Halle aux Bles, as she had told me, I didn't see anything other than just more gray buildings, so I asked one of the passers-by where I could find the Manneken-Pis, to which the man pointed across the street to a spot on one of the gray walls that had been scooped out and something indiscernible from where I was standing was located. I crossed the street, and I stood in front of a tiny stone statue of a boy taking a piss into a little fountain – nothing more. And it wasn't even well sculpted. This was the extent of our sightseeing tour of Brussels. Now I understood the young concierge's reaction. When I got back to the hotel, the concierge and I looked at each other and burst out laughing. It turned out she was French, so we spent the next half-hour reminiscing about Paris. Apparently she hadn't been home in about six months, and was homesick; there was a boyfriend in the equation.

XXVI

The next day we took a bus to the Brussels Airport and boarded a Sabena flight chartered by HIAS to New York. All the passengers were Jewish immigrants – expendable people. I thought of President Roosevelt's decision at the height of Hitler's Final Solution to deny *The Saint Louis*, a ship carrying Jewish immigrants, from docking in New York. Roosevelt knew that by barring *Saint Louis's* entry, he was sentencing those Jews to death, and that's exactly what happened.

The propeller-driven plane looked like it had been pulled out of a long retirement just for this one flight. Once we were sitting inside the plane, the two wing-mounted propellers started spinning, causing the entire plane to vibrate so violently that the small cups of water the stewardesses had handed out to us as we were boarding the plane became inadequate to contain the sudden storm, resulting in furious waves crashing on people's laps. At that point, I noticed a group of Orthodox Jews who on cue pulled out their prayer books and started davening and chanting in unison the "Giverot", the prayer affirming God's power.

Eternal is Your might. Oh God; all life is your gift; great is your power to save!

With love You sustain the living, with great compassion give life to all. You send help to the falling and healing to the sick. You bring freedom to the captive and keep faith with those who sleep in the dust.

Who is like you, Mighty One? Who is Your equal, Author of life and death, Source of Salvation?

I thought the part where it said that God will 'send help to the falling' was particularly appropriate, as we were in a plane that only divine intervention would keep from falling out of the sky.

The plane was supposed to fly from Brussels to Gadner, Newfoundland, the nearest point on the other side of the Atlantic, as that was the plane's maximum range, but as we all suspected it got into trouble as soon as it took off. Three out of its four engines died, and we made an emergency landing at Shannon, in Western Ireland. The last half hour before we landed, the plane was bouncing all over the sky and everyone on the plane was convinced that it was going to crash. In fact, the two stewardesses, who were trained to conceal their fears in order to avoid panicking passengers, were constantly either pressing their palms together or crossing themselves. They may have thought that carrying a load of Jews had something to do with their predicament.

But once we landed at Shannon, we were given the royal treatment. The airline and the crew were so relieved that we didn't crash that they arranged for an incredible feast at a local hotel and hired two terrific Irish tenors to entertain us as we were eating and drinking our way into oblivion. This was memorable, and also very symbolic of what all of us immigrants were going through, a death and a rebirth. And it had to happen in Ireland, a place I always thought was located half way between the world of reality and that of fairytales. Although I'm sad to admit that I never returned, I know Poldy has been back many times, as he considers himself the earthly transmutation of his namesake, the mythical Irish Jew Poldy Bloom.

The following day, we reboarded our beat-up little plane and flew on to Gadner without a hitch, and then on down to New York.

To my surprise, America turned out to be tougher and more challenging than I imagined but, at least for me, it became the place where men stopped being a goal in my search for self-affirmation. I am not saying that I spent my years in America like a nun, but unlike my European period, their passing was like riding a roller coaster, an amusing quick thrill, and once it was over I was perfectly happy, even relieved, to be on my way along the crooked walkways of this carnival I call my life until I decided to climb on another ride. As the years passed, I gradually committed greater chunks of my time to the task of educating this country girl. I took a myriad of adult education courses ranging from literary criticism to understanding art to appreciating the opera, visited museums sometimes as often as three times a week, and became a fixture at the local public library. America offered me the opportunity to affirm myself as a *grande dame*, no less grand than Mrs. Feingold in her heyday.

Yet looking back on my life in Europe, with all its near crashes, I loved every minute of it, and I wouldn't change anything ...or at least I wouldn't admit to it, or else I might go out of my mind. Take this as the adventures of a woman in love with life, no more no less. If there are any regrets, I'll deal with them during that long sleep that awaits me.

Greta turns off the recorder and places it on the night table. She's finished. She was afraid she would not be around to the end, but here she is. She feels good about it.

She unfolds the letter that came with the recorder and rereads the last few lines for the millionth time.

I've been angry at you for over fifty years. I know you've tried to make amends in the past, but they were not sincere. Tell everything in this recorder and I'll listen and decide if I should forgive you. Remember it was not something that you did to me personally, though that was what you always mistakenly thought, but it injured me grievously nonetheless. I want to forgive you. The rest is up to you. I am not promising anything, but I am very old and alone and I would love to have you again in my life, like in those early days when we were both so young and full of romance and hope and we walked through Chishmigiu Park and held each other tight and you told me that you were a tough country girl and you'd always protect me.

Greta looks again at the signature. She knows that if Coty forgave her, she would be ready for the end.

Made in the USA
Charleston, SC
24 November 2014